FAIR ISLE
AND ITS BIRDS

By KENNETH WILLIAMSON

The Sky's Their Highway (1937)

The Atlantic Islands (1948)

Identification for Ringers (1962-4)

By KENNETH WILLIAMSON and J. MORTON BOYD

St Kilda Summer (1960)

A Mosaic of Islands (1963)

FAIR ISLE
AND ITS BIRDS

KENNETH WILLIAMSON
F.R.S.E., M.B.O.U.

with
A LIST OF THE BIRDS OF FAIR ISLE
by PETER DAVIS B.A.

Illustrated with photographs by
JOHN PETERSON
F.R.P.S.

OLIVER & BOYD
EDINBURGH AND LONDON
1965

OLIVER AND BOYD LTD
Tweeddale Court
Edinburgh 1

39A Welbeck Street
London, W.1.

First published   1965

Printed in Great Britain by
Robert Cunningham and Sons Ltd., Alva
for Oliver and Boyd Ltd., Edinburgh

To
ESTHER

FOREWORD

Sir Arthur Duncan

WHEN, at the end of the last war, Ian Pitman and George Waterston asked me to join them in floating the Fair Isle Bird Observatory, I thought that it was a foolhardy enterprise. The fact that the enterprise has succeeded leaves me unconvinced that my first thoughts were wrong but sure that they were both unimportant and irrelevant.

Our aim was to provide facilities for the study of the migratory birds on a permanent basis which could only be done by having a permanently manned base on the island. This was the main aim. The two ancillary and almost equally important ones were, and are, to provide a training ground for young naturalists, and, by the flow of visitors using these facilities, to bring a new source of interest and income to the islanders and thereby postpone the evacuation of the island.

The three of us made a brief, but memorable visit to the island, which convinced us that the naval buildings were suitable for our purpose; it also gave me my first chance to see the sunset from the west cliffs of Fair Isle, an evocative experience like watching the sunrise on the Himalayan snows from Tiger Hill or its setting in flame and orange over the Great Karroo. Thereafter all that remained to be done was to find the cash and the man. Thanks to the generosity of various Trusts, notably the Pilgrim Trust, and many naturalists we were able to secure sufficient funds to make a start. To find the man was all important and without our extreme good fortune in finding that the job interested Kenneth Williamson the venture would certainly not have succeeded so rapidly. When the Williamson family abmigrated to Oxford, we were again most lucky to get Peter Davis to take over.

These two, our first wardens at Fair Isle, have written this book; and those who read it will quickly understand how the F.I.B.O. achieved its pre-eminent position as the leading bird observatory of its kind in the world, pioneering techniques that have become standard practice, throwing considerable light on many facets of bird migration, and making the bird observatory system a great, and mainly British contribution, to scientific ornithology.

The work goes on, sustained by voluntary contributions, and I would ask any reader who enjoys this book and finds the account of the work interesting and stimulating to remember this, and, remembering, to help us by becoming a subscriber to our work on Fair Isle. Full information can be obtained from the Honorary Secretary, F.I.B.O., 21 Regent Terrace, Edinburgh 7.

Gilchristland, Closeburn
1965

CONTENTS

CONTENTS

PART III
A LIST OF THE BIRDS
OF FAIR ISLE
BY PETER DAVIS, B.A.

PHOTOGRAPHS

TEXT FIGURES AND MAPS

INTRODUCTION

MY WIFE AND I agreed to go to Fair Isle to organise a hostel and research centre for the study of bird migration in the spring of 1948: we were not the first to find George Waterston's enthusiasm infectious, and the idea presented a challenge. But the story of Fair Isle Bird Observatory does not begin there, nor do I regard myself in any true sense as its first director. Forty years before one of the great Scottish naturalists, Dr William Eagle Clarke, had thought deeply about migration problems as he wandered through the tiny fields surrounding the whitewashed crofts, his gun ever ready to secure an unfamiliar bird, his scalpel always sharpened to prepare specimens for science. He trained an islander, Jerome Wilson of Springfield, to hunt and work with him—and for him when his own duties called him back to the Royal Scottish Museum in Edinburgh. Occasionally too he had the company of a kindred spirit, when the yacht *Sapphire* dropped anchor off Klingers Geo and Mary, Duchess of Bedford, and her maid-servant climbed the steep cliff path and installed themselves at the Pund.

By 1912 Eagle Clarke's diligent collecting, his museum studies and his thinking about the why and wherefore of the startling bird-movements he had witnessed at Fair Isle and other remote places, such as the Flannans and St Kilda, were ripe for publication, and his *Studies in Bird Migration* remained a standard work in this field down to the nineteen forties. By 1921 he felt he was getting too old for this strenuous game, and he made a last visit to his fabulous bird-isle in the company of a younger and more active man, Rear-Admiral James Hutton Stenhouse. They bothied in the Duchess's old cottage at the Pund. George Stout of Field, who became to Stenhouse what

Wilson had been to Clarke, said of this visit, "They lived on bad food and good whisky for a fortnight!" During the next decade Stenhouse may be said to have wardened Fair Isle. In 1929 he too felt the advancing years and began to look for a successor; he found an eager one in George Waterston, who had just left Edinburgh Academy.

George was not able to go to Fair Isle until the autumn of 1935, when he and A. G. S. Bryson stopped the northbound steamer off the South Harbour and were rowed ashore in an island boat. (It is an interesting point, in view of the considerable number of visitors to F.I.B.O. nowadays, that theirs were the only new faces the islanders saw in 1935, while neither Jerome Wilson nor George Stout had met an ornithologist for six years!) George made annual visits till 1939, by which time his great ambition was to establish at the isle an observatory for the trapping, ringing and study of migrant birds similar to the one which he and other young Edinburgh ornithologists had already started on the Isle of May in the Firth of Forth.

The war must have scotched thousands of ambitions, but at least one burned more brightly throughout those barren years. George was captured in Crete in June 1941 and was a P.O.W. in Germany for the next two and a half years, during much of which he was a sick man. But he had ample time and leisure to think of Fair Isle and what ought to be done there to reap the best possible harvest from its great ornithological potentialities. He fired a fellow-prisoner, Ian Pitman, an Edinburgh lawyer, with his enthusiasm and ideas, and their plans gradually took shape. If George ever had misgivings as to the practicability of establishing a field research station in such an isolated corner of the British Isles, they probably disappeared for ever during the voyage when he was invalided home via Gothenburg in 1943, in an exchange of wounded officers arranged by the Swiss Red Cross. The liner was escorted northwards through Norwegian waters, and then headed west: at dawn there was a shout 'Land ahead!' and everyone who could rushed on deck for a first sight of the old country. To one man the experience was something more than just that—it was an omen, a promise of things to come. For the land was Sheep Craig, with Fair Isle beyond bathed in the soft light of an October morning.

George Waterston bought Fair Isle from the then proprietor, Robert Bruce of Sumburgh, in 1948, and the bird observatory was launched as a public Trust with Sir Arthur Duncan (later the energetic Chairman of the Nature Conservancy) as chairman, Ian Pitman as treasurer, and George as secretary. Grants of £3,000 from the Pilgrim Trust and £1,000 for scientific equipment from the Nature Conservancy, together with many private donations and the annual subscriptions of the 'Friends of Fair Isle', helped to put the venture on its feet. My wife and I planned and supervised the conversion of the former Naval Headquarters at North Haven into hostel and laboratory, and had charge of the observatory and its scientific programme until late in 1956. Peter Davis, who had been warden of the bird observatories on Lundy and Skokholm, then took over until 1963, when he was succeeded by Roy Dennis.

The first chapters of this book tell something of Fair Isle, its scenery, history and people, and of the birds which breed there on moor and cliff, and which were our special interest in the summer months. The second part (chapters ix-xvi) is concerned with bird migration, and more particularly with the growth of our knowledge in this field in recent years—a development to which Fair Isle and the other British bird observatories have contributed much. The study of the field sciences in Britain has always been thrice blessed with a wealth of amateur endeavour eager and capable of being directed towards a definite goal, and the work of the bird observatories over the past twenty years stands as a triumph of co-ordinated effort of this kind.

So far as this book is concerned, it is only fair to say that a number of the ideas developed in it are personal ones, and are not universally accepted. The book, however, is a record of a personal quest which occupied me physically and intellectually for upwards of a dozen years, so the reader must bear with me if I sometimes seem to see the 'mysteries' of migration in sharp focus. Acknowledgements are due to many people. The earlier chapters contain material which has appeared in articles in *Scotland's Magazine*, *The Scottish Field*, *The Countryman*, and talks given for the B.B.C. Various aspects of the migration problems touched upon in later chapters have received fuller treatment in ornithological journals, and I thank the editors of all these publications for permission to reproduce the material here. I should like to express my gratitude to the Fair Isle Bird Observatory Trustees and the Council of the British Trust for Ornithology for permission to use in this present form the results of research carried out on their behalf, both at Fair Isle and later when I was Migration Research Officer of the B.T.O. at Oxford. I am also grateful to my friends George Waterston, O.B.E., F.R.S.E., and Peter Davis, B.A., for reading and criticising parts of the manuscript; and to John Peterson, F.R.P.S., for making his splendid series of photographs of the isle available to illustrate the book. Grateful acknowledgements are also due to the Director of the Meteorological Office, and the Controller of H. M. Stationary Office for permission to reproduce figs. 11-17, based on charts published in *The Daily Weather Report*. My wife and I owe much to many friends who came as visitors to the observatory between 1948 and 1956 and shared in our work. We remember those years with the greatest of pleasure for still another reason, conscious of the debt we owe to the island folk for their help, hospitality and friendship. Of all our memories of a wonderful island these and not the birds are likely to be the most enduring.

Part I

THE ISLE AND ITS BREEDING BIRDS

CHAPTER I

FOLK AND FESTIVALS

FAIR ISLE is more isolated than any other part of inhabited Britain. Its two thousand acres of field and hill and forbidding cliffs rise starkly from the ocean fairway between Orkney and Shetland, and it is 25 miles from each. If you stand on the top of Ward Hill, 712 feet up, on a clear day you will see the flat isle of North Ronaldsay, its only contour a lighthouse tower, away to the south, while in the other direction are the sharply contrasting Fitful and three-humped Sumburgh Heads where Shetland Mainland gives herself up to the sea. Fair Isle is a gem among islands, mild, fertile and friendly; and many more people have admired her picturesque form from the B.E.A. aircraft which fly daily between Sumburgh and Kirkwall than have set foot on her shore. Yet of all Britain's remote islands this is much the easiest to visit.

Like too many of our islands Fair Isle has seen good times and bad—days of tragedy and sorrow, troubled times of indecision when the world beyond the sparkling waters seemed careless, even callous, of the fate of her declining community. Since 1948, when the Bird Observatory was established to study migration and other ornithological problems, she has had much publicity, and has played host to nearly three thousand visitors from urban Britain. These people have not only enjoyed their holiday amid the beauty and fascination of her scenery and wildlife, but have also made friends among the island folk; they have helped in no small way to dispel the islanders' natural shyness and reserve, and allay the fears that come from too much loneliness. Socially and economically this invasion has done the islanders a power of good, putting them at ease with the outside world, while it has also served to focus attention on their peculiar problems of survival.

It has been said that the Shetlander is a fisherman with a croft, and the Orcadian a crofter with a boat; and although the Fair Islander's contacts have long been with the northern group of islands, his economy today is more akin to that of the Orcadian. But it was not always so, for down to the mid-nineteenth century fishing was the main source of the island's revenue. In the early seventeenth century Sinclair of Quendale in Shetland had a booth at Fair Isle where he traded with merchants from Hamburg—perhaps on the same site as the old fish-store now falling into decay alongside the strand of Mid Geo. Barry describes the latter days of this period in the *Statistical Account of Shetland* of 1793: "In their pitiful skiffs they go to the fishing ground, almost out of sight of land, where they catch plenty of fine cod, ling, tusk, skate, halibut, mackerel and saithe." Such success continued until the middle of the last century, and one story has been handed down of a fine summer when the Factor valued the island's catch at £99 19s. 6d. and the Laird was too stingy to make it up to £100!

That was before the Atlantic climate began to change for the worse, towards the close of the nineteenth century. The increasing activity of depressions forging north-east towards Iceland brought milder winter weather, and made the summers wetter and windier than before, so that the range and activity of the small boats were restricted. The superior cod migrated northwards to seek colder waters, where its food is most abundant, and the inferior haddock (which Barry doesn't even mention!) took its place. Today even the haddock fishery is barely sufficient for subsistence needs. The islanders complain that steam trawlers and dogfish have combined to reduce the catch, the professional fishermen cleaning out the inshore grounds, and the 'dogs' eating or spoiling such haddocks as remain before the long-lines can be raised.

The change to a more agrarian economy has not led to any loss of affection for the sea, still less to any deterioration in the art and skill of boat-handling in the tricky tidal streams. How often have we greeted an island friend with the words, "It's a lovely day!", to be answered, "Aye, too lovely to be ashore!" The small boats, mostly built in Shetland nowadays, are drawn up on the beach at Kirki Geo or lie snugly in the 'noosts' fashioned from the escarpment behind. These 'yoals' may be less vital to the Fair Isle economy than they were, but they are not allowed to remain idle on good summer days if the slightest pretext can be found for putting to sea. There is no music more pleasing to Fair Isle ears than the grating of shingle beneath the keels as they are run down to the tide's edge.

In olden days the Fair Islander frequently put his craft to another use than the fishing—a use which was perhaps unique, and which helped to breed in him and his descendants that splendid faculty for seamanship which neighbours to north and south have long acknowledged and admired. When ocean-going vessels glided proudly under full sail through the wide channel separating Orkney and Fair Isle the island-men often rowed a dozen miles and more to trade their eggs, chickens, mutton, fish, vegetables (and the hosiery knitted by their wives) to passengers and crew, who were glad enough to come by fresh food for the long and tedious voyage ahead. This 'passing-trade' was stimulating as well as profitable for the island-folk, being almost their only contact with the wonderful outside world of which they knew so little. There is a good yarn telling how a man was asked, on stepping ashore from such a trip, whence the big ship had come; he had traded well, and doubtless his cry of "Halleluja, halleluja!" was joyful with good cause. He was not in the least abashed when a companion corrected him, saying the ship was homeward bound from Honolulu!

With the fishing prosperous, the passing-trade at its peak, and occasional wrecks to add spice to life, timber to the yard and sometimes a little ready cash to the pocket in the form of a well-merited reward, the eighteenth and early nineteenth centuries were a palmy time. At the close of the eighteenth the population increased by a quarter, and continued rising for fifty years until some 360 souls were somehow contriving to make a living at the isle—mainly Irvines, Williamsons, Eunsons, Stouts, Leslies and Wilsons. With the advent of steam one source of prosperity quickly disappeared, for there is nothing to be gained by trying to chase a steamship in a sixern or a yoal. There were also disasters at sea. The Reverend John Mill, the visiting minister in 1779, wrote that four homes had been ruined, for "the heads thereof were drowned carrying into the isle supplies for their families". Jerry Eunson records how, in the summer of 1851, the first yoal to set out with hosiery and other goods for sale in Shetland was lost with all hands at Horse Holm off Scatness, leaving "four rocking cradles" behind in the isle. A similar disaster took place at the isle itself near the end of the century. The change in the climate, besides limiting the fishing, also brought an unusual number of bad harvests, and as the century drew towards its close hardship and poverty descended on Fair Isle.

Depopulation began with a mass emigration of 137 men, women and children to New Brunswick in 1862, and it has been going on at a varying rate ever since. When St Kilda gave up the unequal struggle against isolation and a growing consciousness of the comforts of the outside world in August 1930, there were still over 100 people at Fair Isle; but when the Bird Observatory was begun in the summer of 1948 the total had fallen to 63. Nevertheless, there was no serious talk of evacuation: instead, people's thoughts turned to modernisation, and we saw the work-oxen taken away on the coal-boat when she came in mid-July. Although there were tears in many eyes as the big flit-boat took the last patient beast to the steamer, the islanders were soon admiring the brightly painted tractors and 'iron horse' ploughs brought by their boat *The Good Shepherd* from Shetland. The ploughman became mechanic almost overnight—a challenge and a change that islanders everywhere have had to take in their stride.

With the fishing no longer remunerative the Fair Isle folk have had to fall back on the crofting and what are collectively termed 'ancillary tasks'. Crofting is not a full-time job; you work hard at 'da voar', the spring sowing, but thereafter the tempo of life on the land is slow till the succession of rye-grass, oats and potato harvests in 'da hairst'. So there is ample time for tending the sheep on the hill, mending the roads, rebuilding a cottage, caring for the telephone lines and G.P.O. 'booster' apparatus, and serving as Coast Watcher or Lighthouse Occasional. There are a few pleasant and perhaps profitable summer days when the haddock lines are shot, or a good-sized halibut is caught, or a boat-load of 'piltocks' (half-grown saithe) is fished from close inshore. And nowadays the lobsters which lurk in cracks and crannies all round the rocky coast come in for special attention, the catch being taken off on board *The Good Shepherd* and sold in Shetland, whence it is flown south to market from Sumburgh Airport; but this, like the weaving in the winter months, is a newcomer to that heterogeneous assembly of ancillary tasks.

This native versatility of the crofter was of inestimable help to us in transforming the group of near-derelict naval huts at North Haven into a habitable—indeed, extremely comfortable —field study-centre. The available labour was by no means unskilled, and our working party contained a first-class joiner, two competent plumbers, and a good enough electrician—all, of course, self-taught. We found the tempo of life very different from what it was in Edinburgh: there were days when nobody turned up for work, either because some other task had priority, or perhaps because it was too fine a day not to go fishing; but such absences made little difference in the long run, since the men always made up for lost time by working in the evenings or on Saturday afternoons, and for the normal rate of pay. They were very punctilious in observance of their obligations to us as their employers. Soon after work on the hostel began, we wondered why they suddenly developed the habit of staying on till six o'clock in the evening—and then we realised it was because they felt morally obliged to make up the time lost during the rather hilarious tea-breaks we instituted in the kitchen in mid-morning and mid-afternoon.

If the work sometimes progressed slowly, there were compensations. I remember helping our foreman, Rock Jamie, to lay lino one day. A professional would have done the job in half the time, but I beg leave to doubt that he would have done it so well. Rock Jamie was not content merely to put down lino: he must first look at the floor from several angles, then fill up all the cracks between the floor-board sections with thin slivers of wood, and finally crawl round on his knees with an adze levelling the irregularities where the sections joined. This took up most of the morning, and only then was he ready to put down the covering. When he had finished he was quite certain that he'd done the job to the very best of his ability. This pride in doing work well, and indeed a personal and often creative interest in the scheme, was general, and engendered a happy relationship that was to last for the whole of our stay.

Among the other tasks there was also, of course, 'the Boat'— the 27 tons diesel-powered smack built at Buckie and called (by whose inspiration we know not) *The Good Shepherd*. She is the second island boat of that name, and Fair Isle's lifeline— the only physical means of communication with the outside world, the fetcher and carrier of mails, freight and passengers to and from Grutness pier at the southern tip of Shetland Mainland. She is subsidised by the G.P.O. and provides a small income for the families who have shares in her. She now makes the trip twice a week in summer, a hundred miles all told, to link up with the arrival of 'the Steamer' from Aberdeen; but formerly it was only one trip a week, weather permitting, all the year round. If you get a good day you can reach Fair Isle in a little over two and a half hours from Grutness and (if you fly north by B.E.A.) five hours from Glasgow or Edinburgh, or seven from London.

It was in relation to *The Good Shepherd* that the spectre of evacuation first raised its head menacingly in 1953. It was a condition of the insurance agreement that the boat should be drawn up on the slipway at North Haven to ensure protection from winter storms, between 1st October and 31st March each year. A primitive hand-operated winch did the job, its long iron handles requiring the exertions of a dozen stalwart men for upwards of an hour in the early morning and late evening of 'Boat-day'. (Somebody once remarked, during a 'spell', that it could not have been very different from this on the medieval rack!) When two families departed for new homes in Shetland, and another emigrated to New Zealand, there remained barely sufficient manpower to perform this essential task. Indeed, after the launching (which required few hands, since gravity was a great help), some of the crew had to return ashore to help haul up the heavy cradle, thus delaying the departure of the boat. Any further reduction would have spelled disaster for the whole community, since it would have become impossible to maintain the link with Shetland. Fortunately the Zetland

County Council came to the rescue, improving the slipway and installing a power-driven winch, to the cost of which the islanders themselves (and many 'Friends of Fair Isle') contributed £300. Quite apart from alleviating the manpower problem, the new winch so speeded up the launching and hauling that *The Good Shepherd* gained well over an hour on the round trip—an important saving in the winter months which enabled her crew to complete the journey in daylight.

When we left in 1956 the native population was down to 44, and the subject of possible evacuation was on everyone's lips, though none had any real desire to go. It was at this critical period that the National Trust for Scotland, which had taken over the responsibility for the island from George Waterston in 1954, laid plans with Zetland County Council for improving the harbour, installing running water and electricity in the houses, enlarging and improving the homes of those who had growing families, and introducing handloom weaving as a winter craft. Some newcomers joined the community and stayed for a time, but attempts to inflate the population in this way have not yet met with permanent success. It is unlikely that they will. Reviewing the current situation, Peter Davis expresses the view that there will be a "succession of romantic enthusiasts who will enjoy the novelty of island life for a few years, and then depart". Practically all the applicants who have so far come forward for the vacant places at Fair Isle have been escapists from civilisation who look at island life through rose-tinted spectacles; such people are by nature 'intellectuals' and nonconformists, with no chance of succeeding in a community which "inevitably values practical far above intellectual abilities, and which seeks to exact a high level of conformity in nearly all individual and communal activities, including, of course, religious practices".

There is also a biological problem—in fact, two problems. Nearly half of the existing community is on the wrong side of fifty, and can hardly remain active for more than a further decade. The possibility of an able succession to carry on the native skills has been completely thwarted by a curious and inexplicable imbalance in the sex ratio—for of a score of children born in the past three decades, all but one have been boys. The great majority have naturally emigrated, or will almost certainly do so on completing their education outwith the island. Even if we assume that immigration *could* make good these losses, there is still the problem of competition, in the biological sense. The relatively few families that remain would be unlikely to dissipate the remunerative accumulation of 'ancillary tasks' that has fallen to their lot, and without a share of this to bolster the subsistence crofting, it is difficult to see how any incomer could succeed. Much of the recent development sponsored by the National Trust for Scotland has been aimed at improving amenities rather than reinvigorating the economy, and with the economy at its present restricted level it is hard enough for anyone to achieve a reasonable standard of living as the reward of hard work on land and sea, and the sublimation of individuality to the demands of community life and thought.

The kernel of the whole problem is perhaps the same today as it was eleven years ago when the men sweated and strained at the long-handled winch above the North Haven shore. Davis writes: "Even if the crew of *The Good Shepherd* relished the idea of introducing outsiders into the crew, which at present they do not, they estimate it would be at least ten years before an incomer would have a working knowledge of one of the trickiest crossings in northern Europe. The transport problem is therefore the rock upon which the whole enterprise is most likely to founder."

§

There were two important days in the Fair Isle week, and the Sabbath was the first. The double event of Sunday was the religious gathering. There is no religious bigotry at Fair Isle: the same folk attend both Church and Chapel, going to the one in the morning and the other in the evening—the order of attendance being reversed on successive Sundays. Chapel services are conducted by a lay preacher, James Wilson of Schooltown, whose uncle was the preacher before him. The Church has a missionary, whose wife is responsible for the School. Each Sunday the psalms and hymns are sung with a gusto that would put most mainland congregations to shame, and although the sermon is listened to with due respect, it does not escape caustic criticism afterwards if it falls short of the high standard expected.

You may well be mystified when told by some member of the congregation that this church was once under the sea. This is true enough in an oblique sort of way, for when the building blocks were brought to the isle there was no quay upon which to land them, so they were dumped overboard in South Harbour at high tide, and manhandled on to the Kirki Geo beach at successive ebbs. The place-name Kirki Geo, however, probably has a more prosaic explanation; it may well have been the site of an earlier church, close to the existing graveyard on whose cliff-top walls the fulmars sit and cackle in courtship while interesting migrants lurk among the graves.

The second important day during our period at the isle was 'Boat-day'. Officially this was Wednesday, but occasionally there were delays, especially in winter. At the observatory, 'Boat-day' was all hustle and bustle from the crack of dawn, beginning with an early greeting to postmaster Douglas Stout over the telephone, and a request for up-to-the-minute information. If the lights were lit in the cottages Douglas assumed that the boat would go, and we put Plan A into operation. This was simple. We knocked at the bedroom doors to rouse departing guests, murmuring encouraging (but not necessarily truthful) remarks about the weather and the state of the sea, and then put an equivalent number of eggs in a pan to boil. If the lights were off in the village Douglas assumed that the crew had not liked the look of the sky and had gone back to bed, and we operated Plan B, which was to follow their example.

The only fault with Plan B was that it tended to introduce too many potential 'Boat-days' to the week and made utter confusion of the calendar. Also, it upset the visitors. One would imagine that the prospect of an extra day or two of carefree holiday in such pleasant surroundings would act like a tonic on these escapists from the slavish routines of civilisation, but it hardly ever seemed to work out that way. Even the nicest people became irritable when the weather and the boat's crew conspired to dislocate their carefully laid plans for sacrificing body and soul once more to the humdrum round of urban life; and much the worst were those who had had the foresight to dose themselves with remedies for a form of sickness they were not to be permitted to endure.

However, one best remembers those happier dawns when all went well and the lorry rumbled down to the quay, and the men laughed and joked as they launched the flit-boat to ferry luggage, mail-bags and passengers to *The Good Shepherd* as she swayed expectantly at her moorings in North Haven. If it was autumn the lambs were given the lee-side and the passengers were left to fend for themselves. The chain rattled as the boat was freed from her moorings; the *plop, plop* of the diesel engine snatched at the still air, heckling the distant concert of the grey seals on Kubbi Skerry, and soon the ship was a white speck on a dark waste with the lighthouses of Skroo and Sumburgh winking playfully at each other over her dipping mast. Eight hours or so later eyes ashore were straining to observe her return. She would come white and graceful as a winter swan to her moorings, and the rattle of the chain being taken up would signify the end—and beginning—of another week.

Not everyone was down at the quay to see her return, eager for a sight of new faces, or curious to know what her cargo contained. For on the afternoon of 'Boat-day' the mail-bags were among the first items ashore, to be whisked away to the Post Office, where the unoccupied element of the community waited in keen anticipation, whiling away the time in a buzz of gossip. The little white Post Office often looked as if it would burst at the seams with the press of humanity within, and if you could squeeze past the parked prams and cycles and motor-bikes and in through the door you were lucky.

The mail-sorting was ceremonial, and the buzz of conversation gave way to a quiet, expectant hush when it began, with Douglas intoning the surnames and the crofts and putting each item carefully into an eagerly outstretched hand. When the last letter had been delivered, and read there in the Post Office, there was more gossip about absent friends and relatives—this time refreshingly authentic and up-to-date. Then the all-important C.O.D. parcels were claimed; naturally the Fair Isle housewives do a good deal of their shopping by post, and there are colourful catalogues for a wide variety of goods among the newspapers and magazines in every cottage. Soon the lorry appeared, dropping crofters and cargo here and there by the wayside, and gradually everyone drifted home to sample the fresh bread and 'fancies' which *The Good Shepherd* had brought.

The tidal range at Fair Isle is small, from about six feet at springs to three feet at neaps; even so, the pier built by the Northern Lights Commissioners at North Haven years ago hardly got its toes wet at high tide, and was out of reach of the smallest flit-boat at low water. The mail-boat could be brought alongside only on rare occasions, and then for a brief period only, so that flitting sheep, cargo and passengers was a time-consuming occupation. Sometimes the passengers had to scramble the last few yards over rounded boulders draped with the wrinkled belts of slippery oarweed. In 1958 all this was changed when a deep-water pier, an extension of the existing inadequate one, was constructed at a cost of £9,000—a joint undertaking by the Zetland County Council and the National Trust for Scotland. This tremendous improvement to the harbour facilities means that not only the mail-boat, but also much larger vessels such as the annual coal-boat, can be moored alongside at any state of the tide, and discharged with complete efficiency. Moreover, units of the Shetland fishing-fleet can now tie up and shelter securely in North Haven if the need arises.

I visited Fair Isle with the National Trust's 'Islands Cruise' ship M.S. *Meteor* on the day the new pier was officially opened. There was a sprinkling of Zetland County Councillors and other Shetland friends of the isle who had come with M.V. *Earl of Zetland* from Lerwick, and altogether the hospitable islanders played host to some 250 people on this historic day. After the speech-making, which was short and to the point, the tape was cut by George ('Dodie') Stout, the Skipper of *The Good Shepherd*, and the throng dispersed 'down the isle' to have lunch in the Village Hall. The water smiled with reflected sunlight, the gay flags and bunting clapped hands in the breeze, and although there was no brass band to provide music nobody cared. The song of a wren on the Stack o' North Haven, the cackling of fulmars under Hoilie and the wood-wind rejoicing of

oystercatchers on Buness made a far more authentic accom-
paniment to the simple ceremony.

§

Twice or thrice every year a snap decision is made to climb
Sheep Craig, a massive sandstone stack joined to the height of
Vaasetter by a razor-edge of crumbling rock which not even
the rabbits can pass, and therefore accessible only from the sea.
A number of sheep, Cheviot or Cheviot-Shetland cross, graze
the eleven acres of rich grassland on its sloping top, and these
have to be 'rooed' in June or July for their wool, and revisited
in autumn to remove the season's lambs, and sometimes to
change the tup. The small boats, their outboard engines
purring, take the assault party from South Harbour round
Meoness, inside the stacks of Da Burrian and Da Fles, and
across the Wick o' Hesswalls to the low sloping slabs at the foot
of 'the Rock'.

There is a thrilling approach to this landing which the Fair
Isle men use if they want to give their guests a special treat, for
the boat can be sailed through a long and eerie tunnel which
pierces Sheep Craig's south-east point. This tunnel forks about
half-way through the rock, and even on the calmest day the
surge of tidal currents where the three passages meet in twilight
is an alarming sight to the uninitiated. It is with a sigh of relief
that one feels the boat steadying up after her plunging progress
through the swirling cauldron of frothy water, and sees the
welcoming glimmer of sunlight in the cave-mouth ahead.

The first part of the ascent is easy enough, a climb up an
inclined face of rock to the beginning of a narrow ledge which
interrupts the precipitous north wall of the Geo o' Sheep Craig,
and affords an impressive view of the inky waters beneath—a
view which effectively halts a number of visitors at that point!
The men stride along the ledge as though it were Princes Street,
disdaining to use the rope handrail which lesser mortals (if they
get so far) find a great help. At the far end of the sloping ledge,
where it meets the inner wall of the geo, a galvanised chain
hangs from the cliff-top eighty feet above. The chain is safe
enough (they will tell you it is tested twice a year—by the first

man up!)—and anyway, if it is any comfort, your friends will lower a rope from the top and see that it is well and truly tied round your middle.

Up you go, hand over hand, grasping the chain for dear life and finding precarious footholds in the cliff-face, while sulky fulmars spit at you from their nesting nooks on either hand. Soon the last climbers are sitting on the plush sward at the cliff-top, taking a short breather and discussing tactics for the operation against the sheep. As you look around you notice that all the animals have fled to the highest part of 'the Rock' and stand there etched against the skyline, impudently challenging the men to toil to the top and chase them down! You may hear a wren or a rock pipit singing on the cliff below, or a skylark somewhere against the blue above. The nesting gulls, among them a number of greater blackbacks, wheel over-head cackling their anxiety and alarm, for many have chicks in the long grass. On the opposite side of the chasm the puffins stand outside their burrows to stare with comical curiosity at this untoward intrusion.

Beyond the puffins, in the south-east corner of 'the Rock', there is a fairly flat promontory, and here a pallisade of rope netting is rigged up to serve as a fold. When this is done every-one expresses the hope that the sheep will go in at the first time of asking, for nobody fancies the idea of toiling twice to the summit on this warm summer's day. When all is ready for the 'caaing' a few men climb aloft while we others conceal ourselves in depressions and behind rocks low down near the netting, so that we can rush from hiding at the proper moment and con-tain the sheep. Soon, peeping round the rock, we see the sheep spilling down off the summit and wonder how they can possibly stop before gravity takes them over the edge; but they do, huddling together and turning warily to watch their pursuers and consider the next move. This is the critical psychological moment for concerted action on the part of all the men, who rush whooping from their retreats and steer the flock neatly into the hastily improvised 'cro'. The lambs are examined (there are usually between fifteen and eighteen accompanying the dozen ewes), and the ram and the ewes are clipped, their fleeces being folded and stuffed into sacks.

While all this is going on you should have time to climb to
the summit of 'the Rock'—believed to be about 420 feet—and
get a new prospect of Fair Isle, looking south-west over the
diminutive whitewashed cottages and chequered fields of the
crofting land, west across the dark moorland to the dome of
Ward Hill, and north over Buness and the two Havens to the
three humps of Sumburgh Head in the distance—and perhaps
even farther to the island of Noss if it is an exceptionally clear
day. There may be time to peer over the edge in a few places
in an effort to locate the peregrines' eyrie, for in some years a
pair nests at Sheep Craig though usually their home is on the
western cliffs. Formerly this was also the site of a white-tailed
eagles' eyrie. Soon you will notice that the netting is being
gathered up down below, and it is time to descend. The boat is
hailed, and the last member of the party is soon on his way
down the chain to the narrow ledge, the wool-sack slung over
his shoulders. The top of 'the Rock' is once more the domain
of the baaing, disgruntled sheep (now up at the summit again!)
and their neighbours the puffins and gulls, who are likely to
keep undisputed possession for the next three months.

§

Yet another island festival must be recalled with affection—
the annual visit of the coal-boat. Formerly peat was the staple
fuel, as on other islands of the north and west, but a combination of circumstances led to its decline. The best quality peat-
banks on the northern flank of Ward Hill were worked out
years ago, while the demand grew less as open hearths were
gradually replaced by cottage ranges and newer types of cooker.
Moreover, the summers have become too wet for the protracted
business of cutting and drying the turves to fit smoothly into
the calendar of Fair Isle life, so that it is much cheaper in terms
of time and labour to use imported coal.

Some time in June or July a small collier comes north from
Methil on the Fife coast with a year's supply of coal for the two
lighthouses and fifteen crofts, also the Schoolhouse and Bird
Observatory—a load of well over a hundred tons. For a
fortnight before her arrival the coal-boat is the main topic of

conversation, and everyone prays that the wind will keep out of the north-east so that she can lie snugly in North Haven until her precious cargo is discharged. Usually she goes to the Orkney light-stations first, and her progress is followed with keen interest from the conversations between Principal Keepers over their short-wave radios. At length the news that she has left North Ronaldsay flashes through the isle, and all is made ready for her reception.

We well remember the hours of apprehension one autumn morning (she was late that year) when the collier arrived off the isle in a thick fog and *The Good Shepherd* put out in a hurry to find her and guide her into North Haven. It was like a game of hide and seek, for as soon as *The Good Shepherd* got into the Wick o' Furse the collier stopped blowing, and the island boat searched in vain. The men returned dismayed, thinking she must have decided to make for Lerwick; but no sooner were they ashore than *Columbine* started blowing again, this time somewhere south of Sheep Craig. There was nothing for it but to let go the mooring-chain and begin the search anew. This time *Columbine* was found and escorted in, being duly warped to the Stack o' North Haven on one side and a cavernous hole in the cliff-face of Hoilie on the other.

The biggest of the flit-boats (there's a tall story that the Vikings built her!) was always pressed into service on this one occasion, and for the rest of the year comprised Fair Isle's moth-ball fleet; it brought coal ashore by the ten-ton load, and the bags were lifted on to the quay by a small hand-operated crane. There was that never-to-be-forgotten occasion when this crane, unlike the men who toiled and sweated beneath it, groaned loudly and toppled into the sea—fortunately without seriously injuring anyone. The remaining ninety tons of coal had to be manhandled from the flit-boats to the shore, a back-breaking job, especially at ebb tide when slippery weed swathed the rocks below the quay.

Even so, the weariness at the end of the day was merely physical, for unloading the coal-boat was always a happy occasion, the men working together in harmony and swapping yarns about island events and worthies of past generations, in their fluent and richly-musical tongue. Between whiles there

FIB B

were halts when the hostel maids came down to the quay
bearing tea-trays in their lilywhite hands, and poked malicious
fun at the 'nigger minstrels' they served. Those men who
delivered coal on the lorries could never get away from a croft
whose storehouse they had filled without taking some refresh-
ment from a grateful wife, and they were constantly chafed on
their return for having taken time off while the pile of bags at
the harbour grew ever higher. It was all the best of fun, and
the last load ashore in the gathering dusk brought a great sigh
of relief, for there are few things more important to an isolated
community than to have the winter's fuel safe and secure
beside the cottages.

§

The Fair Isle folk have long been impressed by the flood of
birds which descends on their fields from time to time in spring
and autumn when tired migrants are blown across the North
Sea from the Skagerrak and Continental coasts. An intelligent
interest in these transient visitors, fostered by their exceptionally keen powers of observation, has made men like James
Wilson of Schooltown and James A. Stout of Mires—both sons
of fine bird-watchers—accomplished artists in the identification
of birds. And there are others whose knowledge, while not
outstanding, nevertheless combines to put Fair Isle in a unique
position for a rural community. The isle has a quite remarkable
ornithological grape-vine, an invaluable accessory to the Bird
Observatory's work.

New birds, especially when they happen to be really rare
ones, make unforgettable occasions, and one I am never likely
to forget was my first Pechora pipit *Anthus gustavi*, a Siberian
species of which there were then about a dozen known occurrences in western Europe, all at Fair Isle. With a friend,
Edward Skinner, I had spent a long morning trying to get a
good look at a 'peerie' brown bird as it skulked in the Schooltown cabbages, but when disturbed it merely hurtled with a
loud and almost explosive *pwit* into the Quoy cabbage-patch
across the way. We never saw it well, but by eliminating every
other small brown bird we could think of we concluded it might

be a Pechora pipit. We decided to ask Jimmy Wilson to look at it; being one of the few men in Britain who have ever seen the species, he would be sure to know.

So I knocked at the Schooltown door, and Jimmy stood there in his shirt-sleeves, his youngest son in his arms. "Fine day!" he said, and I agreed, adding, "Can you spare a moment to look at a strange bird in your cabbages?" He could, and did, and when the bird rose from cover he saw it no more clearly than we had done, but, hearing its distinctive note, he said without a moment's hesitation, "That's a Pechora pipit!" We were overawed. Where else in the whole of Europe could you knock on a man's door and ask him to confirm a putative Pechora pipit in his cabbage-patch?

Every community needs a good, healthy field sport, and Fair Isle is no exception; its interest in birds is sometimes far more lethal than intellectual. There is plenty of outdoor exercise to be had, of course, in rounding up the sheep on the hill, or during those joyful escapades on 'the Rock'; but the real exercise and excitement are reserved for the late autumn, when the woodcock spill out of a rough wintry sky on to the brown heather of hill and moor. Woodcock are good to eat, and provide the isle with one of its few profitable exports—but it is concern neither for the inner man nor the family exchequer which makes woodcock-time so attractive to the men. They have just finished a long spell in the field lifting the 'taties' and chopping off the turnip-tops, and now is the time for some well-earned relaxation. They rise before dawn to feel the pulse of the wind and study the sky, and if the signs are good they are quickly on the road, each man heading for his favourite reach of the hill. And woe betide any 'cock' that dares to cross, or sit in, his path!

As my own particular field sport was trapping and ringing the redwings and blackbirds which always came in with the 'cocks' I was a mere listener-in to this festival; for even in the half-light shotguns were popping all over the place, and misty plodding figures moved to and fro in the grey curtains of swirling rain. All day long the talk was of woodcock—how many there were, how many there might be tomorrow if the weather held, whose marksmanship seemed likely to put him at the top of the league table—and who had wasted the most cartridges. Fieldy George, the island's arch leg-puller, retold the story of how he had once shot 101 'cocks' with 99 cartridges, and, warming to his task, went on to tell of even more unlikely things. Sometimes, at the close of such a day, we would be sitting in the cosy parlour at Lower Leogh enjoying an evening's bridge, and Jerry Stout would argue heatedly with me between the bidding (to the intense annoyance of our wives) as to the route by which the day's woodcocks had come. Jerry could never stomach the newfangled migration theories of Bird Observatory days, which to his mind left far too much to the whims of the wind and far too little to the navigational skill of the birds.

Those and similar social evenings at other homes were a sheer delight, and afterwards there was the cycle-ride home with the rain at our backs—or perhaps a lift on the lorry, towards the crackling, ever-shifting coloured folds of the *aurora borealis* which reduced the revolving beam of Skroo Lighthouse to the meanest of gleams. At other times we took our entertainment in the little cinema which was established, largely through the efforts of the Queen's Nurse, Miss Margaret Cairns, in the Village Hall; but more often, both there and in the Coronation Hall at the Bird Observatory, social affairs took a more energetic form. Usually such evenings began with a whist-drive—always a deadly serious business at Fair Isle—and after a respite for tea and buns the evening soared to new heights of cheerful bonhommie as islanders and bird-watchers alike took off their jackets and joined in the dancing. With the 'boys' from Stoneybrake and Houll and one or other of the lightkeepers coaxing a riot of music from their fiddles, guitars and piano-accordions, the evening accelerated through saltations of reels, old-fashioned waltzes, dashing white sergeants and the like. There was always the grand climax of 'the Sheep Hill'—and if you are curious to know how that is done you must go to Fair Isle and find out!

Then came a second round of tea and biscuits long after midnight when the blackbirds and woodcocks were beginning to fall unseen from the inky sky, and after that we joined hands and sang 'Auld Lang Syne'. The villagers donned their hats and coats and clambered aboard the Leogh-Taft lorry, pulling a huge tarpaulin tent-like over themselves to keep off the rain. The engine roared into life, and, still singing, they were rushed off into the night. If the Fair Isle folk worked hard they played hard too, and as we watched them go from the shadowy huts at the foot of the hill we wondered if there was any small community which effervesced with so much good humour, and had so huge an appetite for life.

CHAPTER II

MAINLY HISTORICAL

FAIR ISLE is dominated by Ward Hill, a gentle moorland dome which rises to 712 feet above the sea. The top of it, and the upper reach of Swey below the dome, was a wretched rubbish-dump of war-time litter—battered brick and concrete walls, stout wooden gantries, broken bits of radar aerials, rusting corrugated iron sheets from gale-torn Nissen huts, scattered items of electrical and electronic equipment, to say nothing of an inestimable number of miles of cable and wire. The radar installations were the last of a long line of 'watch and ward' stations which began with the beacon lighted in the year 1135 to warn Earl Paul of Orkney of the approach from Shetland of a Viking fleet.

Almost as bad as the mess on the hill-top are the long bands of concertina Dannert-wire which snake across the moorland from Auld Jeems' Hill in the north round the West Hill Cups to the impressive cleft of Guidicum. The only good thing to be said of these pitiful barriers is that they provide some cover for migrant birds, unless we can also count on the credit side the surety that some day they will have crumbled into dust. Not so the concrete gun emplacements and ugly brick buildings and the rusting machinery they were set up to protect, and this part of Fair Isle, alas, is forever scarred. Some of the mess has recently been cleared on the initiative of the National Trust for Scotland—to the dismay of the islanders, who value the ruins for the shelter they give to the hill sheep in winter and early spring.

On the seaward slope of the hill there is a steeply canted triangle of green ground, Da Toor, its apex a narrow bridge separating the chasms of North and South Fellsigeo. You can descend the latter with some difficulty to the beach inside

Matchi Stack, below Skinner's Glig; and if place-names mean anything at all Erne's Brae, a little to the south, was probably the site of a white-tailed eagle's eyrie not much more than a century ago. (Sheep Craig on the east coast is also said to have been a sea-eagle site.) The view southwards, looking past the Ranges o' Guidicum, takes in perhaps the most colourful and diversified cliff-architecture of the island; but in the other direction the sheer black gash of North Fellsigeo is awful in the extreme. It was the scene of a courageous night rescue in the spring of 1955, when an islander unwisely attempted single-handed to rescue a fallen ewe and her lamb, and finished up with a broken thigh on a narrow ledge fifty feet above the sea—miraculously alive. It was midnight before he was found, and four hours more before he was strapped to a mountain rescue stretcher and laboriously hauled in the fitful light of Tilley flares to the top. This remarkable feat earned for the whole island the Carnegie Hero Fund's bronze medallion—their highest award—now displayed in the Village Hall.

Past Guidicum the coast recedes beyond the shelving grassy slope of Lerness, to the south of which another crumbling earth-bridge between the heads of North and South Naaversgill gives adventurous access to Burrista. Like Da Toor, this long narrow slope harboured many puffins in the first two summers of our stay, but latterly this picturesque species has decreased con-siderably in number. The coast rises again to the whale-back hill of Burrashield, which is severed half-way along its length by another dark and dismal cleft called Troila Geo. Down below another puffin colony inhabits a small boulder-slope, locked in by the high precipitous walls. Looked at from above, the gloomy boulder-strewn interior does indeed impress one as a highly desirable residence for trolls, those wicked fairies which so plagued the minds of the superstitious Norsemen. I have shown in *A Mosaic of Islands* how place-names with this root, in the Faeroe Islands and on Rhum of the Inner Hebrides, are associated with Manx shearwater rookeries, the nocturnal clamour of which mystified the Vikings and (one hopes!) struck fear into their hearts; and although I have listened for shear-water voices here and elsewhere along the west coast during nocturnal prowls, Troila Geo has invariably proved disappointing, though it is exactly the kind of situation where a shearwater colony might have existed years ago.

The next hill to the south, cleaner and greener than Burra-shield, being grassy and not a mixture of recumbent juniper and heather, is Hoini, over the hill-dyke which reaches the edge of the land above the picturesque gap of Gunnawark. Among the great boulders of the storm-beaches below, as on many similar places around the coast, is a big colony of shags, and when ringing the young one has to pass between the north and south beaches by lying flat on one's back and wriggling through a man-sized hole in the rocky point. As one walks the length of Hoini there are many fine stacks diversifying the coastal panorama, and inland the chequered crofting land extends to the low southern coast.

Ahead, the whole of the southern aspect is dominated by Malcolm's Head, also a place of 'watch and ward' since the island made its bow in history as Fridarey of the *Orkneyinga Saga*.* Etched against the skyline of this magnificent headland, with the thin strip of Orkney hazy-blue 25 miles away, are the ruins of the blockhouse built at the time of the Napoleonic war, cheek by jowl with the modern coast-watchers' hut, for it is here that the island-men keep a vigilant look-out to sea when the gales are at their worst. Between Hoini and Malcolm's Head the low land is broken by the Reevas, twin blow-holes inside the western cliffs. The cavern which brings the tide into the southern one is still arched over by a narrow green bridge, but the roof of the northern cave is said to have collapsed with a thunderous roar early one morning at the beginning of the present century.

§

Fair Isle has a few antiquities, though it is by no means so richly endowed with early monuments as Orkney and Shetland. It seems never to have attracted the archaeologists, and so far

---

* The isle is mentioned in *Njal's Saga* (translated by Magnus Magnusson and Herman Pálsson, 1960), which was written down towards the close of the thirteenth century. It was the springboard of Kari Solmundarson's mission of vengeance against the burners of Njal Thorgeirsson and his family; he stayed with the laird, David the White, during the winter of 1013-14.

as we can recall this was one of the interests which did not take advantage of the facilities afforded by the Bird Observatory, though we had botanists, mammalogists, entomologists, philologists, marine biologists and others during our stay. (There was even one gentleman whose ambition over many years had been to perambulate the whole of the Shetland coastline, and who stayed at the Observatory so that he could complete this delightful task!) There are, of course, many richer fields to tempt the active archaeologist, and the few much-broken tumuli and promontory forts of Fair Isle are not a sufficient attraction while the march of progress threatens so many important sites on the mainland. As for ourselves, we have only a nodding acquaintance with affairs of the distant past: they provoke in us interest and wonder, but do not tempt us to indulge in the sin of digging up sites which are better left as they are until someone with the knowledge and special training for such work comes along. The folk-culture of the isle has been well served by a few devoted students, among whom must be mentioned island-born Jerome Eunson, who has set down the haf-names and fishing-marks, and has listed the wrecks; and the late warden Peter Davis, who with the islanders' help has collected and mapped the place-names.

There is no doubt that Fair Isle shares with Orkney and Shetland a very long history of habitation, for the evidence is everywhere on the moorland and in the rough pastures of Hoolalie between Setter and Pund. The tumuli and earthworks in this region are elaborate and their complexity baffles understanding, while the remains include what is, according to the Royal Commission on Ancient Monuments, probably the largest mound of burnt stones in Shetland. The present wall separating in-bye from outfield runs across the island from Gunnawark to Hesswalls, only a few yards outside an earlier earth rampart, the Feely Dyke, now honeycombed with rabbit burrows. There are the remnants of an interesting promontory fort on Landberg, beside Mavers Geo, directly behind the Bird Observatory, and there the rabbits occasionally dig out bits of crude pottery.

An old stone dyke, probably many centuries old, runs downhill from Troila Geo on Burrashield to the Sukka Mire below, and there is a similar dyke of irregularly spaced boulders across Ulieshield linking Easter Lother Water and Golden Water. Here and there the remains of stone circles plague one's imagination—like the one to the south of Lerness, inside Burrista, and what must once have been a far more impressive structure in Homisdale. Here a pair of 'portal' stones stand above the heather, and other boulders are clearly aligned towards them; but many of the stones which formed this fascinating complex have obviously been built into the local plantacrubs in which cabbage seedlings are raised.

So it is that we turned, in something akin to frustration, to the more tangible antiquities of a comparatively recent epoch. Yet here too, sophisticated far beyond its isolation, Fair Isle has little of interest other than its corn-drying kilns and watermills on the Shetland model. How often, as a change from birds, have we not looked into the now roofless kilns at Shirva (nicely thatched until about 1954), at Springfield (the only one

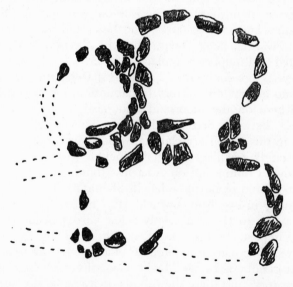

Fig. 1. Stone Circles near the Brae of Lerness, possibly the foundations of an oblong hut with beehive-shaped sleeping chambers. The larger one is about 9 ft. and the smaller one about 6 ft. 9 ins. internal diameter.

with a window), and beside the slate-flagged house at Barkland —especially Barkland, which has the only remaining hand-quern at Fair Isle.

In these buildings the threshing and winnowing took place before the green barley was dried in the apse-like oven built on to the gable wall. The procedure seems to have been much the same as in the Faeroese *sodnhús*, which I have described fully in a previous book, *The Atlantic Islands*. A fire was lit on the floor of the oven, and the sheaves were placed on a platform or shelf of wooden laths about four feet above, so that the ears were thoroughly smoked and dried. Afterwards the grain, if not ground in the hand-querns (that at Barkland stands on its own bench in the main section of the kiln-house), was taken to one or other of the mills.

There are the remains of mill-dams at the head of Vaadal and on the Gilsetter Burn just behind the Gully Trap. The isle had several mills, all served by this stream. There was Vaadal Mill below the Brae o' Tarryfield, Pund Mill just below the observatory's little plantation at the mouth of the glen, Leogh Mill across the road next to the Gilsetter marsh, and Shuny Mill at the dam behind the Gully Trap. It is just about possible to make out the sites of these mills (they are fortunately all plotted now on Davis's place-names map), but the only two where much original masonry remains are the Shirva and New Mills using the same race above the waterfall at the head of the Gill o' Finniquoy.

Fig. 2. Corn-drying Kiln at Shirva.

§

An Irish verse of the time of King Cormac MacArt tells how a beautiful handmaiden was relieved of the daily drudgery of grinding by hand-quern when the king brought a millwright across the sea. 'Over the sea' has been taken to mean Scotland, but although 'clack-mills' of a similar kind to King Cormac's were once common enough in the north and west of Scotland it is hardly likely they were much used there, if at all, before his day. Watermills seem to have been commonplace in Ireland by the seventh century, generally associated with religious houses, and the *Annals of Ulster* tell of one Constantine, king of Damnonia in Britain, who abdicated and became

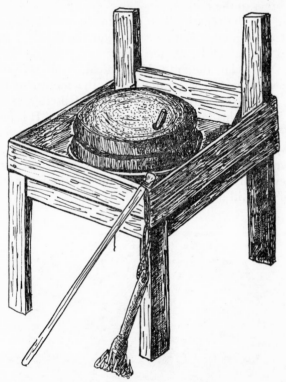

Fig. 3. Hand-quern, mounted on a wooden stand, and a flail in the Barkland drying-kiln.

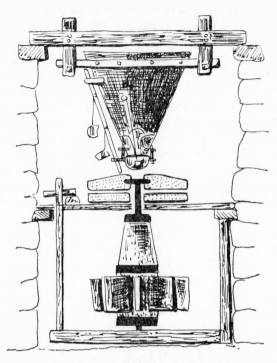

FIG. 4. Mechanism of a horizontal watermill, described on pp. 30-32. In some the grinding stones were set on a bench in the upper house, in others they were on the floor (as shown here). The 'tirl' driving the upper stone had eight or more wooden blades, usually canted to take the maximum force of the incoming stream. The 'sword' and 'lightening-tree', a device to adjust the aperture between the millstones, was a feature of mills with a Norse influence.

At left: The 'tirl' of New Mill, Fair Isle, showing the sockets for the canted wooden blades; and the iron 'sile' which joined the axle to the upper millstone (not to scale).

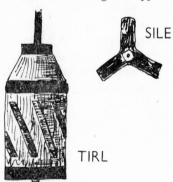

SILE

TIRL

miller to an Irish monastery. Scottish rural milling doubtless
drew its main influence from the Vikings in the ninth and
tenth centuries, and the existence of marked structural differences between the early mills of Scotland and Ireland lends
colour to the view that they had an independent origin.

These primitive mills were of the 'horizontal' kind—that is
to say, the wheel lay horizontally on the stream-bed, driving
an upright axle, instead of turning in a vertical plane and
driving the millstone by means of a horizontal shaft and intermediate gearing as in the much improved Roman type of mill.
There is a picturesque simile, dating from about the tenth
century, in which the action of this horizontal wheel is likened
to the famous whirlpool of Correy Vreckan, between Scarba
and Jura. Compared with the later Roman type the horizontal
mill was a diminutive affair, the 'tirl' (wheel and axle) being
contained in a cellar or underhouse hardly two yards square
and open at two sides so that the stream had an uninterrupted
flow.

The mechanism of the early Scottish and Fair Isle mills
doubtless differed only in minor detail from one I sketched
while its tirl and millstone were rattling away, smothering the
whole interior in a smog of fine particles of brown flour, at
Saltangará in the Faeroe Islands in 1942 (fig. 4). The axle
passed into the mealhouse through a central hole in the fixed
netherstone and engaged the upper millstone by means of
an iron 'sile', so that this stone revolved at the same rate as
the wheel. Corn was fed to the 'eye' of the upper stone from
a hopper suspended from the roof, often by straw ropes, and
the flow from this container was usually regulated by means
of a 'shoe' with an adjustable spout. A shaking motion was
given to this shoe, or to the shoe and hopper combined, by the
jolting of a fixed stick, or stones tied by string, which were
allowed to drag against the turning millstone.

At the beginning of the nineteenth century mills of this kind
were numerous among the Scottish Isles, and Henrey Evershed
wrote in 1874 that half-a-dozen families often co-operated in
building a mill, using it in rotation. There was a similar
arrangement in most of the Faeroe villages—not always atten-
ded by happy results, since one on Nólsoy was called Tvistur,

meaning 'to argue', because its owners could never agree whose turn it was to grind! Sometimes the mills were owned by the richer farmers, or by the clergy, but in Faeroe at any rate were often lent to the poorer folk free of charge. Only a rogue, an old Faeroeman told me, would demand a fee for so small a service!

Yet despite the praise of the Irish poet, the watermill seems to have become a mixed blessing to many communities. In Scotland legal means were adopted to compel people to use the watermills instead of their hand-querns, while in England almost every manor had its Roman mill by the close of the eleventh century, the peasants being under obligation to use it to the profit of the lord, and to the farmer or miller who more than paid for his lease by the toll he extracted. Sir Anthony Fitzherbert scathingly remarked in his *Boke of Surveying* of 1539, "ther be soo many diversities of taking tolle that I shall not take uppon me to telle howe . . . but doubt ye not, the mylner will be no losers." Manx millers were apparently not more honest than their brethren across the waters, and a common epithet applied to a dishonest person was *goaill foilliu keayrt*—'taking toll twice'.

Nevertheless, down the centuries the ancient hand-quern and the primitive watermill existed side by side; and on one Faeroe island, Koltur, I found a tiny wooden mill with its horizontal wheel harnessed to a hand-quern so that the farmer could disconnect the apparatus and do the work himself when the burn ran dry. There does not ever appear to have been a watermill on St Kilda's only suitable stream; in 1819 Mac-Culloch noted that every household had its own quern, and broken pieces of these can still be found among the rubbish lying inside the deserted cottages.

Shetland mills, like the Fair Isle ones, were solid stone-built structures with a roof of straw thatch. (I have seen a photograph of the New Mill, taken during the first world war, when it was last used, showing the straw roof.) Sometimes the mill-stones were on the floor of the mealhouse, and sometimes they were mounted on a wooden bench. Many of the mills I examined in the Faeroe Islands were replicas of Faeroese homes in being made of timber, superimposed on a cellar of basalt

stones; they were roofed with green, grassy turves packed on top
of a layer of imported birch-bark. Here and there, however, I
found bigger and entirely stone-built mills so much at odds
with the traditional domestic architecture of the Faeroes that
they may well indicate Shetland influence. This would be
understandable, since Lerwick was sometimes visited by
Faeroemen in their twelve-oared boats during the eighteenth
and nineteenth centuries.

There were tantalising differences in the structure of the
horizontal mills in the British area, one kind being typically
Irish, and the other characteristically Norse. The Irish mills
had the more elaborate wheel, comprising a large number of
narrow vanes carved into a spoon or ladle shape, the better to
grip the force of the water. In the Hebrides, Orkney, Shetland,
Faeroe and Norway the wheel was degenerate by comparison,
consisting of eight or twelve flat boards, sometimes canted at
an angle where the inflow was thrown downwards from a
trough. Yet in one important respect the Norse mill was
mechanically superior to the Irish, having a lever mechanism
by which the aperture between the millstones could be controlled, so that the miller could grind coarse or fine as he wished.
The spike or 'gudgeon' at the base of the tirl pivoted in the
middle of a horizontal beam, the 'sole-tree', one end of which
was anchored to the wall of the underhouse and the other
affixed to an upright lever or 'lightening-tree' which could be
raised or lowered by a sword-shaped handle resting on the
bench. This lever does not appear to have been a feature of
the Irish mills at all, the gudgeon resting on a hollow stone
on the stream-bed—so to this extent the Scottish variety represented a distinct engineering advance.

It seems that some Irish influence must have penetrated to
parts of the Highlands, however, for a mill at Kirtomy in
Sutherland was of this kind, and MacCulloch, describing what
he calls 'the Highland Mill', speaks of an axle turning "on any
casual stone by an iron pivot", with a wheel of "sixteen or
eighteen rude sticks, scooped at the outer ends like a spoon".
There is some evidence that both kinds occurred in the Isle of
Man, but that is hardly surprising in view of Manx cultural
connexions with both Ireland and the Hebrides.

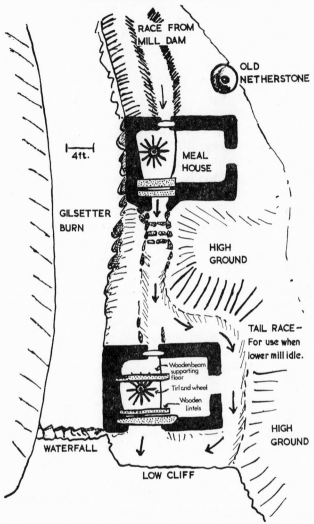

FIG. 5. 'HORIZONTAL' WATERMILLS AT FAIR ISLE

A plan of the Shirva and New Mills (now in ruins) beside the Gilsetter Burn at Finniquoy. The race issuing from the dam in the marshy field above ran through both underhouses, where the flow turned the 12-bladed tirls; it could be diverted when the lower mill was idle. There was little room for the miller: his working-space measured approximately 12 ft. 6 ins. (of which nearly 5 ft. was taken up by the millstones) by just over 7 ft., while the height from floor to thatched gable was about 5 ft. 6 ins.

FIB C

Despite this overlap, the suggestion is strong that the two kinds came into the British area by different routes. King Cormac MacArt, with the welfare of his beautiful handmaiden at heart, may well have sought his millwright in southern France or Spain (or even deeper in the Mediterranean world), where the wheel-spokes were similarly ladle-shaped. The horizontal mill may have come to Ireland along the great west-coast trade route that had meant so much to Irish culture since the days of the megalith builders around 2500 B.C. The mechanically superior Norse mill was in all likelihood brought to Scandinavia by Swedish Vikings raiding and trading down the Volga and other central European rivers to the Near East, and then introduced to northern and western Scotland, Shetland and Faeroe during the ninth and tenth centuries.

Today the problem of their origin is purely academic—what is of more urgent importance is the problem of their survival. When Sir Walter Scott visited Shetland in 1814 there were no fewer than 500 mills, but now nearly all have fallen into rack and ruin. We saw one at work in Dunrossness ten years ago, and along a short stretch of the stream at Spiggie in the same parish we often admired a splendid series which could have been rebuilt as a show-piece without much trouble or expense at that time. At Vementry in Aithsting a mill was restored by Donald Cross some years ago, and there are probably a few elsewhere which could be saved from ultimate decay. The Ministry of Works maintains a fine mill in Orkney. We commend to the National Trust for Scotland the rebuilding of the fine pair, the Shirva and New Mills, whose tirls and millstones are still *in situ* beside the waterfall at Finniquoy. It would be a thousand pities if so splendid a memorial of Norn and Celtic peasant culture as this, the most primitive engine in the world, were to disappear from the British scene, yet there is a grave danger that this could happen within the space of the next few years.

§

There have been stirring episodes in the history of Fair Isle and not least among them were the many wrecks which took place on its red sandstone rocks before the lighthouses gave some measure of security to shipping in 1892. 'Fair Isle—Isle of Wrecks', Roland Svensson called it in his book *Lonely Isles*—and certainly this place has had more than its due share. Fortunately wrecks are few and far between today, and there has been no serious loss of life in the present century. It was a different story years ago when the only warning of impending doom was given by the now derelict rocket-firing emplacement on Tarryfield, almost in the middle of the isle.

Fair Isle lay on the route of ships bound between Baltic ports and the New World. This fact enabled the islanders to carry on a profitable trade with passing vessels in fine weather as they sailed through 'the Hole' between Orkney and the isle; but in foul and murky weather these same vessels were often drifted much too close to the cliffs for safety by the strong tides. Svensson reproduces a list of the known wrecks compiled by Jerome Eunson, an islander who has done much painstaking research into Fair Isle's story. We may assume that the record for the eighteenth and early nineteenth centuries is almost certainly incomplete, and many sad events forgotten, but the years 1868 to 1918 are doubtless better documented and give a truer picture of the dangers attending navigation in these perilous waters. During that half-century no fewer than thirty-three vessels of all sorts and sizes, from the fishing-boat *Intrepid* to the destroyer H.M.S. *Caradoc*, skirmished with the cliffs, and many became total wrecks.

This long cavalcade of destruction is not without its brighter side, for the island-men emerge from this period of their history with a magnificent record of courage and brilliant seamanship which does the small isle resounding credit. Their knowledge, skill and fortitude not only saved many ships, but also succoured hundreds of lives. In the two years 1868-69 alone they rescued nearly 800 German emigrants together with the crews of the two ships, *Lessing* and *Gazelle* of Bremen, which were taking these people to start a new life in the New World. *Gazelle* was fortunate and got off the rocks of Klingers Geo through the exertions of the local boatmen, who succeeded in warping the ship to a safe part of the cliff until the weather eased. The German government rewarded the isle with £100.

Lessing had not been nearly so lucky the year before: she ran fast aground in Klaver Geo west of Sheep Craig on 22nd May, and there can be no doubt that the 465 souls aboard her would have perished but for a stirring rescue operation mounted by the Fair Isle men. Klaver Geo has no beach, only precipitous cliffs, but Hesswalls close by has a little shore at the back of which a tortuous sheep-track scales the cliff—and the island-men ferried the 465 people to this beach by working their small boats through a narrow archway in the rocky point separating the two inlets.

The galvanised chain up which the men now climb to the top of Sheep Craig is a relic of the *Lessing*, and the ship's bell now calls the islanders to Church. How the islandmen got on to the Sheep Craig before 1868 is not recorded, but that they were grazing their small brown Shetland sheep on its grassy top many years earlier is known from the *Diary* of Sir Walter Scott. He visited the isle in the Trinity House yacht in 1814 and wrote: "One immense portion of rock is separated by a chasm from the mainland. As it is covered with herbage on the top, though a literal precipice all round, the natives contrive to ascend the rock by a place which would make a goat dizzy, and then drag the sheep up by ropes, though they sometimes carry a sheep up on their shoulders. The Captain of a sloop of war, being ashore while they were at this work, turned giddy and sick while looking at them." If performed without a fixed rope or chain (as seems likely), then for cragsmanship and sheer nerve this must be ranked second only among regular climbs to the St Kildans' ascents of Stac Biorrach in the sound between Hirta and Soay.

The ship *Hertigan* of Christiansund went to pieces against that 'literal precipice' on 14th December 1876, all hands being lost, but thanks to the islanders' toughness and competence in boat-handling other vessels fared much better. One was the Danish ship *Dronning Louise*, outward bound for Rio de Janeiro with coals from Newcastle: she struck on the south-east coast on 11th August 1884, but a Fair Isle boat put out an anchor and got her off. The crew had to leave her for three days because a gale blew up, but she rode it out and they eventually got her into Lerwick for repair. Twice in 1916, once with *Cio*, a barque of Farsund in Norway carrying a cargo of maize, and on the second occasion with the barque *Sterna* of Copenhagen, the Fair Isle men put out kedge anchors and enabled the vessels to get off the rocks.

Many ships, however, stuck fast and became total losses to their owners. The Dunbar whaler *Blessed Endeavour*, outward bound for Greenland in April 1798; a Dutch smuggler with a wasted load of gin in 1817 (the mate and the boy sat for three days on the Stack o' North Haven before they were rescued); the *Rover* of Kirkcaldy with timber from Nova Scotia, dismasted during an Atlantic gale in October 1831, and thrown on to the rocks at Hesswalls where none but the mate survived—and so the catalogue goes on. It was an ill wind in the proverbial sense that cast S.S. *Duncan* ashore in thick fog in July 1877: she was bound for Archangel with a Glasgow preacher as passenger, and the islanders benefited to the tune of a Sunday sermon (a rare luxury in those days) and the christening of eight of their children.

Local knowledge of the winds and tides has not always conferred immunity for Jerry Eunson's list enumerates several Shetland packet-boats which have come to grief at the isle—*Star of the West*, *Golden Fleece*, *Rising Sun* and others. Even the island boat has had her troubles, and the ancient drifter *Lord Curzon* which first took us to Fair Isle on an unseasonably stormy day in June 1948 was making the run—reluctantly, it seemed—only because *The Good Shepherd* was on the slip, having run aground in North Haven about eight weeks before. In the late summer of 1955 a Shetland motor-boat, *The Planet*, struck a rock off Buness in thick fog and holed her stem badly: she made water fast, and the skipper ran her full speed into North Haven and beached her on the sandy shore. It was a sad blow for the owners and crew, for the previous night the nets had brought her 130 cran of herrings worth about £400.

The cargo had to be abandoned, of course, and for the whole of August life in the vicinity of the observatory was made almost unbearable by the noxious stench from the oily scum which rose from the decaying fish. The bird-life of North Haven underwent a rapid and remarkable change, and it seemed that all the gulls of Fair Isle converged to vie with one another, day and night, for the sunken treasure—resting in dappled white quiescence on Hoilie when the tide was high, and milling around in a snow-flurry at the ebb. There were greater and lesser blackbacks in all plumages and stages of moult, and of course hundreds of herring gulls—for once living up to their name. A few early common and black-headed gulls arrived, and there was an immature glaucous gull which preferred to remain in Shetland waters rather than go home to Iceland for the summer. The bonxies pitched into the fray with the rest, but the arctic skuas preferred to pirate their herrings from the well-fed gulls.

§

The most glamorous and historic of all Fair Isle's wrecks took place in 1588, when the scattered remnants of the Spanish Armada were trying to make for home round the northern tip of Scotland. The flagship of the Hulk Squadron of hired transports and stores ships, *El Gran Grifon* of Rostock, commanded by Juan Gomez de Medina, became a total loss outside the dark and gloomy Swarts Geo.* Most of her complement of 300 soldiers and marines was saved, but for many of the poor wretches it was merely a postponement of the end. At the time there were seventeen households on the isle (about as many as today), but of "savage people whose usual food is fish, without bread except a few barley meal bannocks cooked over the embers," according to an eye-witness account in the archives of the Royal Academy of History in Madrid. The translation by Major Martin A. S. Hume goes on: "They have some cattle —quite enough for themselves for they rarely eat meat. They depend mainly upon the milk and butter from the cows, using the sheep's wool principally for clothing. They are a very dirty people, neither Christians nor altogether heretics. It is true that they confess that the doctrine that once a year is preached to them by people sent from an island nine leagues off, is not good; but they say they dare not contradict it, which is a pity."

* She had in fact rounded Cape Wrath and got as far south as Galway Bay, only to be storm-driven north-eastwards to her destruction at Fair Isle: see Michael Lewis, *The Spanish Armada* (1960), pp. 201-2.

The master and mate of the lost vessel and about fifty others perished, mostly from starvation, between landing on 27th September and departure on 14th November, when a ship sent by Andrew Umphrey of Berry took the survivors to Quendale in Shetland, whence they later re-embarked for Anstruther in Fife on the next stage of their long journey home. There is perhaps a memento of the lost master and mate and others of the crew in the place-name Swarts Geo where *El Gran Grifon* foundered: for this is a curiously hybrid name, half German (and certainly the events of that September day were black enough by any standard) and half Norn, *geo* meaning a narrow inlet. Rostock, like Lubeck and other free Hanseatic ports, was a Roman Catholic enclave in the Lutheran states of north Germany, and if the transport was hired there she would almost certainly have on board a German master and crew.

There's a story at Fair Isle that the mortality among the Spaniards and their allies was not due entirely to starvation, but was largely brought about by the guile of the natives, who foresaw that these unwanted guests would very soon eat them out of house and home. So the Fair Isle folk roasted an ox in the Round Reeva when the beach was dry at ebb tide, and invited the strangers to the feast. They plied their guests with plenty of good meat and strong drink, and many were either helpless or asleep when the islanders stole away—just before the rising tide rushed through the great archway in the cliff and swept the somnolent Spaniards into the deep water outside. This grim barbecue has a fine medieval ring, but somehow seems quite alien to the character of island life. It is less likely to be true, one feels, than that other yarn that when the Spaniards came over the Brecks of Busta, their steel armour gleaming in the sunlight, the natives supposed they were being invaded by a heavenly host!

§

It has been often said that the colourful Fair Isle hosiery patterns were taught to the islanders by the unfortunate Spaniards, but the claim, which seems likely to have arisen through a fancied resemblance of some of the patterns to

Moorish work, need not be taken too seriously. Such patterns are much older in northern lands than the days of the Armada, and there is a close family kinship between those of Fair Isle, the Faeroe Islands, Iceland and Norway. Like the horizontal watermills with which we began this chapter, they probably owe their presence to Norwegian settlement of these areas in the ninth and tenth centuries, after their introduction to Scandinavia by the forays of the Swedish Vikings down the Volga to the lands of the Near East.

The garments which today are trade-marked at the Village Hall 'Fair Isle Made in Fair Isle' (to assert their precedence in the peck-order over 'Fair Isle' garments made in Shetland) pay scant attention to tradition. The variety of articles has widened in recent years to embrace tea-cosies, egg-cosies and other novelties, and new and more intricate patterns have been developed. The use of bright colours is also a relatively modern technique, and although most of the present-day dyes are of chemical origin, a few are still processed from the roots and leaves of wild plants. (If you are bold enough to ask a Fair Isle wife how, your temerity will reap its just reward of a sweet smile and a firm rejoinder, "Ah! that's *our* secret!") Several different motifs may be used in one jersey, each repeated in alternating bands round the garment, against a natural fawn or grey or *moorit* (dark reddish-brown) ground. Basically each motif is a fairly simple geometrical device, and the art and skill consists in the elaboration of the patterns and careful blending of colours. It is in this that the Fair Isle womenfolk have had— and still have—such marked success, and adept as they are with the needles (for a housewife will produce a jersey or cardigan inside a week), the supply can hardly keep pace with the demand. All the knitting is done to private orders, mostly from hostel visitors, and nowhere can you buy the genuine Fair Isle garment in a shop.

Mrs Babs Stout once knitted a jersey for me which she claimed was in the traditional Fair Isle style; it had eight different geometrical motifs, each in a lozenge-shaped frame, and each repeated round the garment in successive bands. This bore a much closer resemblance than the modern types to traditional Faeroese work, though in Faeroe there is a much greater demand for natural wools, bright colours and lavish patterns being reserved mostly for children's wear. There is great richness and imagination in the variety of motifs in traditional Faeroese designs, as can be seen from Hans M. Debes's interesting study *Føroysk Bindingarmynstur*. Many of these patterns have their own names, and stylised animal—even human—forms are common. *Hundagongur* is a lifelike picture of small dogs walking round the jersey as small dogs should, nose to tail; there is *kettunøsin*, 'cat's nose', and *gasareyði*, 'goose's eye'; and a favourite, especially for the border of children's jumpers, is of men and women hand in hand in the unique Faeroe ring-dance. In olden days woollen underwear had distinctive patterns from place to place among the islands, while many designs —such as *Katrinamynstir*—commemorate the long-forgotten wives who presumably invented them.

The Naval 'anchor' and the 'Norwegian star' are evidence of external influence on Fair Isle work, and in Faeroe the alternation of large and contrasting motifs in bright colours is known as *Hetlandsmynstir* or 'Shetland knitting', suggesting that the idea was introduced from the south. The Faeroe wife uses only one needle for a garment like a pullover or cardigan, a long round needle with ends of hard steel but pliable as wire in the middle. In Shetland and Fair Isle six or even eight straight needles will be used to knit such a garment, depending upon the vital statistics of the intended wearer; one of the needles is held fast in a perforated pad affixed to a leather belt worn around the knitter's waist, so that as the garment grows the weight of the wool does not have to be supported by hand.

CHAPTER III

MISCELLANEOUS RESIDENTS

THERE are two creatures which run to distinctive insular races more readily than most, wrens and mice—and Fair Isle has both. Shetland also has a distinctive wren, a rather large and dark reddish-brown one, abundantly flecked with brown beneath; but although this bird was described and named *Troglodytes t. zetlandicus* from specimens collected in Dunrossness parish less than thirty miles away, the Fair Isle bird is very different as wrens go. It is a paler and brighter brown above, more rufescent on the lower back and rump, and suffused with grey on the head and neck in fresh plumage; it is also a little whiter and less heavily marked beneath. Curiously, its plumage inclines more towards the still paler brown and whiter wren of St Kilda, *T. t. hirtensis*—perhaps the result of convergent adaptation to similar conditions of climate and exposure. I decided our bird was as worthy of a scientific name as the others, so called it *T. t. fridariensis*, Fridarey being the name given to Fair Isle in the *Orkneyinga Saga*. The choice also seemed apt because the insular field-mouse had been christened *fridariensis* by N. B. Kinnear in 1906—and in the Faeroe Islands the local wren, *T. t. borealis*, is known picturesquely as *músabróðir*, 'brother of the mouse'!

I have written at length in both *St Kilda Summer* and *A Mosaic of Islands* about the habitat and habits of the wrens of Fair Isle, comparing them in particular with their relatives at St Kilda. Suffice to say that the Fair Isle population is very small, between 45 and 50 pairs, but that within the limitations imposed by its rigorous environment it seems to be very successful. It is strictly a bird of the cliffs, especially in geos with tide-washed stony beaches, where I have seen wrens feeding among the wrack as rock pipits do. They are to be seen in the gardens and cabbage-patches of the crofting area from late summer onwards when the young are dispersing, but I never knew a pair nest in the village, and indeed the only 'inland' nest I found was a hundred yards from the sea in the lower mill at Finniquoy.

The east coast, with its many indentations (especially in the region of the Wick o' Furse), and the great cliffs under Ward Hill, were usually their stronghold; but Peter Davis found that there was a definite tendency for the birds to concentrate on the lee side of the isle, so that a cold easterly spell in early spring would result in most of the wrens taking up territories along the western cliffs. Their song is wholly delightful, louder and more vehement (but also more stereotyped) than that of either the common or St Kilda wrens.

The Fair Isle bird's distinctness from Shetland stock is proof of a long period of isolation, and of the efficacy of 25 miles of open sea in checking dispersal. Only once during our stay did we take a Shetland wren in one of the traps, but occasionally in most autumn seasons we would get examples of the migratory Continental wren, probably Norwegian birds. Their more russet upper parts, less vermiculated under parts, slightly smaller size (but above all the facility with which we could handle them!) were good characters for identification. Unlike these comparatively docile visitors, our own wrens struggled and squirmed with surprising strength and vigour for such small mites, and no bird was more wily and difficult to secure. You could never induce panic in a Fair Isle wren; he would move quietly around the trap funnel looking systematically for some imperfection in the wire-netting which would permit his escape. Indeed, the time-honoured remark on finishing the construction of a new trap was, "All right, now let's find a wren and see if it works!"

§

So far as mice and wrens are concerned, islands are open-air laboratories where Nature's experiments in evolution often proceed along entirely different lines. There are field-mice in Iceland, generally regarded as a race of the common long-tailed field-mouse, *Apodemus sylvaticus*, but the breed is absent from the Faeroe Islands. Instead there is a wild-living form of the house-mouse, *Mus musculus faeroeensis*, which thrives among the vast sea-bird colonies on the great cliffs, not infrequently nibbling the lunch-packets of the fowlers when their attentions are otherwise engaged. Those inhabiting the island of Mykines in the extreme west are sufficiently different from other Faeroese mice to warrant subspecific separation as *M. m. mykinessiensis*; they are more robust, with larger feet and longer tails, and evolution seems to have carried them along much the same path as the now extinct St Kilda house-mouse, *M. m. muralis*. Meanwhile, the ships bringing produce from the Continent have introduced the typical race of the house-mouse to Tórshavn, the capital, and although the strain is diluted there, Nólsoy four miles across the sound still has pure Faeroese stock.

Farther to the south-east Shetland has both house-mice (of the typical form, commensal with man) and field-mice; and at least three of the local populations of the latter show distinctness from one another—*A. s. granti* on the main islands, *A. s. thuleo* on Foula 16 miles west of Mainland, and *A. s. fridariensis* at Fair Isle. Fair Isle also has house-mice, now confined to the crofting area; they are dependent on man and are bigger and yellower beneath than the common European house-mouse, but have not yet been given the distinction of a separate name. They may easily gain one in the future, provided Fair Isle keeps its human population. If it does not, then the house-mouse will almost certainly succumb to competition with the more vigorous field-mouse, as happened at St Kilda after the evacuation of 1930.

Like its St Kilda counterpart, the Fair Isle field-mouse is a large and handsome animal. The adults have bright foxy-red fur above and are white below, with a prominent yellow spot on the chest. They weigh between 40-50 gm., or very nearly twice as much as a mainland field-mouse. Immature specimens, especially those under about 30 gm., are very dull by comparison, like young St Kilda specimens—dark grey-brown with a blackish line along the dorsum. In this respect they are very similar to mainland *Apodemus*.

I have to admit, regretfully, to having slain a number of these field-mice, for when the wild autumn days brought cold winds and rain they invaded the observatory kitchen in embarrassing strength. I have never understood the way of a woman with a mouse: once or twice on the hill, when searching burrows for wheatears' nests, my hand clasped something soft and warm and I drew forth a mouse; Esther looked upon it admiringly, almost fondly, showing not the least sign of dread. But a mouse in the house is, as every man knows, a monster! So traps had to be set, and whenever the weather was too bad for birding, or there were no birds about, I whiled away the time making up 'skins' of *A. s. fridariensis* for the cabinets of the Royal Scottish Museum.

In my nursery rhyme days there was a tall story about three blind mice which had the temerity to chase a farmer's wife. I have come across two of them, one at Fair Isle and the other at St Kilda, and hope one day to run across the third. The St Kilda one was feeding in broad daylight among the stone *cleitean* behind the village, standing on its hind-legs with its forepaws reaching up the grass-stems and bending them, then pulling the seed-heads towards its muzzle with what I can best describe as a hand-over-hand action. I wondered why it was not aware of my presence as I stood over it, until I bent down and a close scrutiny revealed that it was sightless. If I put my hand close to its head it was momentarily alarmed, for presumably it could then smell me—but when left alone it continued to feed in this stereotyped way. The other was among long matted grass inside the Mill Trap at the head of Finniquoy; I had disturbed several mice on crawling under the low wire-netting roof, and this one was left sniffing its way haltingly along the runs which led to the mill wall. Doubtless the wire-netting umbrella gave it a far better chance of survival than it would have had in the open, with gulls, skuas and migrant kestrels always about.

Although one can find field-mice almost anywhere on the island—even in the village, for they invade the stackyards along with house-mice in the autumn—they are commonest where the heather cover is good and stoneworks of various kinds provide shelter. They do not apparently range far from home, and on the lower ground their distribution is restricted to the immediate neighbourhood of plantacrubs and drystone dykes. At North Haven, where they have the cover of the observatory huts and the harbour store, and there is no lack of food, they nest from late April onwards, the first young appearing in mid-May. In summer they feed mainly on the caterpillars of antler and various noctuid moths, but in autumn subsist mainly on grass and weed seeds.

We caught a house-mouse among the Observatory buildings in the late summer of 1948, the only one we saw there in eight years; it must have been one of the last survivors of the Royal Navy's occupation, which ceased in 1945. Jiro Kikkawa, who made a study of the mice in May 1956, trapped a house-mouse on the edge of the village at Barkland croft, which had been deserted since the winter of 1951. This must have been their last outpost, since Field, two hundred yards nearer the hill, had only field-mice. Field George often brought me specimens for skinning, and the interesting thing is that this appeared to be a discrete group in which the adults had the same dark grey-brown pelage as the immatures. I fancy there are field-mice on top of Sheep Craig as I have seen small burrows there, but nobody has yet been able to examine this even more isolated group.

§

The island has no horses, though the Norse place-name Hesti Geo, south of Malcolm's Head, indicates that a venerable connexion with the isle was severed when these animals were finally banished in the thirties. In the heyday of the Shetland pony trade, when large numbers were bred for draught work in the coal mines, the laird kept a herd on Skadan, the grassy stretch between Kirki Geo and the South Lighthouse. In 1804 there were about 70 ponies, but only a dozen remained by 1928. They were useful for bringing home peats from Geordie's Cup and Auld Jeams's Hill, and a shallow pool on Byerwall got the onomatopoeic name of Da Sprittery Hole because of the splashing water when the islanders allowed the ponies to cool their fetlocks on the way home from the hill. Practically all the haulage and ploughing were done by heavy oxen down to

1948-49, and when coal from the annual steamer banished the drudgery of protracted peat-cutting, the ponies became super-fluous to the island economy.

Fair Isle's list of mammals is brief enough, and there are few creatures between the extremes of mice and whales. The ubiquitous rabbits, fortunately never stricken with the horror-sickness myxomatosis, compensate somewhat for the damage they do to the pasture by providing a winter sport and useful food-crop. There is a liberal sprinkling of black ones, big white-collared ones (whose ancestors are said to have escaped from a careless lighthouse keeper), and pure albinos with shining pink eyes—though the latter do not appear to survive very long. There are no rats nearer than *The Good Shepherd's* storehouse at Grutness—and every care is taken that they get no farther. Shetland has plenty of otters, but the 25 miles of swiftly flowing water in Sumburgh Roost has proved an insurmountable barrier to their conquest of Fair Isle. In the early years of our stay feral cats, a relic of the Army and Navy occupation, lived on Ward Hill and the western cliffs, but towards the end few remained. Otherwise, the only wild mammals were seals and cetaceans.

The usual breeding time of grey seals—at least where they can haul out in numbers and comparative security—is October and November, but I have seen small white-coated young on the twilight beaches inside Fair Isle caves as late as April. Probably, since their numbers are large and suitable caves are few, there is a good deal of competition for nursery space and a protracted breeding period in consequence. We saw occasional porpoises, and every autumn schools of white-sided dolphins, on south-wards migration from the arctic, raced through Sumburgh Roost in company with *The Good Shepherd*. One of the best bits of animal film I have seen was shot by a Shetland friend Theo Kay one morning when a number of these sprightly dolphins, meeting the mail-boat, turned about and swam for an hour or more alongside.

Shortly before our arrival in June 1948 an example of the little-known Sowerby's whale, one of the larger toothed whales, was stranded in Klingers Geo, providing food for the ravens and hooded crows for months; and what I believe to have been a large bottlenosed whale, *Hyperoödon rostrata*, spent the whole of

a summer's afternoon lying idly in the water between Landberg
and Goorn, its long dark back showing just above the surface.
In striking contrast to its sluggish behaviour were the incredible
circus-antics of a couple of bottlenosed dolphins, *Tursiops
truncatus*, which escorted *The Good Shepherd* into North Haven
on the afternoon of 1st August 1956, and sported there and in
the Wick o' Furse for several hours afterwards. We had
excellent views of the distribution of black and white on their
fat bodies as we looked down from Hoilie, and found them
most exciting to watch, for they frequently leapt clean out of
the water—no mean feat for creatures which must have been
more than twelve feet long, and broad in proportion. They
took a fancy to the isle, for they were back in the Wick o' Furse
on a number of occasions down to 27th August.

§

When the mountain everlasting and the violet butterwort
were at their best on the heather moorland the eiders began to
wander there in search of an inconspicuous hollow in which to
make their grey-brown downy nests. We saw little of this
prospecting, for it takes place at night—if one may so describe
the brief twilit hours that link the summer days together. But
we often saw the commencement of such journeys as the pairs
came ashore on the South Haven shingle, overlooked from our
sitting-room.

The journey inland was invariably slow and tedious, with
frequent pauses while the mates admired each other, or perhaps wondered which way to go next. It was, moreover,
always on foot, and whenever I saw an eider on the wing at this
season it was flying towards, never away from, the sea. Some
five weeks after that first journey in her mate's company the
duck has to return to the sea on foot, this time with her brood
of three, four or five young. Sometimes she has another female
with her, an 'aunt' or 'nursemaid' or whatever you please to
call her, who helps the mother to conduct her brood on their
hazardous way across the skua-infested moor. One leads and
the other brings up the rear, and at the first sign of danger both
squat down and the ducklings scuttle under their wings. Who

Milens Houllan dominating the Old Red Sandstone cliffs of the north coast; in the middle distance is the nameless pointed stack, with the Cathedral Rock and grey seal skerries beyond.

The Bird Observatory from Hoilie, with the Sheep Craig and Vaasetter beyond. Note the bird-trap between the bedroom huts.

these aunts are, whether failed breeders or immature non-breeders, and how they attach themselves to prospective mothers, and when, I do not know; but as a number of mothers succeed in finding one, it would hardly seem to be a matter of chance. Two eider ducks have been found sharing the same nest in Orkney, but the shared broods I have seen were too small to have been the progeny of two females. It is just as well that such help is available, for the drakes show no interest in the young, and in any event they have gathered by this time in bachelor parties of up to thirty or so on the sea. An observant voyager on board *The Good Shepherd* should see something of them, for usually there is a big 'raft' of drakes swimming off Sumburgh Head, all in moult and many unable to fly.

I have seen arctic skuas stooping at these eider families, but they do not appear to be a serious threat to the young; the squatting ducks lunge upwards menacingly, and the skuas seem disinclined to press home an attack. It may be a different story with the more rapacious bonxie. At St Kilda in the summer of 1963 the eider's chief enemies were the ravens and greater blackbacked gulls. Descending the hillside above Village Bay one afternoon, I saw a raven dancing with huge, grotesque hops around a tiny pool where a duck with five ducklings at her side was striving to keep him at bay. Overhead were other ravens, their pinions etched like greedy fingers against the sky, and it seemed to me the odds were altogether unfair. So, much to the eider's annoyance, I gathered up her brood and marched down-hill with the ducklings in my hands. She tottered over the heather in my wake, rushing frantically to overtake us whenever the ducklings cried out loudly, so that sometimes she was actually walking beside me. No fewer than eight ravens kept pace overhead as we went downhill to the shore, as bizarre a procession as you could wish to see.

Let us return for a few moments to that exploratory uphill walk before the female selects her nesting-hollow in the juniper or heather, or in the shelter of a rock. Does she remember, for her brood's sake, the route by which she and her mate walked to the spot? Or, put another way, is this twilight trek an adaptation which guarantees the safe arrival of her flightless ducklings on the sea when the journey is accomplished in

FIB D

reverse? This seemed to me a reasonable supposition, for in this way natural selection might ensure that those birds which learned an easy route, uninterrupted by impassable ditches, stone walls and sheer cliffs, would rear the most young—so that in the fullness of time the capacity for good pathfinding would become inherited and almost universal.

It is nice to have theories, but this one had soon to be discarded! One day I found a mother eider and three ducklings blundering about inside the Double Dyke Trap, a large wire-netting affair. I released the parent without much difficulty, and she waited nervously a few yards away while I disentangled her young from the 'baffle' behind which they had imprisoned themselves. When reunited they set off towards the edge of the cliff a hundred yards away, mother leading and the ducklings following obediently at her tail, almost tripping over her feet at every step.

They came to the edge of the cliff at a point where I knew there was a fifty-foot drop, below about twenty feet of shelving brow, and to my astonishment the duck walked clean over the edge, her brood scuttling loyally behind. She had her wings and was all right—but they had none, and after slithering and tumbling for a few yards they bounced off into space. When I reached the spot she was swimming unconcernedly down below, but only two chicks were bobbing behind her; they had fallen into the water, but the third had had no such luck, and lay inert on an exposed rock. I turned away, reflecting that either I had witnessed the exception which proves the rule, or natural selection is perhaps not the all-powerful force we are sometimes inclined to believe.

Sometimes a visitor with no knowledge of the ways of birds would turn up at the observatory clutching a woebegone baby eider in his or her hand, and recount how he or she had found it all alone beside the road or on the moor. The best thing to do under such circumstances, of course, is to leave well alone—the mother bird is seldom very far away, quietly watching and waiting her chance to return. Fortunately, it is the easiest thing in the world to get an orphan eider adopted. All one has to do is walk along the brows until one sees a group of brown ducks swimming idly offshore—and one does not usually have to go farther than Mavers Geo or Finniquoy. Descending to the beach, you place the downy mite at the water's edge and marvel at the shrill, piercing quality of its cry as it takes to the sea. No sooner do they hear the whistle than the sleepy brown ducks are galvanised into action and swim rapidly towards the noise. The youngster attaches himself happily to the first one to arrive, and she swims into the bay the very picture of pride. If nature has been uncommonly mean in not giving mother eiders a better bump of locality, she has at least made up for it by giving the ducklings that compulsive whistle, and providing a plethora of potential 'aunts'.

§

The cliffs of the north coast, from Wester Lother to Da Nizz, have much of interest—a wealth of fulmars on the barer places, small colonies of puffins on the grassy slopes, groups of guillemots next to the sea, while here and there the loud song of a Fair Isle wren sounds strangely out of place among the cackling and laughing of the gulls. Above the head of Wirvie Burn you can lie on the grassy edge at Milens Houllan and watch the ebony wings of anxious ravens as they fly croaking against the blue sky, or look below to count the fat slug-like bodies of grey seals basking on the skerries of the Stacks o' Skroo. One of these stacks is so massive and high-pointed at the landward side as to have earned the names 'Cathedral Rock' and 'Kirk Stack', and it has kittiwakes nesting and crying on its walls.

From nearer the North Lighthouse, above Easter Lother, the diversity of the red sandstone cliffs with their long grass slides, deeply eroded geos and picturesque sea-worn arches commands admiration. There is a high needle-pointed stack pierced by an archway beneath Milens Houllan, but in spite of being one of the most impressive features of the whole beautiful coast, it does not seem to have achieved the dignity of a name. Beyond it the play of sunlight and shadow freckling the sea is broken only by lace ribbons of white water where Lowery's Strings, the swift tidal races, run their course. Far away to the north-west the blue hulk of Foula rises in the haze, superb in her proportions.

Not far from Skroo Lighthouse the road runs by a gigantic blow-hole, the Kirn o' Skroo; you can descend into a sort of upper basin ringed by fallen boulders and scree in which storm petrels are said to have nested in the past. From the edge of this basin, opposite the precipitous north wall, you can peer down into the abyss of the blow-hole proper, to a small boulder-beach where the sea pours through a dark tunnel. Here the white-winged tysties rest and whistle among the rocks. The constricted grotto, with only the long dark tunnel giving them access to the sea, seems to suit them to perfection, and more than once on a May afternoon I have lain on the edge and watched a score of birds at rest on the boulders, sporting in the clear water, or standing in nooks and crannies at various heights on the dark walls. They were well worth a little of one's leisure time.

They swam and dived together in the joy of courtship, the leading partner seeming to fly submerged with a slow rhythm that showed off its square white wing-patches contrasting with black plumage, its legs outstretched in a scarlet trail behind. As soon as this bird surfaced its companion scurried to the front, lowered its head under the water to swim with rounded back, and then submerged until its dark body was swallowed by the underwater shadows and only that vivid red trail and the butterfly-motion of the white wing-patches marked its progress. The birds on the ledges and rocks (underneath which many would soon lay their eggs) kept up a continuous high-pitched whistling, the brilliant red of their throats matching their leg-colour as they did so; but soon the love-play so excited them that they too fluttered into the placid pool sixty feet below me and joined in, the beauty of their water-ballet holding me entranced.

We looked out upon another little colony of tysties from the windows of our sitting-room, for several pairs nested under the cliff of Buness on the opposite side of South Haven. These birds were much the most accessible of the many nesting at Fair Isle, and when the tide was low we looked for their eggs and chicks underneath the boulders and in the narrow fissures and tiny caves. Nests containing young were not difficult to find, for the tystie chick is 'house trained' and all you have to do is look for the pink-and-white sludge of faeces which marks the outside latrine.

This is the only British auk which lays two eggs, but the rearing of an equivalent number of youngsters is the exception rather than the rule; the eggs are laid at two-day intervals, and as incubation begins with the first, the elder chick has an unfair start in life. We visited one nest regularly from the hatching of the young in mid-July; the youngest chick seemed to do well over the first four days, increasing his weight from 43 to 76 gm., but after that he languished and was dead within the week. Probably the older and sturdier one monopolised the parents' attentions and got all the food. This bird attained adult weight —360 gm.—after three weeks in the darkness of his tiny cave, though he did not leave the nest for another ten days. Another youngster, almost fully fledged in dappled grey feathers on 7th August, weighed 440 gm.—or 60 gm. more than the heaviest adult we managed to capture at this site. In some years the South Haven colony would be flooded by high waves whipped up by a southerly storm, and no young at all would survive.

§

The pair-bond between the small brown twites, which take the place of linnets in the isles, is so strong that it was not unusual in the summer months to trap male and female together. Even if one escaped during a 'drive' a little patience was all that you required, for the free bird would do all in its power to be reunited with its mate, and would often find its own way into the trap. Not infrequently one found a twite singing cheerfully on top of one of the catching-boxes, serenading another of opposite sex inside.

There was more than observational evidence for this extraordinary fidelity of the mated pair, for our records of retrapped birds gave much support. One pair, indeed, were taken together in the Observatory Trap one season on 7th June, 16th July, 1st October and again ten days later, showing that the pair-bond survives the breeding season and continues beyond the period of the post-nuptial moult, when most species appear to have lost all interest in sex. We were unable to discover if the mating is renewed in the following year; both birds of this pair were retrapped next summer, but always separately. In another case a female was recaptured with different mates in August 1952 and June 1954, but of course she may have lost her original partner through natural causes in the meantime.

We found very few twites' nests, despite the fact that it was a common enough bird. Many of them breed on the cliffs in inaccessible positions, but others nest among the hummocks of thrift and scattered rocks of Buness, and in heather a little way inland from the cliff-brows elsewhere. When visiting Unst I found a pair nesting in ivy against the Post Office wall—a typical house-sparrow niche. The twite is a late breeder, since the best time for raising young is when the weed-seeds ripen in the late summer.

The twite seems destined to become a rare bird at Fair Isle and elsewhere in Shetland, for much of the seed-corn imported in recent years has been predressed with mercurial preparations, or with dieldrin and similar hydrocarbons. Peter Davis found a number in the last throes of paralysis as a result of ingesting this poisoned food, and there is little doubt that those which escape a lethal dose have their breeding success impaired, since the toxicity passes into the eggs. What is happening at Fair Isle is only a faint reflection of the poisoning on a far vaster scale that is threatening song-birds in orchard and agricultural country the world over.

One summer we had a nest under observation from a hide for approximately 70 hours all told; it was in late July, when the four youngsters were between six and thirteen days old. At this nest the cock took no part in feeding the young, leaving his mate to do all the work; but in another on Vaasetter, found with five newly-hatched chicks on 2nd August, the male took just as active a share as his mate throughout. Indeed, we saw the pink-rumped male of the first nest on only four occasions, on each of which there was a brief courtship display culminating in copulation, after the hen had fed the young. This she did at remarkably regular intervals of a little under half-an-hour, spending usually from a half to a full minute at the nest. On two mornings when we were (literally!) up before the lark we found that she began feeding her family at 03·15 and 03·30 hours G.M.T.—and as she made her last visit at about 20.45 she had a 17½ hours' working day!

Of all the ground nests of small birds the twite's is about the most open and exposed, and its position would soon be obvious to any predator if it were not kept scrupulously clean, for the white faecal sacs would quickly give it away. The mother bird was fastidious in this respect; her first job in the morning was to carry away the sacs which had accumulated on the nest-rim during the night, and thereafter she removed new ones at each visit. At first she had to rummage around inside the nest to find them, but by about the tenth day the young were strong enough to expel their faeces over the nest-rim. She got rid of at least a quarter of the earlier ones by the simple expedient of swallowing them, but as the young grew bigger more and more of the sacs were picked up and carried to a distance.

The youngsters presented a very odd appearance, for they were being fed on seeds and their crops bulged with undigested food, so that each appeared to be a tiny two-headed monstrosity. They had visitors other than their parents: a young wheatear inspected the nest closely on several occasions in the absence of the hen, and seemed on the point of putting his head right inside, while another which came too near on two occasions when the hen was at home was chased off vigorously. This interest in the doings of quite a different species was intriguing, the more so as it is known that juvenile wheatears will sometimes adopt a late nest of their own kind and help the parents to feed the young. A less welcome visitor had to be forcibly removed: on one visit the hen was greatly agitated and would make no effort to feed the chicks, and the watcher on duty, leaving the hide to investigate, found an ugly black slug *Arion ater* crawling over them.

We weighed the nestlings each evening directly after their last feed. With the exception of the runt (there seems to be one in every nest!) the young had attained an average adult weight —about 16 gm.—by the end of their first week, while one topped 18½ gm. on its tenth day. This and runt, who was 2½ gm. lighter, were the first away, having vanished from the immediate vicinity late on 29th July. The other two followed next morning. The watcher saw the returning hen study the empty nest in apparent perplexity before performing a last quite unnecessary rite—the removal of a faecal sac which one of the departing youngsters had deposited on the rim.

CHAPTER IV

THE ARCTIC SKUAS' COLONY

FAIR ISLE has a unique colony of sea-birds—seventy pairs of arctic skuas. It is unique because nearly every bird carries a combination of coloured and numbered metal leg-bands, and is therefore known individually to the few people who have studied the fortunes of this colony in recent years. When our study began in 1949 there were twenty pairs, so we have watched this young and virile colony grow year by year, and have learned a good deal about plumage variation among the birds, the social structure of the colony, the behaviour of the various age-groups, and the breeding biology of the species as a whole.

There are four kinds of skua in the northern hemisphere and this one, despite its name, is by no means the most arctic in its distribution. Indeed, the somewhat larger pomarine and the more delicately-built long-tailed skuas, lemming hunters of the far north, would better qualify for the name. It is also called Richardson's skua, but a more imaginative name is the Shetland 'skuti-alan', evocative of the bird's swift and dashing flight above the dark heather moorland of the isles. According to the Norn dictionary it gained this name by "swooping down on other birds and belching out a stinking fluid upon them"—a false observation which does the skua much injustice, since the fluid is actually half-digested food surrendered in appeasement by its victim. The skua is a Viking of the skies, a pirate who gains his living by relentlessly pursuing other sea-birds such as gulls, terns and cliff-nesting auks, until they are glad to buy escape by yielding the burden in their crops. The skua takes the offering in full flight, long before it falls to the sea. The Fair Isle name is *kjá*, perhaps not unrelated to the Faeroese *kjógvi*.

The bonxie or great skua hunts in the same manner, and

although he selects gannets and the larger gulls, he and the arctic skua sometimes compete—and not always to the bigger bird's advantage. A member of the mail-boat's crew told me with evident enjoyment how he watched a pair of bonxies harassing a gannet off Sumburgh Head, one pouncing on the luckless bird, the other waiting below for the inevitable reward —and how, with cavalier dash and perfect timing, a skuti-alan nipped in between and carried off the prize! In the winter some arctic skuas may fish for themselves, since they have been reported in parts of the southern ocean where other sea-birds are scarce, but we still have only a fragmentary knowledge of their distribution and habits at that time. Perhaps an individual can feed itself by legitimate means during the off-season if food is abundant, but cannot support a growing family without recourse to piracy. The habit is so strongly ingrained in the breeding season as to permit of no modification: on several occasions I have watched a huge concourse of shags, auks, kittiwakes and other gulls getting food for the asking at a surface-swimming shoal, and the only birds which were having to work (and work hard) for a living were the arctic skuas patrolling the outskirts of the throng.

They are beautiful creatures, and thrilling to watch as they fly with loud yodelling cries above the moor. Their narrow angled wings and long middle tail-feathers give them the appearance of falcons rather than gulls, yet it is to the latter that they are most closely related. Their plumage shows great variation; indeed, the arctic skua is one of the few easily accessible species in which two or more well-defined forms or 'morphs' co-exist in the same colonies. The extreme types look so different that anyone unfamiliar with birds might well believe them to be different species. This pronounced individual variation is genetically controlled and has nothing to do with either age or sex, and part of our programme at Fair Isle was to amass data which would enable geneticists to work out the mode of inheritance of these different morphs.

The so-called pale morphs or 'light phase' birds are much the handsomest, having the back and wings dark brown, the under parts white usually with a more or less distinct brownish band across the breast (sometimes only noticeable at the sides, and in rare cases absent), and the nape and cheeks white suffused with yellow, contrasting markedly with a dark brown skull-cap. At the opposite extreme there is a melanic type, a blackish-brown bird, and between the two there is an intergrading series in which the plumage of the under parts and sides of the head becomes progressively pigmented with brown. Thus, in the dullest and dingiest of pale morphs the dark breast-band is considerably extended and the cheeks and neck are clouded; and in the next stage, the lightest intermediate type, the white feathers of the under parts are entirely hidden by overlapping brown tips, most copious in the pectoral region. These intermediates are in the majority, so it is often difficult from field observation to decide just where a bird fits into the series. Because of this difficulty intermediates have always been reckoned as dark morphs in previous studies, but many of them are closer to the pale end of the series.

H. N. Southern (1943) enquired into the geographical distribution and the causes of this striking polymorphism. The pale bird is relatively scarce in British colonies: at Fair Isle, it has hovered between about 16 and 25 per cent of the adult population, varying in different years. It increases to the north, being generally over 20 per cent in the Faeroe Islands and higher still in parts of Iceland. It increases still further as one proceeds eastwards along the Continental edge into Siberia in the Old World, and westwards towards Alaska in the New, and colonies comprising 90 per cent pale birds have been reported. Nothing is known of the variation in geographical distribution of the darkest birds since, as already pointed out, these have always been lumped with the wide range of intermediates. The variation among these intermediates led Southern to write that more extended quantitative studies were needed on the frequency of birds verging towards one extreme or the other before the genetic control could be properly understood.

Thus very little is known about the problem of inheritance of the various plumage-kinds. Arctic skuas cannot be reared and studied in a laboratory like a population of mice or fruit-flies, and they die quickly if sent to a zoo, so the only way of getting the necessary information is to encourage the birds to initiate their own breeding experiments in the wild. This is exactly what we set out to do at Fair Isle. By ringing each season's crop of young, and keeping a record of their parentage, we hoped eventually to gather information covering several generations. Important to our task is the fact that arctic skuas are long-suffering birds, tolerating a lot of disturbance when nests are visited, chicks examined and ringed, and hides and clap-nets set up to catch them. Throughout the whole period of the study not a single pair deserted the nest as a result of our activities.

The young are divisible into three broad categories corresponding with the light, intermediate and dark morphs of the adults, though the plumage characteristics of each are somewhat different. The pale ones have an abundance of rufous bars and tips on their feathers, the tips being so slight on the under parts that the white of the belly feathers often shows through. As they run the gamut of intermediacy between pale and dark we find a progressive reduction in the amount of tawny or rufous barring, while the belly feathers become increasingly saturated with dark brown. Finally the plumage is almost entirely blackish-brown practically without rufous tips, and the belly feathers are sooty to the base as in the melanistic adults. It should be said that a sufficient number of ringed birds has now returned to the colony as breeders to give us confidence that the juvenile and adult plumages correspond as described. An interesting point is that the juvenile variation finds a close parallel in the plumage variation of adult bonxies, where there is a bright rufous type at one extreme and a dark earth-brown type at the other. Arguing on the basis of ontogeny (that young creatures exhibit primitive characteristics more markedly than their parents) one would guess that the bonxie's plumage is of a more primitive kind, closer to the ancestral skua's.

The outcome of any mating, except a pale x pale one, is unpredictable: from double pale matings we had only the rufous-flecked, light-bellied type of youngster, which suggests that the pale morph is the recessive wild type. When a pale bird mates with an intermediate bird they usually reproduce their own kinds in a brood of two, though not infrequently such a pairing will produce either two pale or two intermediate young. Dark x intermediate and double intermediate matings usually give intermediate youngsters, one perhaps darker than the other; but two intermediates may also throw out a pale chick. The truly melanic birds are much the rarest and we had very few cases of really dark birds mated together; certainly some are heterozygotes, since such matings not infrequently produced an intermediate chick.

§

The skuas return to the island from their winter wanderings in the South Atlantic early in May. There have been two recoveries of ringed birds at Angola, Portuguese West Africa, over 7,000 miles to the south, as well as reports of other marked birds on migration from the coasts of Portugal and Spain. Their route southwards seems to pass through the North Sea, for nearly all the remaining recoveries away from the Shetland-Orkney area have been in the maritime countries of western Europe. Often they were storm-blown birds. We expect to find the same pairs on the same moorland territories at the beginning of each season, and often one member of the pair appears on the scene a few days before the other—which suggests that they drift apart in the winter and make a rendezvous at their nesting-place each spring.

It was not until 1955 that we first caught with the clap-net a former season's chick—an event which we regarded as a milestone in F.I.B.O. history! It happened at the old-established Eas Brecks East site, the nearest one to the observatory. There was little sign of activity in mid-May, though this had always been one of the earliest pairs, and a changed mating provided the reason. In 1954 we had managed to ring the male only, and he had returned. I found the nest on 25th May, and when the sitting bird rose I noticed with some excitement that she also wore a ring. Could this be the event we had awaited so long—a former year's youngster come to the home colony to breed?

When we caught her on 3rd June she proved to be 337.789, marked as "a very dark-looking youngster . . . with belly feathers sooty to the base", at Furse Hillside in 1951. She was now a typical dark morph adult breeding for the first time at

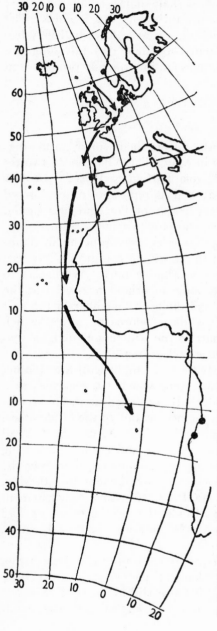

FIG. 6

RECOVERIES OF ARCTIC SKUAS
RINGED AS NESTLINGS AT
FAIR ISLE

In addition to the many which have been 'controlled' at their native colony, two have turned up in Shetland (South Mainland and Foula) in summer when three and five years old respectively, while another was found at Papa Westray in Orkney in its fifth summer. These records suggest that a proportion of Fair Isle skuas join other colonies when they become mature. There is also a British recovery from Aberdeenshire. On the Continent, birds have been reported from More og Romsdal, Norway; three localities in Jutland, Denmark (one as late as 9th November); Mecklenburg, North Germany; West Flanders, Belgium; Asturias, Spain; the Berlenga Isles off Estremadura, Portugal; and Algarve, Portugal, hard by the entrance to the Mediterranean. All except the Berlengas bird, which was in its fifth year, were making their first migration. Only one ringed Arctic Skua has entered the Mediterranean, a Fair Isle bird marked on 5th July 1960 and found at Algiers in the following month. This is probably unusual, for the distribution of the recoveries suggests an autumn migration through the North Sea and English Channel (not round the western seaboard of Britain), outside four years of age. Her parents lost their first clutch to a predator in 1951, and she was the junior chick of a replacement clutch hatched as late as 18th July. The *Skua Journal* for 17th August has this entry: "The dark youngster ran before me this-morning but could not get on the wing. I held him [*sic!*] on my hand and he took off, flying round with one adult following, and the Brae East fledgling attempting to guide him. A few minutes later he flew up from the ground of his own accord: fledging period, 30 days." Both youngsters were still on the moor on 5th September and the dark one was last seen, a single parent in attendance, on the evening of the 7th—a very late date for a family to be still at the isle, though we once knew a parent stay almost a fortnight later than this, caring for an injured chick. One thing about this bird was intriguing: whereas her parents were mild-tempered and never threatened a human in-truder, she herself proved to be strongly aggressive in defending her nest and young, often swooping at our heads as we cycled along the road just below the breeding ground.

The recapture of birds ringed as chicks has shown that most return to the parent colony to breed for the first time when aged four or five years. By the end of the 1962 season 49 such chicks had been retrapped at their first nests: 7 were three-year-olds, 27 were aged four, 11 were aged five, and there were 4 as old as six years. This, in a bird which rears only two young in a good season, argues a potentially long breeding life. The Venables have recorded that an extremely tame bird returned to Leraback on Foula every summer for 31 years, and they were told of another which had come to one of the crofts for

the Bay of Biscay and round West Africa to the wintering area in the South Atlantic. Some indication of the whereabouts of the winter quarters is perhaps given by the recoveries at Benguela and Mossamêdes, in Angola, over 7,000 miles south of Fair Isle. The first of these was found in October of its second year, the other in November of its third year.

food for 12 years. It is doubtful if any of the Fair Isle birds is as old as the first of these, and very few individuals can equal the second. Indeed, only one pair of the 1961 breeders had been together since 1948—though they may, of course, have been coming to the isle for some years before ourselves. It is usual for a pair to be faithful year after year, but divorces do take place, though they usually involve birds of the previous season's intake. In general the young pairings seem more susceptible to change than the older and more experienced birds, between whom the attainment of breeding condition is more closely synchronised.

Divorces apart, changes in mating are usually due to the failure of one or both of a pair to survive the winter at sea, in which event the survivor, be it male or female, claims the territory and finds a new mate—sometimes a similarly bereaved neighbour, but often one of the pool of newly matured younger birds which is always present at the colony. The loss to the effective breeding strength due to mortality at sea and other causes is usually between 10 and 12 per cent per year. The loss is not entirely made up of deaths, since in most years one or more birds (for some reason not known) miss the breeding season, although they turn up again at a new site the following spring.

§

In mid-May two eggs are laid, at an interval of about 48 hours, in a slight saucer-shaped bowl in the moor-grass or heather. Those young females which are precocious enough to nest for the first time at three years of age usually lay only a single egg, often a smaller one than normal, and they not infrequently lose it or the chick through inexperience. Competition with older birds generally obliges the younger pairs to settle on the periphery of the colony, where their nests are more exposed to danger from predatory gulls, ravens and hooded crows. Both sexes share the responsibility of incubation during the next 26 to 28 days, and the sooty-brown chicks generally hatch on successive days, rarely together.

In 1956 we got a new pair on Swey with an abnormal clutch-size of three eggs, none of which hatched. They returned in

The Gill o' Finniquoy, the long and exciting approach to
the Gully Trap.

The varied cliffs of Hjukni Geo and Linni Geo on the west coast,
looking over the fertile croft-land to South Harbour.

subsequent years, again laying three eggs and sitting on them without reward. From 1960-62 another female on the Brae of Restensgeo also laid clutches of three, with no better luck. Meanwhile, there had been two interesting developments in the case of the first pair. The male took a new female in 1961, who laid two eggs in that season, but increased her clutch-size to three in the next, while his original partner found a new mate at Swey West and began producing normal two-egg clutches, though it was 1962 before she at last succeeded in rearing young. Skuas' eggs are fairly large for the bird, which has only two brood-patches, and at first we thought that the birds were unable to cover three eggs efficiently, so that they got chilled; but it now seems more likely that all the eggs were infertile, and the blame seems to have lain with the male rather than his spouse.

At the other extreme there were occasional birds, first-time breeders, which laid no eggs at all and were quite content to sit on a small stone or other foreign body, showing such attachment to the substitute that we even caught them on their nests with the aid of the clap-net and hide. An interesting case-history concludes chapter VI.

The incubation period can be reckoned as the lapse of time from the laying of the first egg to the hatching of the second youngster; or better (since the parent only covers her first egg intermittently in the beginning), from the laying of the second egg to completion of the hatch. During the seven years of our study we found that the period varies from 27 to 29 days, most nests taking from $27\frac{1}{4}$ to $28\frac{1}{4}$ days. For the second egg alone, the normal time was between $25\frac{1}{4}$ and $26\frac{1}{2}$ days: it was always easier to get precise data for the second egg, since one seldom found a nest before the first had been laid several hours, the bird under observation having little urge to return. Because incubation proper really begins with the second egg this 'catches up' with the first so that the young are born seldom more than a day apart, and quite often free themselves from their shells on the morning and evening of the same day. We found a distinct tendency for birds to lay in the early morning.

Meanwhile, there were a good many skuas at the island which had little or no interest in nesting. These were the subadults—or, as we preferred to call them, the Youth Club. First-year birds, which have a recognisable barred plumage due to pale feather-tips, appeared only on rare occasions, and then only for a day or two, and it is doubtful if many of them come north of the equator in their first summer. As most of the Youth Club members were indistinguishable from adults they were probably two, three and four years of age. This Club is of vital importance to the social structure of the skuas' community; for one thing, as mentioned above, it provides a pool of newly matured birds from among which the established breeders can at once get a mate should their former partner fail to return, or defect to another bird. Such an arrangement is invaluable for maintaining the effective strength of the colony, but the Youth Club has a much more vital rôle to play than that.

The Club's members fall into different behaviour categories. There are some birds which are obviously unattached and interested only in having a gay time: they stand around in groups on the rough war-time airstrip, facing up to each other like large pouter pigeons and uttering their yodelling song, or sport together with hair-raising twists and turns in a frenzy of *joie-de-vivre* over the hill. They patrol the various parts of the colony, and although the breeding birds tolerate their presence, sitting adults yodel at them almost aggressively if they dally overhead, as though to remind them that they are trespassing on occupied ground. There is another group whose gay bachelor days are over; they are to be seen going about the colony, or walking up and down the airstrip, in pairs—but they use the Club as a centre and have no territory of their own. Then there are the more senior birds which, having paired in the previous season, forsake the Club and stake out a territory on the moor, where they sit in the heather for long periods of the day, but make no attempt to nest as a general rule.

This is an oversimplified picture, because the second and third categories may easily become telescoped in a good season. This is the real value of this pool of sub-adult birds to the community—and, taking the wider view, to the species as a whole, for it contains potential breeders who are always available to swell the effective ranks of the colony if the season should prove unusually favourable. Thus, if there is a glut of sand-eels around the isle so that the kittiwakes and auks 'never had it so good', competition among the skuas is reduced and there is room for a bigger intake of breeding birds. Conversely, if food is scarce the rate of increase is depressed, because the Youth Club has to spend more of its time competing with the Establishment for the bread of life, and in consequence has little leisure or incentive to undertake domestic affairs. This 'group-selection' is not just a perquisite of the skuas; it has been shown by Professor V. C. Wynne-Edwards, in a recent book, to be an aspect of the evolution of social behaviour universal in the animal world.

§

The young are lovely and entertaining creatures, able to scramble about in the heather a few hours after their birth. While the female covers the second egg of the clutch she keeps up a delightful, low-voiced conversation with her first-born as the intrepid fellow explores the vicinity of the nest, stumbling home from time to time to seek the warmth of her breast feathers. The male is often in attendance and is very solicitous at this time, clearly proud of his family, and when the second chick is ready the two are led from the nest and taken different ways. In general, we think they remain apart during the whole of the fledging month which follows, for it is unusual to find two chicks of a brood lying close together. This dispersal seems to be Nature's insurance policy against complete loss of the brood through predation.

The chicks are most vulnerable at the hatch and during their first few days, especially if the weather is cold and wet, for they have no temperature control and need to be constantly brooded: during the first day or two they lose weight, but with more regular feeding begin to grow rapidly. During the fledging month they have an incomparably lazy time, eating and sleeping in hidey-holes among the clumps of heather and re-cumbent juniper. A chick may lie motionless for two or three hours at a stretch in his grassy couch, watched over by a vigilant parent from a nearby rock or mound. The adult often relieves the tedium of baby-sitting by picking the crowberries or snapping angrily at the troublesome, tormenting midges.

Such exercise as the youngster takes coincides with his meal-times. The parent who has been hunting returns and circles the territory, voicing a special low call-note *kaa-ow*, which appears to serve both as a greeting to its mate and an advice of its intentions towards the chick. At any event, the young ones often stand up when they hear the note and describe in no uncertain terms the aching void in their stomachs. Occasionally the chicks come together for a meal, but this seems to be very rare; more usually the parents visit each in turn, alighting beside the young bird. Then the hunter regurgitates the partly digested fish on to the ground, leaving the chick to help himself if he is well grown, but feeding him from the bill if he is still very small. Then the rôles of the adults are reversed —the erstwhile hunter takes up his post on the rock or mound, and his mate flies out to sea to look for exercise and a fish-laden kittiwake to chase and rob.

When the young one has finished his meal he walks a matter of fifty yards or so across the territory, often stopping once or twice to indulge in some vigorous jumping and wing-flapping exercise to strengthen his growing muscles. At a later stage this activity also assists the protrusion of the wing feathers from their blue waxy sheaths; by taking daily measurements of wing-length in growing skuas we found that the rate of feather-growth is not even, but occurs in periodic bursts. Shortly the chick finds a new hiding-place and settles down to await the next meal, which may not come for a couple of hours or more. Here again is an insurance against destruction of the brood by predation, for any food remnants (perhaps even the strong taint of half-digested fish on the vegetation) might well attract four-footed enemies, with evil consequences for any chick that did not move far from its last feeding place.

A well-feathered chick is often allowed a short stroll between meals if the coast is clear. In such cases the guardian adult flies round the territory and, dropping low over the resting young-ster, gives it permission to wander by uttering the low *kaa-ow* note. The young one will 'freeze' at once into cover should any disturbance mar his exercise and the parent rise from the mound with a shrill bark of anger, *ya-wow*, *ya-wow*. Whenever a raven,

crow, gull or bonxie appears on the scene the moorland becomes
Bedlam, every skuti-alan in sight and hearing rising to the
attack and hustling the intruder unceremoniously from the
nesting-ground. It is the closest thing I have seen in Nature to
the Spitfire *versus* Heinkel 'dog-fights' which were such a
memorable feature of those warm summer days along the
south coast of England after Dunkirk.

When the young are really quite big their parents sometimes
leave them unattended while they go off to join a noisy social
gathering on some part of the hill. ("The skuas are having a
picnic!" Hervør, aged 5, would say on hearing the wild
yodelling music away over the moor.) I never saw a guardian
adult take time off like this without first making one or two
short stoops at the young bird's hiding-place, as though to warn
him to remain as quiet and unobtrusive as possible during her
absence. There is undoubtedly a very close understanding
between parents and young.

In a good season the young skuas get on the wing between
27 and 29 days after hatching, and in a poor season when food
is not easily come by they may take up to 34 or 35 days to
fledge. This is well shown in table 1 which gives the mean
value for the fledging of the two chicks of a brood over five
successive seasons for the same individual pairs. The first year
was an exceptionally lean one, the second showed some improvement, and 1951-53 were good. During the last three
years there were often a lot of non-breeding kittiwakes at the
south end of the isle, attracted by what appeared to be an
abundance of sand-eels, and doubtless this plethora of potential
victims made life easier for the skuas. In these good years the
breeding success (reckoned as the number of chicks reared in
the colony from the total eggs laid) was higher than in the
leaner years, as one would expect: in 1955 and 1956, for example,
it reached 70 and 72 per cent respectively, but in 1960 (which
was also a bad year for auks and kittiwakes) the skuas' success
was only 57 per cent.

We watched many a youngster's maiden flight, and he was
always guided round the limits of the home territory by a
watchful parent and rudely jostled in mid-air if he showed
signs of straying out of bounds. In the early days of the post-

TABLE I

MEAN FLEDGING-PERIODS OF BROODS OF THE SAME PAIRS OF ARCTIC SKUAS IN 5 SUCCESSIVE SEASONS

Season	A	B	C	D	E	F	G	H	I	J	Average
1949	—	34	33	31	35	$33\frac{1}{2}$	34	34	—	—	$33\frac{1}{2}$
1950	$32\frac{1}{2}$	$30\frac{1}{2}$	$30\frac{1}{2}$	$33\frac{1}{2}$	31	30	33	32	30	29	31
1951	$28\frac{1}{2}$	29	$28\frac{1}{2}$	—	32	27	—	—	29	$29\frac{1}{2}$	29
1952	28	—	$29\frac{1}{2}$	28	29	29	30	28	—	—	29
1953	28	28	$29\frac{1}{2}$	$28\frac{1}{2}$	28	—	30	29	$28\frac{1}{2}$	$30\frac{1}{2}$	29

One pair, a double pale nesting on the Mire of Vatnagard from 1950, had consistently short fledging-periods: 27 days for their only youngster in 1951, 28 and 26 days for their two chicks in 1953, and 27 and 26 days for their two chicks in 1954.

fledging period the two young of a brood spend a large part of the day trying out their wings in pursuit-flights over the home ground, and later they visit or are visited by the young of their neighbours for the same purpose. Frequently, too, they play with the sub-adult non-breeders who are continually moving about the colony at high summer, and whose presence is tolerated by the parent birds at this late period, although earlier they are often scolded and told to move on by the aggressive yodelling cry.

The young are fed by their parents as before, but with this difference—that often now the returning parent makes his hungry offspring pursue him for several minutes before he will alight and give up the food he has brought. We have often wondered, as the crying youngsters try to emulate their parent's marvellous twists and turns, if this is the first step in their training for a life of highway robbery. If it is, then the fact that the young require to be taught suggests that this habit of 'kleptoparasitism' is a recently acquired one in the evolutionary sense. After a week or ten days the young are taken out to sea, and doubtless their further education begins in earnest where the kittiwakes gather to feed in the tide-rips. Soon it is September and their education is complete—and during the first days of the month both parents and young disappear from their moorland home and begin the long journey to the southern seas.

CHAPTER V

THE BONXIES

THE origins of the skua tribe, like those of most birds, are shrouded in mystery, but are none the less intriguing. Today the northern hemisphere boasts four species, of which the subject of this chapter, the great skua or bonxie, is much the largest; and the southern hemisphere has other forms which are conspecific or at least very closely allied with it. Since the smaller *Stercorarius* skuas (or jaegers as they are called in America) migrate into the southern hemisphere they may have originated there, in which case their branch of the family may have been forced out of Antarctica as a result of intense competition during the Pleistocene epoch, leaving the other branch of more powerful birds in supreme control.

Certainly it is more than likely that the species radiation which has given us the arctic, pomarine and long-tailed skuas took place in the north, for while polychromatism is a marked feature of the plumage of arctic and pomarine, and has been recorded in the long-tailed (though it is excessively rare), it is not found in the bigger birds. Their variation is of quite a different kind in which individuals take on a dark brown, straw-coloured or a beautiful rufous aspect; and it would seem that the world's skuas must have been effectively isolated in two distinct groups when the genetic changes which have given us 'pale morphs' and 'dark morphs' in the smaller birds began. The juvenile plumage in all three species is rather like that of the bonxie, and as there is no material difference in the plumage of young and old in this and the southern skuas, it is probable that they are the least specialised and most like the ancestral form.

During much of their evolution, therefore, these two groups must have remained apart, and there seems little reason to doubt that the bird we call the bonxie is a comparatively recent immigrant from south of the equator. From such museum material as I have seen I would say that the population to which it is most nearly akin is that of Tristan da Cunha and Gough, and these islands may well have provided the spring-board for its return to the northern hemisphere. The present-day distribution of the bonxie accords closely with the North Atlantic storm-track, a fact which suggests a relatively recent appearance on the scene. It has colonised southern Iceland, where perhaps 80 per cent of the world's bonxies breed (though its numbers have decreased there in recent years), and the islands that stand in the path of the northern depressions—Faeroe and Shetland. Only in the present century has it tried to make new gains on the fringe. It secured a foothold in Orkney about 1914, in Caithness about twenty years later, and has recently begun to breed regularly in Lewis. It nested for the first time at St Kilda, 50 miles west, in 1963, and is now thought to be breeding sparingly in south-east Greenland.

All this lends point to the study of the small group of birds which has been trying hard for a number of years to colonise Fair Isle, near the periphery of its range. Here we may be witnessing an attempt at range expansion made possible by the bonxie's remarkable recovery from the decimation it suffered in the middle of the nineteenth century, when persecution imposed a severe check on its natural increase. In Faeroe and Shetland the eggs, and later in the season the fat full-grown young, were heavily cropped by hungry crofters, and by the 1880's this fine bird had disappeared from Skúvoy, its classic home in Faeroe, while in Shetland it was reduced to a few pairs on Foula and at Hermaness on Unst. There, Thomas Edmonston appointed a watcher in 1891 to guard the interests of the seven remaining pairs; they had increased to over a hundred by 1925, and to nearly 300 pairs by 1949, having spread meanwhile to many other parts of Shetland. The Venables (1955) estimated that some 1,200 pairs (among them many non-breeders) were present in Shetland by 1952, over three-quarters of them on the three isles of Unst, Foula and Noss; and as the first and last places are reserves of the Royal Society for the Protection of Birds there seems no reason why the numbers should not continue to grow. Indeed, the recovery has been so substantial that some form of control on the main breeding grounds is already desirable in the interests of weaker species, for the bonxie is a rapacious and predatory bird. It has been argued that the present level of damage to the kittiwake, eider duck and oystercatcher is not seriously menacing these species; but unless there is a commensurate increase in the more usual victims, gannets and the larger gulls, intraspecific competition may force the bonxies to turn to new food sources. A situation might arise where predation pressure becomes greater than the weaker species can tolerate.

§

There is traditional evidence in Patrick O'Neill's *Tour of Orkney* of 1806 that the bonxie nested at Fair Isle at the beginning of the nineteenth century, but it is not known to have done so in the present century until about 1921. George Waterston recorded three pairs in 1936 but only one in 1943-44. During our first seasons, 1948-49, four pairs nested, and five young were raised by six pairs in 1950. The next summer saw a drop to five pairs, which mustered only four young between them; but in that year a further six pairs held territory without breeding—a larger percentage of non-breeders than in any season before or since. Five of these six pairs returned in 1952 and so the breeding-stock was doubled. But it was a disastrous summer. Although ten pairs had the full clutch of two eggs, six eggs proved to be infertile and others disappeared during the incubation period; it is doubtful if more than eight young survived, which would give a breeding success figure of about 40 per cent against the arctic skua colony's 82 per cent in the same year. The 1953 season was nearly as poor, but the next one was better, and by 1955 it looked as though the bonxies had at last turned the corner.

The bonxies do not form a single crowded colony like the arctic skuas, but are scattered in little sub-colonies or isolated pairs over the eastern and northern parts of the isle. The Vaasetter moor has always attracted a few, and so also has the rather wet area of the Mire of Vatnagard and Cup o' Hey Doo below Ward Hill. From the beginning one or more pairs have nested on the wide grassy slope above the north-west cliffs at Dronger, with a fine outlook across the Atlantic to the bonxie stronghold of Foula 45 miles away. The oldest pair of all was close to the observatory, in the middle of Eas Brecks: they were there in 1946 when there were only half-a-dozen pairs of skutialans on the isle, so this territory perhaps antedates the founding of the arctic skua colony. These bonxies were always the first to return to the isle, in early or mid-April, and except in 1950 (when there was a change of mating) their eggs always appeared between 3rd and 8th May.

The moorland of Byerwall has been bonxie ground since a pair of arctic skuas were ousted from it in 1951, and the northern part of Sukka Mire (the 'sinking marsh') has had a pair since 1953. Closer to the airstrip there was a handsome couple, the female an extremely dark earth-brown bird, and the male almost fawn colour with a strong rufous tinge on the nape and rump. So strikingly different were they that a lady visitor, caring naught for physiological exactitude (and why indeed should she?), dubbed them Desdemona and Othello—and the names stuck! Up to our departure in 1956 they had managed to lay one infertile egg in every clutch except their first, when the single egg so often laid by birds in their first breeding season did produce a chick.

Owing to preoccupation with our growing colony of arctic skuas we were seldom able to pay as much attention to collecting data on incubation and fledging among the bonxies as we would have liked. In 1955 an intriguing pattern emerged. Eas Brecks, as always, was the first pair off the mark, and their youngsters had the longest fledging periods, 47 and 49 days. The two pairs at Vaasetter and the Byerwall birds laid in mid-May as usual and hatched their young between 4th and 16th June; the fledging-period for three of these chicks was 45 days, while the sole youngster at Byerwall took 46. Desdemona and Othello raised one chick between 20th June and 3rd August (44 days), while a late pair at Thione reared their brood in 41 and 42 days from hatching on 27th-28th June. Thus, as the season advanced, the fledging-periods grew shorter, and one wonders if this situation reflects the increasing availability of food towards high summer, when the gulls and other victims of the bonxies' aggressive kleptomania are busy providing for their own growing young. In earlier years we had known longer fledging-periods, particularly 1949 (which was bad for arctic skuas too), and 1948, when two young on Vaasetter took 54 and 55 days.

There is little direct evidence of the length of time it takes birds to mature, compared with the now abundant data for the arctic skua. Each year we ringed all the youngsters we could find, but it was not until 1954 that we had a ringed bird at the isle which we felt sure was one of our own. During that summer it was a free-lance wanderer about the moor, and when resting usually chose one of the hummocks in Homisdale, where it was made unwelcome by the smaller skuas. Next year it moved to a part of the hill overlooking the Brae o' Restensgeo, and found a mate. We recognised it as the same bird because it had peculiar white eyebrows, and when the pair returned and nested on the Brae in 1956 I determined to recover the ring. The hide and clap-net technique had proved successful with arctic skuas, and there seemed no good reason why it should not work with the bigger birds.

But I had reckoned without taking account of the powerful frame of these pugilistic creatures! I waited with mounting excitement in the hide as the ringed bird ambled to the nest. I let her settle, and gave the cord a hearty pull. The net fell cleanly, but to my chagrin she stood up to her full height, arched her wings, and literally elbowed her way from under the net. I tried again a few days later but she was too wily to return, so we decided to give her a week or so to get over the shock. On 21st June Esther operated the net while I crouched in another hide, ready to spring into action and forestall another escape—and it was a case of third time lucky. The ring was one we had put on a Vaasetter chick on 17th August 1950, so its wearer had begun to breed at six years of age. The ring was rather worn so I decided to replace it, and during the ensuing minutes I was never quite sure who was 'controlling' who, for 3 lb. 2 oz. of bonxie flesh and muscle takes quite a lot of handling! Since that day two further birds ringed as chicks have come to hand as first-time breeders, both at four years of age: abroad, a 1951 youngster came to grief in its fourth winter at Bermeo in northern Spain, while one of the last young bonxies I handled at Fair Isle, three days after the incident described above, was in Julianehaab Fjord in south-west Greenland on 24th June 1958.

§

Over the years we were able to see something of the inter-action between the two skua populations, and some interesting points emerged with regard to the dominance of the bigger over the smaller birds in securing living-space. The bonxie shows a preference for rather wet patches or close-cropped grassy areas above the cliffs, while the skuti-alan prefers the dryer heather-moor and avoids the grassy zones. Both, how-ever, may be attracted to the damper areas with long grass and scattered pools, so there is no clear-cut ecological division and a proportion of the two are in direct competition for nesting-room. In both species the same pairs will return to the same places, once they have established a territory, year after year.

The bonxie may be bigger and more powerful than his neighbour (he weighs between $3\frac{1}{2}$-$4\frac{1}{2}$ lb. against 1 lb. or so for the smaller bird), but it is not by any means a matter of brute strength winning the day. For one thing, the bonxie is no match for the agile skuti-alan in the air, and any bonxie which ventures over the skuary is assured of a rough passage, being harried relentlessly with a chorus of *ya-wow, ya-wow* cries which calls up all the arctic skua reserves for miles around. In 1949 a pair of bonxies tried to nest at the heart of the skuary in Homisdale, but were so badgered by the smaller birds that their single egg became chilled, and they deserted the site. Occasional non-breeders also tried to 'muscle in' from time to time, but met with no better success.

A young pair's best chance of establishing a territory lies in joining one of the existing sub-colonies like Dronger or Vaasetter, or in selecting ground on the fringe of the skuary where the smaller birds are thinly distributed. The chief reason why the larger species finds it difficult to hold ground in or near the centre of the skuary is because newly-mated birds do not attempt to establish territory until late in the spring, by which time the neighbouring arctic skuas are already defending nests, and are quite capable of looking after their own interests. Many new pairs do not lay in their initial season; they may make one or two nest-scrapes and defend them against human intrusion with a weak (one might say a token) aggressive flight, but for the most part they are content to sit on a mound, and are usually tame and easy to approach. Should their chosen area adjoin the skuary there is no change in the *status quo* in the first season; but in subsequent years their earlier return upsets the smaller birds' breeding rhythm, causing them to shift their ground and so delaying the start of incubation by a week or more.

The bonxie holds the trump card—the important advantage of an earlier return to the nesting ground in his second and subsequent seasons. The older pairs turn up at the isle in early and mid-April and have taken full possession of their ground by the third week in most years. When the arctic skuas put in their first appearance at the beginning of May they find the bonxies prepared to stand their ground; and when the skutialans have really settled in at the end of the second week most bonxies are already defending eggs. Those unfortunate arctic skuas which find a pair of the bigger birds on or too near their original pitch are obliged to cut their losses and go elsewhere.

The pressure exerted on neighbouring arctic skuas by a pair of bonxies is much greater than the intraspecific pressure within the main colony, since bonxie chicks are more active than young arctic skuas, and have a roving disposition. The reason for this difference in behaviour may be that the young of the smaller bird are more susceptible to predation, and are more retiring in consequence. The larger bird has few natural enemies, and certainly the young show more boldness and move about a good deal more in the open, so demanding a much more extensive fledging area than their lesser relatives.

As a result, there is a marginal distance at which nesting arctic skuas will tolerate a pair of bonxies during the incubation period, but will remove their chicks each year to a more distant fledging area within a week or so of the hatch, to counter the danger implicit in the expansion of the great skuas' territory as their young grow in size and activity. Four nests on the perimeter of Eas Brecks were in a marginal zone of this kind, the arctic skuas moving outwards from their nesting territories after hatching to put the greatest possible distance between themselves and the old-established bonxies. From 1948 to 1953 inclusive a pale *x* dark pair at Eas Brecks North nested on the edge of the moor, overlooking the Lighthouse Road, which they regularly crossed to a belt of heath called the Brae o' Roskilie within a week of the hatch. They moved gradually north-west along the Brae until, after ten days or so, they reached a wetter area dominated by a good look-out hillock above the Furse stream; and here, fully 300 yards from the nest, the chicks grew up and flew around after fledging.

Thus, pressure from the bonxies forced upon this pair the necessity for separate nesting and fledging territories in the same season; and it is of interest that in 1951, when they lost their eggs on 11th June and no replacement clutch was laid, they moved within six days to the fledging ground and stayed there for the rest of that season. In 1954 the bonxies put their nest a good deal farther to the east than usual, causing the Eas Brecks East arctics to shift ground to the north, so that the North pair was crowded out. They went off to their customary fledging ground at Furse and completed a clutch there on 28th May, a week later than the East pair, and for the first time since we had got to know them they went through the full breeding-cycle in the one place. They were successful, and this enforced move established a habit, for they returned to the new area for the full season in subsequent years.

§

One year we kept a close watch on the family life of a pair of bonxies while the chicks were still very young. The first one hatched on the morning of 15th July, the second on the following evening, but this chick was dead by the morning of the 20th. It probably died from starvation, brought about because the youngster did not respond properly to the behaviour of its parents when they brought food to the nest. We were impressed by the significance of the actual nest to the family circle during the first few days, for although both youngsters left it as soon as they were dry from the shell, the empty pad remained the focus of the parents' attention. The young were called up and brooded there at night, and eight out of twelve feeds witnessed on 19th July took place at the nest, the incoming parent alighting there and calling to the chicks. Twice the younger chick did not go to the nest, and at other times it was slow; and despite its pleadings it was not given food, or managed to secure very little. The older chick ceased to return to the nest on the sixth day, and thereafter was given food wherever it happened to be.

Both parents took turns at the task of hunting, and while one was away the other stood on guard on a nearby mound, leaving it only to give chase to passing ravens and gulls. Short, low sounds were often uttered by the watchful parent to comfort the chick, and to while away the time it picked and ate crowberries or strolled to a nearby pool to drink. When the hunter returned it flew calling overhead, and was greeted by the mate and by hungry plaints from the young one. Sometimes the adult went straight to the chick, but at others it alighted briefly at the mound beforehand, and then walked to the chick with downcast head, making convulsive movements of the head and throat. Then it regurgitated the partly digested food on to the ground, and helped the chick to feed. Such meals rarely lasted longer than two minutes and took place at very irregular intervals, varying during our watches from 5 to 87 minutes. On the fourth day after the first hatch twelve feeds were counted in a six hours' watch.

Although the male often fed the youngster direct, it was perhaps more usual for him to transfer the food to the female, who then satisfied the youngster while the male stood vigilantly over them—sometimes taking part in the feast, if his mate permitted. Once the female returned after a long absence and settled on the mound, apparently not disposed to feed her offspring; the male circled low over the chick, calling, and returned to his mate, as though to remind her of her duty— but he had to repeat the procedure twice more before she capitulated and went to the chick.

After a slow start (which is usual also with arctic skuas) the lone youngster grew quickly. He weighed 60 gm. on hatching,

the second chick 62 gm., and both were at the latter figure at
07.00 hours on the 17th. At the end of three more days the
older one had put on 33 gm., the younger one only 7 gm. (it
was found dead next morning), and subsequently his best increase during any one day was of 34 gm. on the eighth. By
07.00 hours on the tenth day he had put on over 170 gm. since
his birth at an average rate of 19·4 gm. per day. The bulk of
the weight increase took place between midday and dusk, and
as would be expected there was little or no gain during the
night. In fact, the first-born lost weight on his first two nights
by 3 gm. and 2 gm. respectively, and subsequently the best
overnight increase he showed was of 5 gm. on two separate
occasions. We also weighed the young of the Eas Brecks pair in
the same year, but at a much later stage of development: the
older youngster attained maximum weight at four and a half
weeks, and the younger one at four weeks, after which they
remained steady at 37-39 ounces until they flew when seven
weeks old.

On the whole, bonxies are a little more exciting to watch
from a hide than their lesser neighbours. The guardian bird
has a pretty display when greeting the returning mate, lifting
its wings high above its back to show the white flashes at the
base of the primary feathers, and at the same time bowing its
head to say *hek*, *hek*, *hek* in a hard and tuneless voice. On a
number of occasions both birds, after sitting quietly for some
time on the knoll, would rise to their feet and display in this
mannner simultaneously; at other times they would display in
flight, the wings upheld in a deep 'V'. Besides serving as the
greeting ceremony and mutual display, wing-raising and its
reiterated call-note are used to advertise the birds' ownership
of a territory. We saw the behaviour practised against other
bonxies as they visited, or merely flew overhead on their way
to and from the sea; also against intruding ravens, crows and
herring-gulls, and even such innocuous neighbours as rock
doves and oystercatchers. More than once we saw the action
stimulated by sheep grazing too close to the nest. It was also
evoked by the Taft-Leogh lorry rumbling along the road a
quarter of a mile away, and (perhaps not so strangely after all!)
by a B.E.A. service aircraft which flew low overhead.

§

Another summer Jack Peterson and I decided to observe and photograph the early days of the chicks at a nest on the Gowans. We put up a couple of hides some days before the hatch, so that the adults could get used to them, and we spent some time inside on the day the first chick appeared. It was soon clear from the behaviour of the parents that something was radically wrong: they were visibly distressed, and frequently nonplussed, apparently because certain of their actions did not meet with the expected response from the youngster. At first we too were at a loss, but when I left the hide and took the youngster in my hand I saw the cause of the trouble—for the chick had been born blind. The eyelids were sealed together, and although later I tried bathing them with warm water and managed to open them a little the slits were minute, and the young bird was obviously sightless. Its movements on the ground were very different from those of a healthy chick, for it shuffled along on the flat of its legs, the head carried low. It often fell on to its back and had difficulty in righting itself. Probably we ought to have killed it for quite clearly it was doomed to die, but the behaviour of the adults had been so puzzling that we decided to watch a little longer.

When we were back in the hides the male approached with a low *aa-ow* call, in obvious anxiety, and invited the chick to accept brooding, squatting down on his legs and fluffing out his breast feathers. Now the rule is that the offer to brood is made at a short distance and the chick's duty is to respond to the call-note and attitude of the parent; but although he was only a few inches away the male waited in vain, for the chick could not see his intention and so was unable to respond. He grew more and more uneasy, but did not seem able to modify his behaviour to accommodate the youngster—the next move was up to the chick, not to him. Finally he did change his position, but instead of going to the helpless chick he went to the empty nest and satisfied his unrequited urge to brood by sitting on that. Here he seemed reasonably composed, lifting his body occasionally and shuffling a little, and looking under his belly as if he expected to find something there—and all the time the sightless chick lay cheeping only a few inches away.

His mate had similar difficulty. She settled near the chick and offered to brood it, but apart from turning to face the piping youngster as it stumbled around her, adopting the same invitation posture for a few seconds in each new position, she made no effort to take the initiative. After three minutes of this she did move towards the chick and actually settled on it, whereupon its piping ceased, and she gave vent to a contented *tup* at short intervals. The male also squatted in a brooding position behind his mate, perhaps stimulated by the young one's cries, and when all was well he went off to a distance to sit on the moor.

The female, who had come in from hunting, next made an effort to feed the youngster, but this was no more successful than the brooding had been, and for the same reason. She stood close to the chick making regurgitation motions, the half-digested food slavering from her bill; but the blind chick, of course, could not respond to this invitation either, and because the young one did not go to her for food she could only stand unhappily by. It is remarkable how stereotyped the mechanism of invitation and response has become in such simple and fundamental activities as brooding and feeding the young: it is as though each separate movement acts as a link in a chain, a stimulus eliciting the next, and if at any point the chain breaks there is no flexibility, no room for manoeuvre, and the behaviour pattern cannot reach fulfilment.

CHAPTER VI

ARCTIC SKUA DIVORCES

WHEN you are engaged upon a long-term study of a species you have an uncontrollable desire to hoard masses of facts, figures and miscellaneous observations against the day in five, ten or twenty years' time when you will settle down to write up the results. The trouble is that field-work, although it may answer some of the original, simple problems, has a habit of throwing up others of greater complexity—and so that day of reckoning gradually recedes into the mists of the future. Then, quite suddenly, you are called upon to change your way of life, and much that you had hoped to do to tie up the hundred and one loose ends is lost in the limbo of good intentions. That is the only apology I can offer the reader for what is, I fear, a half-baked story. There will be no carefully constructed tables, no graphs, no histograms, but just a plain and doubtless over-simplified account of the goings-on inside a small community of birds, helped out by one or two simple diagrams to make the whole thing more intelligible —I hope!

I see now that we sowed the seeds of much trouble for ourselves, and for Peter and Angela Davis who followed us, as far back as 1949 when we decided to put numbered aluminium rings on the legs of as many skua chicks as we could find, in the hope that one day we would discover what proportion returned to breed at the colony of their birth. Then, in 1954, we found we could catch fully grown skuas with remarkable facility merely by arranging a clap-net so that it collapsed on top of the sitting bird when we tugged at a line taken to a hide a dozen yards from the nest. By this means we set out to catch and colour-ring as many adults as we could, always substituting dummy eggs for the bird's own, which we kept warm during

Fig. 7

Arctic Skua 'Divorces'

Each box represents a territory: those territories where matings changed are shown in relation to neighbouring ones where they did not (and which have been left blank). The date of occupation is given between the appropriate male (♂) and female (♀) symbols. The arrowed lines indicate the change of mate and territory of the bird in question: e.g. the 1955 male at K joined the female at L in 1956, while his mate moved to territory M in Furse, replacing a female captured by the male at N whose own mate went off with a young male to Wirvie.

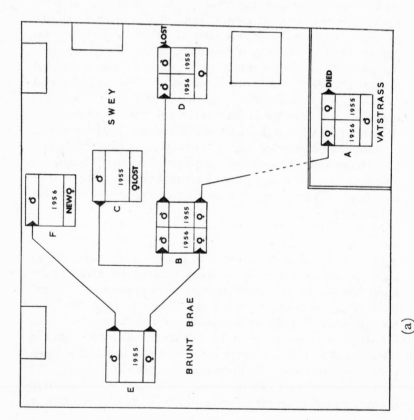

(a)

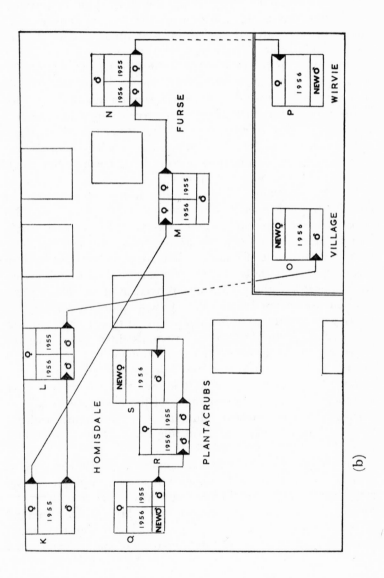

(b)

the operation in a tin filled with cotton-wool. We found we could also adapt the clap-net technique to catching non-breeding adults at their favourite preening-place on the edge of a small communal bathing-pool next to the airstrip. This was an even more thrilling sublimation of the hunting instinct, since there was no compulsion on the bird to return to its property; one watched one's hoped-for quarry arrive, bathe, walk round the pool (and often, alas, depart!) with mounting excitement—almost unbearable if the bird was clearly a sub-adult sporting a ring. There were always volunteers for this pastime, and I remember the consternation among the males in the lab one day when a most attractive young Danish under-graduate wanted to have a go. I warned her the job required a great deal of patience. "Oh, I have much patience!" she replied, delightfully mispronouncing the last word. She tried, and her 'passions' were well rewarded.

We did not catch all the nesting-birds in one season, of course, but made good headway in 1955 and 1956. Peter, who took over the direction of the observatory's work in 1957, carried on, and by 1962 the arctic skuas' 'Who's Who' was rapidly getting out of hand, all but a few of the 140 breeding birds being personally known. So far as Esther and myself were concerned, the year which proved most stimulating was also our last at Fair Isle, 1956. Of the 51 pairs then nesting 92 birds (not counting non-breeders) carried both numbered and coloured rings, and had their credentials entered on a massive chart which we always carried in the field, together with Hervør's box of multi-coloured crayons. Even without the evidence of ringing we had long known that certain birds are together year after year, for many of the birds had highly in-dividual characteristics of plumage and behaviour. Indeed, it seemed likely that the general rule was that they chose their mates as we had done—for life.

On the other hand, the skuas sometimes had their passions too, and we had known matings change—but until our colour-ringing programme really got under way we were without the means of discovering what circumstances brought such changes about. And then, in 1956, we were shocked to find that arctic skuas have their triangles and separations and divorces just

like human beings, and that (as in human communities) in-
compatability may be held to cover a multitude of conditions.
The matrimonial tangles of 1956 were very complicated ("What
they need is a Marriage Guidance Council!" Esther said), but
Peter and Angela's experience in subsequent years suggests that
this was a rather exceptional season.

§

At the head of the small green valley of Homisdale, sheltered
from the nor'west winds by the rising moorland of Swey, and
from the sou'westerlies by the low escarpment of Peerie Brae,
there is a group of square drystone enclosures in which some
of the Fair Isle families raise cabbage seedlings before trans-
ferring them to the crofts. They are called plantacrubs, and I
have always felt a little unfriendly towards them because they
have swallowed up bits and pieces of what must have been a
most interesting ancient stone circle. For a number of years a
pair of skuti-alans nested close to the plantacrubs, while
another pair nested just over the rim of Peerie Brae, the 'Little
Slope' at the end of the airstrip above. Although on different
levels of the moor the two nests were usually not more than
eighty yards apart.

In the spring of 1956 the male at Peerie Brae deserted his
wife and home and joined the plantacrubs female down below,
and they reared two chicks close to the walled plots. His former
mate stuck to her old territory and we saw her there on many
occasions until well into June. Then, on the 22nd, we found a
nest; and next morning, after waiting in a hide for the change-
over on the eggs, I was able to add the credentials of a new male
to our growing dossier. Meanwhile, the usurped plantacrubs
male took a new mate who we also caught, and who turned
out to be a bird ringed as a chick in 1952. This new pair
sliced off a goodly portion of the plantacrubs estate, nesting
near the 'portals' of the half-buried prehistoric circle, so that
we then had three pairs occupying an area almost at the centre
of the colony where for years past there had been only two.

That was a comparatively straightforward case of the eternal triangle, but meanwhile a much more complicated tangle was unravelling itself not very far away. Late in the previous season, when her chicks were only a few days old, the female of the Vatstrass pair at the eastern mouth of the valley met with an accident and had to be destroyed. She was a militant creature, and it seems more than likely that she struck the telephone wires when stooping at some passer-by. To his credit, her mate reared the two youngsters single-handed in the normal fledging time of 30 days.

He was back early in 1956 and set about finding a new mate, attracting a female who had already had one successful season at a site on Brunt Brae. This, 'Burnt Slope', is the next moorland rise beyond Peerie Brae as you climb towards Ward Hill, and beyond it lies the eroded and somewhat stony heath called Swey. It is interesting that both place-names derive from heather-burning, no longer a practice at Fair Isle, but obviously a feature of land 'improvement' in earlier days, perhaps when the spring was a good deal dryer than it is now. (Swey, which has a good Old Norse ring, suggests a word which was familiar to me in my Lancashire boyhood days, when 'swealing' meant setting fire to the grass.) It is on this higher reach of the hill that the main expansion of the skuary has taken place in recent years, and the defection of the new Vatstrass female set up a veritable chain-reaction of changed matings in that area which ultimately affected ten birds.

The male she left behind at site 'B' soon found another mate, going to join a female at 'D' whose 1955 partner had failed to show up and was posted 'missing presumed lost' (until he reappeared with a new wife in another part of the colony in 1957). Two birds, each from different pairs, liked the look of the now vacant 'B' territory better than their own, and promptly moved in: both had nested for the first time in the previous year, but in only one case had the 1955 partner failed to come back. The divorcee at 'E' took a new mate, one of the Mire o' Vatnagard chicks of 1953 now breeding for the first time— almost within sight of her parents, still happily together in their eighth year. This was a late, mid-June nesting, and as not infrequently happens with a three-years'-old female, there was only one egg, which proved to be infertile.

§

Homisdale is really the head of two small valleys, one running eastwards to Vatstrass and the other northwards to Furse at the foot of the steep bracken-clothed slope of Swey. Since before our arrival at the isle a 'white-winged mutant' female had nested with a dark morph male at the mouth of Furse among some much-ravaged tumuli which provided the pair with handy vantage-points. She herself was a dark morph, but a partial albino with white patches on her chin and belly and the leading-edge of her wings, and small white spots underneath her eyes. Such 'white-winged mutants' are rare, and she was unique among Fair Isle breeders at that time, though occasionally a sub-adult with similar markings (perhaps her own offspring) has paid a fleeting visit to the colony.

Every year since 1948 this pair had hatched two young, one an apparently normal sooty chick, and the other with exactly the same white markings as the dam: every year, that is, except 1951, when both youngsters were of this partial albino type. At first both showed the white eye-spots, but with the assumption of juvenile plumage the first-born, a very dark bird, lost these marks, though the younger chick retained them. Like all the other chicks of this kind they had flesh-coloured legs and feet, which are blue-grey in normal young and black in the adults. Neither chick survived, one dying when a month old, and the other having the misfortune to strike the telephone wires which span the valley about a fortnight after fledging. In other years our white-marked female reared her young successfully, normal chicks flying in 1950 and 1952, and 'white-winged' ones in 1949, 1953 and 1954.

Unfortunately none of these ever returned to the isle to breed —a pity, for an investigation of the hereditary factors of this curious partial albinism depended upon their doing so. We hoped in particular that one of the apparently normal chicks of the union might return and mate with another normal bird; then, if the new union should produce a 'white-winged mutant', we could be sure that the apparently normal offspring from the Furse family tree was a heterozygote carrying the strain as a recessive factor, and able to pass it on. Nor, up to the present time, has *any* mating of outwardly normal birds thrown up a 'white-winged mutant' chick.

We found the continuance of this picturesque variation most intriguing, and a holiday in the Faeroe Islands in the spring of 1953 made me even more interested. I was sitting beside the lake of Gróthúsvatn on Sandoy, enjoying the sunshine on 21st May, when a dark morph skua with a similar distribution of white feathers to our own bird's alighted on the shore. Later in the week, when visiting my friend Niels á Botni of Nólsoy, I found another 'white-winged mutant' in his collection of mounted birds—in this case a pale morph. After my return I wrote to a number of museums in Europe and America, and personally examined the British Museum collection in London, to see if I could trace other examples of this mutation. I found the British Museum had two specimens collected in the Faeroe Islands in 1875 and 1879 which were exactly like our Burn of Furse bird, and correspondence revealed the existence of other specimens from Orkney, Shetland and Caithness in our own area, and from places as far away as Namsos in Norway, the north coast of Iceland, Godthaab in West Greenland, and Cape Cod in Massachusetts, U.S.A.

My correspondents also found in their collections a number of birds in which the partial albinism was only slightly developed, there being a few white feathers in the carpal region or 'wrist' of the wing—and in general there always seemed to be more white feathers in the right wing than the left! I have seen such chicks at Fair Isle very occasionally in broods one parent of which had the odd white feather in this part of the wing. So there are varying degrees of development of this partial albinism, which first shows itself among the lesser coverts at the bend of the wing, and in a more advanced stage includes a white chin and a small patch on the belly, adding the white eye-spots only in its rarest and most strongly developed form. Moreover, it affects both pale and dark morphs, though in the former the white belly patch is of course occluded, and the white chin nearly so.

I hope the reader will forgive this digression, but the Burn of Furse female was understandably a great favourite, and we looked forward eagerly to her return each spring and followed her home-life with great interest. We were unashamedly distressed when, on my morning round of 21st May 1955, I found her lying dead from no obvious cause beside one of the tumuli from whose scarred top she had watched vigilantly over so many chicks. I performed her obsequies with a sharp scalpel and she now lies alongside some of those chicks in the cabinets of the Royal Scottish Museum. And this is where we take up the original story once more, for if it had not been for her untimely and unexplained demise then another series of matrimonial tangles, interesting in that they resulted in a considerable territorial expansion of the colony in 1956, might never have arisen.

§

The bereaved Burn of Furse male took a new partner, a younger female, about ten days after 'white-wing's' death, and for some inexplicable reason this bird laid single eggs in two different nests fifty yards apart. Because neither she nor he could make up their minds which one to sit on, neither egg brought forth a chick. Next spring the male decided he would have a change, and he took his next-door-neighbour's spouse, breaking up a partnership that had also begun the previous year.

There was a similar unhappy state of affairs at the other end of the valley, in Homisdale. At an old-established territory the female took as her mate a pale morph which, mated with a dusky pale bird, had made their home on Peerie Brae in 1955. The dusky pale bird, thus deserted, filled the vacancy created by the triangle in the Burn of Furse, and so the Peerie Brae pitch lay empty until a new dark pair took it over and laid a single egg in late June. Territories do not lie vacant for long in a flourishing colony, for young pairs which have come to maturity are always moving around on the lookout for a place to settle down.

We were left with two loose ends, the male of the old-established pair 'L' and the female of pair 'N', and it was some time before we found either. They were eventually discovered breeding with new mates in new situations remote from the colony, the former at Busta Brecks in the village a mile away, and the latter on a stony slope overlooking Wirvie half-a-mile to the north of Furse. She had as her mate the other 1953 chick of the Mire o' Vatnagard birds—and this remains the only instance we know from ringing of a brother and sister joining the colony as breeders at three years of age.

In the village the 1955 'L' bird had joined with a female first ringed as a sub-adult at the airstrip pool in 1954, so she must have been at least four and probably five years old. We caught them both in our clap-net in quick succession one afternoon before a sumptuous tea at Busta. They had become so inured to the comings and goings of the family that they scorned our intrusion and disdained the paraphernalia we brought along, and the whole operation was over inside half an hour—a record event. They hatched, but failed to rear, two young, and did not return in 1957, though one turned up in another part of the colony in 1959.

So the jigsaw puzzle was complete. In this case the chain-reaction of changed matings involved a dozen birds, led to the desertion of a good territory at the heart of the colony, and the formation of two new ones (both by birds with previous breeding experience) on the periphery—an expansion which more than doubled the north to south extent of the breeding area.

The point of particular interest brought out by all these mating changes is the instability of the young, year-old pairings. It stands out in sharp contrast to the fidelity of the older pairs, among whom divorce is a rather rare event. In 1956 only six of the fourteen matings established the previous year managed to survive, and these six, it is interesting to note, continued unbroken in 1957. A tentative explanation of this striking difference in behaviour is that the stability of matings depends upon the time of return to the breeding ground in spring, and the rapidity with which the partners come into breeding condition—factors which are no doubt closely integrated. It has been fairly well established that among colonial breeders the older and more experienced members not only come home earlier, but attain breeding condition more quickly, and are generally more successful than the younger and relatively untried element. Austin (1949) has shown this to be true for the common tern in North America, and in our own country Coulson and White (1958) have proved it for the kittiwake. Both species belong to the same natural order as the skuas.

So a delayed homecoming on the part of one of a pair is likely to result in the early bird becoming restive and seeking a new mate, and there is every likelihood that he or she will attract or be attracted by another celibate. When both partners are older and experienced their annual rendezvous among the heathery knolls, and the fulfilment of the breeding urge, are more closely synchronised; and once a pairing has weathered the physical and marital storms of two or three seasons the likelihood is that it will continue unbroken until the death of one or another partner dictates a change. Peter Davis has reviewed this problem of divorce among the skuas in the light of evidence available from the seasons subsequent to our departure from Fair Isle. Out of fourteen divorces between 1956-58 ten, probably eleven, concerned matings only one year old; but in 1959 the situation was reversed, only one of five divorces in that season affecting a pair newly-established in 1958. Of the others, two pairs had had two and the remaining two had had three seasons in company. He supposes that if asynchronous return to the colony is a main cause of divorce, as is highly probable, then in some seasons it can operate among birds in the older age-groups more than among their inexperienced juniors. Gales at sea, for example, might impede the return of old birds and allow youngsters travelling behind to overtake them. There may indeed have been some unusual stress on the Fair Isle skuas on northward migration prior to the 1959 season, since no fewer than twenty-one of the sixty matings which survived 1958 were broken in 1959, fourteen cases being due to the failure of birds to return.

Over the three seasons nearly 20 per cent of breeders with but a single year's experience failed to come back, compared with half that figure for older pairs, and Davis suggests that a higher proportion of younger birds may be attracted to other colonies in the Shetland area (where a few colour-ringed birds have been reported from time to time) in their second adult year.

§

The middle section of Sukka Mire, beneath Burrashield, was first occupied in 1954 by a pale x dark non-breeding pair who returned in 1955. They succeeded in rearing a chick although the female never laid an egg—a seeming paradox which I shall try to explain. In late May and early June one or the other bird gave vigorous 'injury-feigning' displays, as though to draw our attention away from a nest, whenever we crossed that part of the moor; but, watch and search as we might, we were quite unable to find any signs of a nest.

I was watching from a distance on 16th June when the dark bird gave the unmistakable impression of settling on a nest, but on going to the spot I could find only a bare scrape between two hummocks of wiry grass. The bird ceased her piteous crying and 'injury-feigning' antics when I went away and quickly returned to the scrape, which she appeared to be enlarging by pivoting around on her breast. She was sitting there next day, and by the 18th had lined the scrape with grass-stems. A small piece of flattened cartridge-case—a relic of the previous autumn's woodcock shoot—which had lain outside the nest on the 16th and in it next day, now lay just outside it on the opposite quarter. By the 21st it was back in the nest and the birds were assiduously brooding it turn about, and picturesquely 'injury-feigning' in its defence—behaviour which is described in greater detail in chapter VII.

This was a poor substitute for the real thing and we thought we would do better than that, so we put a hard-boiled hen's egg in the nest—and the pale bird accepted it at once. We often looked towards the territory as we did our skua rounds on subsequent days, and always one or other was sitting contentedly. This was very satisfactory from our point of view, for the dark bird had colour-rings and it was necessary to trap her, since owing to fading of the colours there was some confusion of identity with another breeding-bird. She was caught while 'incubating' on the 25th and was found to have fully developed brood patches; she had been ringed as a non-breeder at the skuas' bathing-pool near the airstrip in June of the previous year.

The pair sat on the hen's egg until well into July. We then decided that if the young Breedpiece pair, whose territory lay next to that of Desdemona and Othello just across the moor, showed signs of hatching both their eggs, we would give one to the Sukka Mire pair, because the chances of young and inexperienced birds rearing two chicks in such dubious company were remote. Besides, we felt that the Sukka Mire pair's persistence merited some reward! The Breedpiece eggs were chipped on 14th July, so one was taken and substituted for the hard-boiled hen's egg that evening. The adopted chick hatched early on the 18th, the last chick on the isle to break its shell in 1955. It was well cared for and flourished, flying exactly a month later. Its brother at Breedpiece also survived and got on the wing at the same time, after a longer fledging period of 32½ days.

CHAPTER VII

IN DEFENCE OF NESTS

THE naturalist who elects to spend the summer studying skuas, great or small, should have steady nerves, for he will quickly find himself the victim of intimidation. Both bonxie and skuti-alan are renowned for their aggressive ways during the nesting season, and neither is afraid to drive home his attacks. One of my more uncomfortable moments at Fair Isle was when I took two friends to view a bonxies' nest: one had a good knowledge of birds and knew what to expect, but the other was a Londoner whose interest was slight, and mischievously we did not enlighten him. There was no sign of the birds and we reached the nest without incident; it contained a newly-hatched chick, and with a murmur of delight the Londoner went down on his knees the better to see and touch its silky, buffy-brown down. At that moment an irate parent swept in from nowhere and walloped him hard on the back of the head. He leapt to his feet with an oath and squared up truculently to my other companion. It took all the tact and persuasiveness I could muster to avert a fight.

A blow from a bonxie that is really on target will leave you with a headache for the rest of the day, but although there are more vicious bonxies than skuti-alans on aggregate, I would choose to deal with the bigger bird every time. When he comes lumbering towards you at eye-level the bonxie looks a malevolent, cumbersome heavyweight, and the attack is menacing enough; he may swerve aside (assuming he intends to swerve at all) when less than a yard away. But his movements are more predictable than those of the arctic skua, because he nearly always approaches from the direction of his favourite sentry mound, swinging round after each attack to begin another long run in from the same quarter. Once you have

Climbing Sheep Craig. The ascent is made by a fixed chain in the dark cleft below the group of men. The wall of the rock is dappled white with fulmars.

The scattered crofts as seen from Malcolm's Head, looking north-east to Vaasetter and Sheep Craig.

The crofts as they appear from the hill-ground of Burrashield.

mastered the topography of a bonxie's territory you should be able to manoeuvre so that the war of attrition goes in your favour. It is a useful theory, but in practice you will still qualify for the odd headache because bonxies do not always behave as expected—which, of course, is part of the joy and stimulation of watching them.

The skuti-alan is a far more terrifying proposition if he belongs to the kind whose courage knows no bounds. There were some really wicked customers at Fair Isle whose territories it was always wise to avoid, even if this meant a tedious detour. Practically all will attack sheep and dogs, but many are over-awed by man. Some never attack at any stage of the breeding cycle; others do so towards hatching time and when the young are small, and a minority are vicious from the moment their first egg appears in the third week of May. Such birds have a bad influence on their immediate neighbours, and we have known birds of a normally quiet and courteous demeanour turn into raving Dervishes simply through acquiring a mate of the aggressive kind. An attacking disposition is not necessarily inherited—one of our fiercest females was the progeny of a quiet and undemonstrative pair, and conversely we have known veritable rogues produce mild-tempered descendants.

There are no rules for dealing with this species; an attack may develop from any quarter, and more often than not it will come from behind. The birds fly in at a higher level than the bonxie, stoop and strike whenever they can, zoom upwards, swing round when a dozen feet away, and hurtle down at you again. They quite often hunt in pairs, so that one is going up while the other is on the way down, and your defences are confused and frequently pierced. More than once I have sat on the moor enthralled by the sight of a pair trying to shift an obstinate sheep, swinging above its head like winged pendulums out of phase. Your only protection against the worst offenders is a stout stick held above your head, but I never cared for this after one of my favourite birds knocked herself unconscious for several minutes one afternoon.

Another thing about skuti-alans is that they behave most badly to those who love them most. The Vatstrass female was a case in point; she always went for me no matter who else was with me, and even when Esther and I changed coats and hats one evening she was not deceived. Another female on the Brae o' Restensgeo liked me so little that, after attacking strongly as I walked to a hide-tent on her territory, she spent the next half-hour thumping the roof while I sat inside optimistically holding the pull-cord of a clap-net set to catch her on her return to the nest. We had a grand border collie named Bob Williamson-Dog to whom skuas were anathema ever after that puppyhood day when the Burn of Furse 'white-wing' gave him the biggest hiding of his life. Nothing would induce him to go on the moors with us between May and September; when we left the road he might come along for a dozen yards or so, leaping up all the time at my chest in an effort to dissuade me from the rash enterprise. A bend of the road strikes into the Vatstrass territory, and Eas Brecks East also overlooks the road; both pairs were a hazard to cyclists, of whom more than one finished up in a prostrate muddle of whirling spokes and projecting limbs on the verge.

No wonder the Fair Isle men and their dogs loathed the skuas, for every year at 'rooin' time they had the whole gamut of this unruly mob to run as they herded the sheep across the hill. By hustling the men, and scaring the sheep and dogs, the birds made the day's work a torment and a frustration. The men, I may say, were marvellously good about it, and I do not recall losing a bird or a nest through deliberate human interference. The F.I.B.O. owes the Fair Isle people no mean debt of gratitude for that!

§

While the bonxie is really a dreadful bore in defending his nest, the skuti-alan is as picturesque and exciting as any bird can be, except perhaps the oystercatcher. The aggressive flight is only one trick of the trade—there are others equally interesting and engaging to watch. The bird has a highly developed 'lure display' by which it seeks to beguile the wanderer on the moor to the greatest possible distance from its eggs and chicks. This is a kind of behaviour shared by many birds, particularly ducks, gamebirds and plovers, and it is often referred to as 'injury-feigning'. To the unaccustomed eye the writhing, grovelling bird gives a most convincing impression of hurt, even paralysis, but if you follow its pitiful stumblings you quickly learn that it is all an elaborate deception, for when you are out of harm's way a miraculous recovery takes place. So effective and marvellous is this simulation of injury that it seems churlish to deny that the performer is guileful, and to emphasise that far from being an intelligent act this 'injury-feigning' is the purposeless, panicky product of frustration and fear. Yet its true nature is perhaps as wonderful as the anthropomorphic interpretation would have it be—but for different reasons.

This distraction display shows much individuality in performance, not only between different birds, but in the same individual at different stages in the breeding cycle. When you become familiar with the skuas' versions you can recognise two distinct major forms. In some cases the skua progresses slowly across the heather with her wings twitching and flapping asymmetrically, her head bowing jerkily, and her tail lifted until it is almost at right-angles to the body. The pronoun is carefully chosen, for this is the 'female' type of display. In others the performance has quite a different character. The bird stands on the moor with half-open wings, peremptorily bowing and gaping, and every so often leaps upwards to a height of several feet, descending with outspread wings. This is the 'male' type and it is usually silent, whereas the 'female' kind is accompanied by a curious whimpering recital reminiscent of a young animal crying in distress. With the more vicious pairs this 'injury-feigning' seems to be called forth at a higher emotional level than the aggressive flight, for their first reaction when you set foot on the territory is to attack, and they do not normally resort to the lure display until you are very close to the nest, or handling the chick. As you leave the nest or chick they desist from 'injury-feigning' and begin attacking again, continuing until you have left the nesting ground.

These distraction displays throw important light on bird behaviour in general. In those species whose activities have been closely studied the displays appear to have evolved through the modification of more primitive patterns, such as those associated with threat and courtship. In the distraction display context, these older patterns occur through an accommodation or compromise between the desire for self-preservation on the one hand, and parental protective behaviour on the other. In other words, there is a strong conflict of opposing drives, the one to stay and brood the nest or young, the other to seek safety in flight. The emotional energy produced by this conflict is denied orthodox expression through either of the familiar channels, and is expended through some other activity in the bird's repertoire which, because it belongs to a different sphere of experience and is inappropriate to the current set of circumstances, is called a 'displacement activity'.

It is essential that an effective distraction display should quickly divert the attention of an enemy from the position of the nest by focussing it upon the parent bird. The more conspicuous the performer can make itself, the more effectively will it protect its brood. Common denominators in all such displays, therefore, are extravagance of movement, the presentation of bright or contrasting colour-schemes, and (in some cases) the incorporation of vocal or other sound effects. Those elements from older patterns which best meet these important requirements will tend to become ritualised in this new rôle, eventually becoming fixed in this situation as a new behaviour pattern in their own right. Thus we find that the distraction displays of various species have 'borrowed' and modified those elements, whatever their original function, which most adequately fulfil these demands and have been favoured by natural selection as a result.

In the case of the arctic skua one of the 'borrowed' activities recalls the feeding of the young bird, for an anxious skua will sometimes bow its head vigorously and regurgitate food on to the ground. More than once I have seen a whole fish appear suddenly in this way—to be as quickly gobbled up again! Other elements which have lent themselves as safety-valves for pent-up emotion in the same way belong to the most highly emotional phase of the skua's life, namely copulation. The grovelling, whimpering, tail-tilting bird is the submissive female inviting coition; the jumping, wing-spreading, head-nodding bird is the male attempting to mount and grasp his

mate by the scruff of her neck. Unless one is fortunate enough
to witness the comparatively rare mating act there is no other
way of sexing one's skuas than by studying their lure displays.
Sometimes, over the years, we saw known birds in copulation,
or dissected birds found dead on the moor, and so were able
to check the conclusions drawn from watching distraction
display. Invariably we found agreement.

§

In other species the most striking (and therefore efficacious)
original from which distraction display has evolved is found
in the threat posturing against a rival bird. Occasionally we
caught a snipe or a woodcock in one of the traps; it was difficult
to urge such birds into the catching-box, for they would strut
around like little turkey-cocks lifting, fanning and flicking their
colourful tails. This is a part of intraspecific threat display, and
it is also the chief motif of the snipe's 'injury-feigning'. I had
seen a good deal of it during four seasons in the Faeroe Islands
(and was to see it often again at St Kilda in 1957 and 1963)
and a good performance is perhaps the most singularly beautiful of any of the activities in this category.

I was treated to a perfect gem on the hills near Tórshavn
one summer day in 1945. The bird had two chicks, tiny balls
of russet, silver-spangled down with milky-blue eyes; they were
hiding under a rock, and while I took them in my hands and
ringed them she crept towards me until almost within arm's
reach. For several minutes she held me spellbound. She moved
round me in a half-circle, in a crouching posture with her legs
nearly flat on the ground and her bill pointing obliquely downwards, emitting a loud, harsh call-note. Her wings were sometimes in the normal resting position, and sometimes their tips
drooped underneath her tail and were fluttered and shaken
vigorously. The tail was the most fascinating feature, its movement the most striking and compelling feature of the display;
for every so often she halted, twisting and spreading the feathers
into a vertical fan. Round the edge of the tail, subterminally,
there ran a reddish-chestnut band, and on one or two of the
feathers rather below the centre of the fan an intensely black

spot a quarter of an inch in diameter interrupted the band. She did not hold the fan rigid, except momentarily, but continually snapped it open and shut. Frequently she reversed her direction so as to keep to my front as I knelt on the moor, and having swung round would creep forward a little, always calling, then lean forward with her breast almost touching the ground, the better to get her tail up in the air. Then the fan would start flicking open and shut with that intermittent flashing of buff and chestnut, and always that staring black spot in the middle. Here were all the ingredients of a successful lure display—a weird croaking call to attract attention, a continuous series of abrupt and extravagant motions to hold one's gaze, and bright and contrasting colours startlingly presented.

There are still other sources of material on which a species can draw for its distraction display. In Faeroe the golden plovers used to run quickly with the wing-tips flicking rhythmically but alternately up and down, and the head tucked into their scapulars, so that they looked for all the world like small mammals running away. This 'rodent-run' is a common ruse among purple sandpipers (which contrive to make themselves look like lemmings!) and several other small wading-birds, among which something very like it appears also in courtship display. Doubtless it is a very effective deception when practised against the arctic fox and avian predators whose technique is to pounce on small four-footed animals whenever they can.

§

The oystercatcher, which in some ways is the most polished and always the most entertaining performer of all, uses a terrestrial version of an aerial display which bird-watchers call 'butterfly-flight'; but this is only one of many activities in a repertoire as rich and varied as can be found in the bird-world. Like the skuti-alan it has an aggressive flight when the young are closely threatened, and this may result in physical attack; also, it has a 'false-brooding' posture, a common component of distraction behaviour among waders; and it also indulges in a curious pretence at sleeping (with one eye open!) when it thinks there is danger in the offing but not exactly imminent. There are striking regional differences in the incidence and intensity of these displays. In the Faeroe Islands, where oyster-catchers nest in the fields and on the moors, forms of lure display are general and highly ritualised; in England, where the bird is a shore nester, displays are rare and their performance is poor; and at Fair Isle and Unst at the extremities of Shetland, where many birds are moorland breeders, the behaviour is at an intermediate stage of development.

I have sat for many hours watching oystercatchers, and could sit for many more, for they are among Britain's most fascinating birds. They are handsome in their black and white livery, with long red beaks, pink legs and eyes like glowing coals. Good places to watch them were the green sward of Buness and the steep slope of Goorn—especially the latter, because one could sit on the slope half-hidden by a rock and watch all that went on below. When anxious for the safety of their buffy-grey chicks they are highly demonstrative, but by retiring a little way and sitting inconspicuously on the slope one could reduce the tension. They would return to their daily affairs, feeding and preening, but conscious all the time that you hadn't gone very far and there was still a need to be on the alert. A common attitude on such occasions was 'pseudo-sleeping', when one or both birds would stand quietly on one leg, the scarlet beak pushed among the scapular feathers, and apparently asleep—but always with a ruby eye wide open, watching for the slightest movement.

This 'pseudo-sleeping' is a curious activity, doubtless an ancient and inherited posture since newly-fledged young also do it under circumstances of mild disturbance. Its main function seems to be in flocking behaviour, when birds must ensure that they are not too crowded by their neighbours, and always have enough room for a sudden take-off should the need arise. The South Harbour skerries often held little groups of quiescent oystercatchers, young as well as old, 'asleep with one eye open', on sunny autumn days; and if the party was joined by another every member 'woke up' at once, if only momentarily, until the newcomer had settled down and every-one had shuffled (on one leg) to a tolerable distance. Often you see similar behaviour in other waders, especially when the flocks are resting on a sand-spit at high tide, waiting to feed on the ebb; as the outer ranks are forced higher by the incoming waves hidden beaks are continuously unsheathed while positions are changed. Young fulmars also 'pseudo-sleep' when resting warily on their ledges, half-expecting to be disturbed by the adult birds which constantly fly to and fro close to the cliffs.

One stage higher on the emotional step-ladder is the oyster-catcher's 'false-brooding'. A number of species do this, and if it were a deliberate ruse to lure the watcher to a false nest it would be successful time after time. It is very rare among skuas but not uncommon among plovers and sandpipers, though none is so persistent in its use as the oystercatcher. When you rise from your watch-point and advance a little way towards the birds they 'wake up' and run furtively about with downcast heads, and then one or both will sit down as though covering a nest. Some species, when an observer has been searching for their eggs, have been recorded 'false-brooding' eggs or young which were not their own; thus A. C. Buturlin was kept guessing when looking for a nest of the rare Ross's gull, because the bird continually sat on nests of arctic terns in the same colony as her own. This suggests that the posture arises from a thwarted broodiness, and that in an early stage of development something resembling the bird's own property is required to give the brooding urge temporary dominance over the desire to run away. The oystercatchers have left this primitive stage far behind and with them 'false-brooding' requires no provocation from the environment. A bird will sit down several times within the space of a few minutes, but never in the same place twice; I have seen them sit on unlikely 'nests' on the tops of moorland boulders and in the middle of metalled roads—and I have seen birds brood continually even though their young were on the wing and there was no longer any biological need for such behaviour.

Finally, when you approach too near and step up the emotional level still further, the bird will treat you to the full lure display, though often mixed with spells of 'false-brooding' and the aggressive flight. To see the whole rigmarole at its best you need to be on a Faeroe moor, but sometimes you will get nearly as good a performance at Unst or Fair Isle. The bird moves quickly across the rough ground, in a crouching posture, the wings partly spread and pumping rhythmically up and down, the tail fanned and showing a marvellous contrast of black and white. So long as you follow her the bird will keep going; but if you hang around she will come to rest on a prominent hummock or rock, her head lolling, her beak half-open and gasping, her wings hanging limply and twitching spasmodically.

I call this the 'exhausted bird' posture and it succeeds wonderfully well in giving the impression that the performer is about to expire. It is not by any means peculiar to the oystercatcher, and I have often seen a similar figure in the lure displays of ringed and golden plovers. It is difficult to resist the temptation to rush forward and grab the dying bird—even when you know it is all a hoax!—but if you do move in her direction, the crouching run with beating wings and fanned tail will begin all over again, and will continue until you no longer constitute a threat to her young.

When you meet with this performance at Unst or Fair Isle it is soon apparent that the polished lure display of Faeroe birds is derived from the beautiful 'butterfly-flight' display. In spring, before nesting begins, this seems to have something of the character of a song-flight—or, better, an advertisement flight by means of which unmated birds draw attention to themselves. It is not confined to any particular territory and may cover a wide area, and often a mated pair will find themselves with the embarrassment of a 'gooseberry' who engages in this extrovert activity. The wing-beats are slower and more deliberate than usual and their amplitude is greater, and each full stroke is accompanied by a piping cry. Later in the season, in situations where eggs or young are threatened, Shetland birds perform this same flight over the territory as a 'displacement activity'; and, as excitement increases, they descend lower and lower, finally touching down to run with the same motions as 'butterfly-flying' across the rough ground. Gradually the flying action is slowed down and the movement is more like the typical lure display of Faeroe birds.

It has always seemed remarkable to me that the lure display

and its associated postures have reached their finest development in the Faeroe Islands, because there the oystercatcher has fewer natural enemies against which such displays might prove effective than have oystercatchers elsewhere. To have reached such a high pitch of development as a behaviour pattern in its own right there must have been strong selection pressure—and yet in Faeroe there are no foxes, no otters, no weasels, no stoats to pilfer the eggs or trouble the young. There are avian enemies such as ravens, crows and gulls, but the oystercatcher deals with these intruders by attacking them with its powerful red bill from below. Rats are too recent, and too few and scattered away from the ports, to have exerted any influence. What, then, has brought about this kaleidoscope of contrasting colours and bewildering postures in Faeroe oystercatchers, golden plovers and snipe?

It seems to me that this wonderful range of activities can have evolved only through the need to outwit man and his dog—it does not seem possible that the necessary selection pressure could have had any other source. Men have lived in the Faeroe Islands for little more than a thousand years; but throughout this time it has been their habit to go to the moors in spring to tend their lambs, cut and dry their peats, and round up the flocks for their wool. These are protracted tasks, and during the whole of its breeding cycle the oystercatcher is, and always was, exposed to human interference. Probably, at times in the past, there was also a certain amount of human predation of its eggs. It is not perhaps so very remarkable that, through numerous generations, the oystercatcher has responded to this continual disturbance by evolving these remarkable displays.

CHAPTER VIII

THE FULMARS

A LTHOUGH the skua work was time-consuming, there was another bird we felt we ought to find time to study during the long summer days, and this was the fulmar— our commonest breeding sea-bird next to the puffin. A great deal is known about the numbers and distribution of the fulmar in the North Atlantic: it is a comparatively recent breeding bird in the British area, except at St Kilda, having arrived from Iceland towards the end of last century, via the Faeroe and Shetland Islands. Its phenomenal increase and range expansion have proved a source of fascination to one ornithologist, James Fisher, spurring him to monumental research which culminated in the appearance of a monograph *The Fulmar* in 1952. A good deal is also known about its movements at sea, but knowledge of its behaviour ashore was still so fragmentary in the early fifties that Fisher was able to devote less than a dozen of his 496 pages to the subject. Here was a field that was wide open for investigation.

The chief difficulty in studying fulmars at their breeding places is that the sexes are identical in plumage; also, the full-grown young are so like the parents as to be almost impossible to differentiate unless one has had some experience of watching fulmars closely during the later part of their season. One May day in 1952, looking idly over the cliff at Johnny's Peats, I saw the chance we had been hoping for—two quite dissimilar fulmars were sitting side by side high up on the opposite face. This was a doubly exciting find because the fulmar is polymorphic, and although a gull-like type with white head and under parts and grey wings is practically universal in the British Isles, our seas are visited in winter by birds from the high arctic regions, where the majority have the plumage predominantly

bluish-grey. The St Kildans sometimes killed a 'blue' fulmar
at their cliffs, but otherwise there was only one known case of
such a bird nesting in Scotland, and this had been discovered
and filmed by our Shetland friends Theo Kay and Jack Peterson
at Hascosay the previous year. According to Peter Davis, a
'blue' fulmar bred on Lundy, north Devon, from at least 1948
till 1954.

Quite apart from the intrinsic merit of Upper Blue, as our
bird came to be called, here was a pair in which we could distinguish the partners with ease. But better was to come! I
could hardly believe my eyes a day or two later when I saw
another 'blue' fulmar, not quite so dark as the first, mated to one
of the normal type only a few yards below. I then looked more
closely at the others on the cliff, but there was only one further
pair whose members could be told apart—they were normal
birds, but whereas one had a wholly greenish bill, its mate had
the upper mandible coloured dark brown. So with Greenbill
and Darkbill and the other two pairs to provide the information,
our study of the breeding season behaviour got off to a flying
start. We visited the cliff at least three times a day, often more,
but always first thing in the morning, then just before or after
lunch, and again in the late evening, and were able to note
approximately when each change-over on the single white egg
took place.

The first and most remarkable fact which emerged was the
inordinate length of individual spells spent covering the egg.
This was never left unguarded, and the sitting bird did not
move from it unless the mate was alongside ready to take over
—and this, we found, did not happen very often. There is no
doubt that fulmars can go for a long time without food, and in
all likelihood their feeding areas are many miles (perhaps
hundreds of miles) out to sea. Between 20th May (when we
first saw an egg) and the end of June Darkbill had only five
spells on the egg, averaging five days in length; but the other
birds usually had shorter sessions of about two and a half to
four days each.

Darkbill was a prodigious performer—her longest spell at the
cliff was just short of nine days—and the mate of Lower Blue
was a close runner-up. She had an eight days' session broken

only by a few hours intermission (during most of which she sat alongside her mate) early on the seventh. Moreover, the birds seemed in no hurry to depart for their feeding grounds after the arrival of the relief, and not infrequently the brooding bird sat on contentedly for several hours before handing over. Dark-bill remained at the nest-site for some hours paying court to Greenbill in a mild and sedate fashion even at the close of her nine days' vigil.

Quite a number of change-overs took place either very early or very late in the day, perhaps even during the night: in fact, two-thirds of those at Upper Blue's nest fell in our overnight period, and of forty changes at all nests in the first five weeks of watching, 60 per cent occurred between eight o'clock at night and seven o'clock next morning. The remainder were about equally divided between morning and afternoon. There was none or very little ceremony; sometimes the incoming bird found it necessary to coax his mate by caressing her with the bill before she would hand over, and sometimes there was a spasm of head-rolling and cackling on the part of one or both birds during the change. We thought Upper Blue and Dark-bill were the females of their pairs (though there is no certainty of this), since they took the first spells of incubation and were the more assiduous in attention to domestic duties, as shown in table 2 on p. 110.

A week or ten days before the hatching of the chick the rhythm of incubation changed suddenly, the change-overs becoming more frequent and the majority of spells on the egg being reduced to little more than a day. At the same time there was a marked tendency for the unoccupied partner to stay at the nest-site with the brooding mate. There seems little doubt that this new behaviour was adjusted to the hatching phase, which, in the case of so large an egg, must occupy the best part of a week from the first noticeable activity of the chick inside the shell. But we do not think it is a response to some *observed* difference in the condition of the egg, since Lower Blue and his partner behaved exactly as the others in this respect and their egg never hatched, being presumably infertile. Their brooding urge declined about a week after the hatch was due, and for much of one afternoon the egg was deserted—the first

TABLE 2

NUMBER OF DAYS BETWEEN CHANGE-OVERS AT THREE NESTS OF THE FULMAR

1. Upper Blue Pair
(18th May—10th July)

Blue Bird	$2\frac{2}{3}$	5	4	4	6	3	2	$2\frac{1}{3}$	$\frac{2}{3}$	$1\frac{1}{3}$	1	Total	32
Normal Bird	$1\frac{2}{3}$	4	2	2	$2\frac{2}{3}$	$3\frac{1}{3}$	$\frac{2}{3}$	$1\frac{1}{3}$	$1\frac{1}{3}$	1	$\frac{1}{3}$	Total	$20\frac{2}{3}$

2. Lower Blue Pair
(19th May—10th July)

Normal Bird	?	6	2	$5\frac{2}{3}$	$5\frac{2}{3}$	$3\frac{1}{3}$	$1\frac{1}{3}$	$\frac{1}{3}$	1	Total	$25\frac{1}{3}+$
Blue Bird	6	$\frac{1}{3}$	7	5	3	$2\frac{2}{3}$	$1\frac{1}{3}$	$1\frac{1}{3}$	2	Total	$28\frac{2}{3}$

3. Darkbill × Greenbill
(20th May—8th July)

Darkbill	?	$3\frac{2}{3}$	$8\frac{2}{3}$	$4\frac{1}{3}$	$5\frac{1}{3}$	3	1	$\frac{1}{3}$	$\frac{2}{3}$	Total	$27\frac{1}{3}+$
Greenbill	2	5	4	$4\frac{1}{3}$	3	$\frac{1}{3}$	$1\frac{2}{3}$	1	$\frac{1}{3}$	Total	$21\frac{2}{3}$

NOTE: Three observations were made daily—between 0500-0700 hours, around 1400 hours, and between 2000-2200 hours G.M.T. Thus each period approximates to one-third of a day.

time we had seen fulmars leave their egg unprotected on the ledge. Although one bird returned that evening, and sat during most of the following day, the egg disappeared, perhaps taken by some marauding gull during a later absence. It seems likely that this late period of shorter sittings is initiated by some physiological change which anticipates the hatch, and is adapted to the chick's need for constant brooding and regular feeds during its first week or so of life.

§

Eric Duffey, who studied a group of fulmars on Buness quite close to the observatory, found that an odd relationship existed between the young chick and its parents. The chick's response to any sudden movement close to it is to squat on its tail and throw its head forwards spasmodically, making a loud retching noise and ejecting a stream of oily, evil-smelling fluid at the source of the disturbance. It has been claimed that the young one will 'spit' in this manner when still partly enclosed by the shell, but this is certainly not general and was not substantiated by the half-dozen or so hatching youngsters I have handled. This 'spitting' is the young bird's only defence against predatory gulls, rats and other enemies, and by this means it denies the use of its ledge to passing fulmars (mostly non-breeders) which try to alight on the cliff. It does not (perhaps cannot) discriminate between these and its own parents, at any rate in the early days, and so receives them in the same aggressive fashion. It is customary for the returning parent to land at some little distance from the young one and wait for its initial excitement to die down, when it gradually sidles along the ledge until close to the chick. The chick will accept its parent readily enough if the approach is casual, and will then suffer the grown bird to caress its head and neck with the bill, for in this way the adult stimulates a begging response from the chick. After the first week or ten days there are signs that the young one recognises its parents, for they are permitted to land closer and advance more freely than before. By this time the young one, growing rapidly, is better able to take care of itself, and it is left alone on the cliff for long periods.

The fulmar does not seem to be a hungry bird even when young, and like Duffey we formed the conclusion that it has often to be stimulated by its parent before it will condescend to take the regurgitated, oily food derived from half-digested plankton. There were a few exceptions, as when Upper Blue took over the care of the chick on the evening of 11th July, when it was about three days old. For a time Upper Blue sat beside the youngster, which continually made upward lunges in an effort to reach her bill, and she responded each time by lifting her head away with a brief cackle. Persistence won in the end, and Upper Blue finally shuffled about so that the chick was safely between herself and the wall of the cliff; she spread-eagled her wings to give it greater security, lowered her head, and passed the food into its uplifted beak. When the youngster was satisfied she brooded it.

Begging, however, is a much more frequent routine among older youngsters. Only one, a late-hatched chick, remained at Johnny's Peats by 30th August in 1952. It repulsed an adult which leaned towards it from a neighbouring ledge, but accepted another which alighted alongside soon afterwards. It began to beg from this bird with a harsh rasping noise and a side-to-side swinging motion of the head, fencing now and then with the adult's bill. The newcomer remained quite impassive, its only movement being to shake its head and cackle occasionally at some near-flying bird, one of which it followed after only a few minutes' stay with the chick. Fairly often in the later stages of fledging life such begging would prove successful and the old bird would give the young one food, and always the loud rasping noise accompanied both the meal and the preliminaries.

§

In late August, when the skua field-work was at an end for another year, we could give more of our time to fulmar-watching. The young at Johnny's Peats were then well-grown, the bigger ones almost indistinguishable from adults except for their brighter pinkish-flesh legs and a subtle difference in shade of plumage—clear white in the young, ivory in the old birds. The younger chicks still had powder-puffs of down on the feathers of head and vent, but this was being continually preened off and lay like a thin covering of snow about them. They remain on their ledges for between seven and eight weeks—some perhaps even longer—and begin to leave during the last ten days of the month, departures building up to a peak about the 27th-28th.

TABLE 3

DEPARTURE DATES OF YOUNG FULMARS, 1954

	August								September								
Date	24	25	26	27	28	29	30	31	1	2	3	4	5	6	7	8	Total
No. of Young Flying	2	3	1	3	10	4	2	2	2	5	2	2	—	1	—	1	40

Sheep ready for rooin' in the makeshift cro'.

Puffins and men—residents and interlopers—on the top of Sheep Craig.

The crofting land between Meoness and the west coast, with the
Haa and Chapel close at hand.

Looking in the opposite direction, over the late afternoon shadow
of Malcolm's Head.

When we first started regular watching about 20th August the young were very inactive. They seemed hardly ever to be visited by their parents, and spent most of the day dozing. There were still many birds planing to and fro along the coast, and not infrequently one would fly very close to a young bird, or even attempt to alight on its ledge, whereupon the youngster would rouse itself to 'spit' and snarl at the intruder. Our note-books made rather dull reading: "15.00 hrs. 'A' sleeps, as usual with one eye open; 'B' preens; 'C' stands by to repel boarders." A week later these same chicks were noticeably restless and frequently shuffled forwards and craned their necks over the edge—and to some of them it must have seemed that the sea was a long, long way below! So they went back to their dozing, or preening—or, perhaps, to a little exercise, turning to face the cliff-wall and flapping their wings vigorously. But very soon they would be at the edge again, 'looking over' as we called the habit, and wagging their heads at the sea as though contemplating departure.

In the seasons 1953-54 we were really able to get to grips with the fledging behaviour of the young fulmars because we had campers from Monkton Combe and Merchant Taylors Schools staying on the isle, under the leadership of two of their masters, Paul Witherington and Noel Wylie. They were tremendously keen to help with the work of the observatory, and took the fulmar study in hand. They certainly did not do things by halves, for within a few hours they had put a bivouac tent close to the cliff edge, and two of the party slept there each night, so that the fulmars were under constant surveillance throughout the daylight hours.

These excellent teams made it possible to record the fortunes of close on fifty young fulmars in the two years. The position of each bird was plotted on a chart of the cliff-face, and each was given a letter or number for identification. During the last few days of its home-life the fulmar was far from being "the dull creature to watch" which Duffey had found was the case in an earlier phase. Periods of marked restlessness alternated with periods of repose. Sometimes the youngster would stand precariously on the edge, exercising its wings; at others, it would shuffle along the ledge on a journey of exploration,

FIB H

stopping now and then to nibble the bare earth or tug at strands of vegetation. The vertical cliff-face falling to the sea below the nest became an obsession; time after time the chick would survey the prospect with swaying head, and sometimes would even half-spread its wings. And time after time it would get cold feet, and draw back from the brink to snooze. Nevertheless, it was very often immediately after a quiet period, rather than during a sudden burst of activity, that a bird would embark on its maiden flight.

All this made for great excitement, particularly as we found it quite impossible to predict the approximate time when the great event would take place. We were sometimes kept on tenterhooks for hours, even days, with birds whose actions suggested readiness to go. The boys made great play of this indecision; for sixpence you could have your young fulmar in the observatory sweepstake, but if you succumbed to this temptation your nerves were likely to be in tatters by the end of the week. Our other visitors were drawn, as though by a magnet, to the little bivouac tent, where they sat in the sun chatting with the watchers, their eyes fixed on *their* bird, willing it to depart. Fulmars assumed a prominence in the meal-time conversations which I am sure Nature never meant them to have. There would be a cry outside as one of the boys came cycling down the hill—" 'K's going, 'K's going!'"—and 'K's owner would nearly choke as he bolted his food and dashed out in the general direction of Johnny's Peats. But 'K', of course, was foxing, and continued to vaccilate for another two days! I recall that Laker was doing powerful mischief among the Australians at Old Trafford one year, and as the boys had a portable radio the atmosphere at Johnny's Peats that afternoon was painfully electric. One could sympathise with the visitor who, after a fruitless wait, turned away dispirited with the remark, "If only the fulmars would get out as quick!"

When they did go their flight was quite different from the facile gliding of the old birds; normally they flew with ponderous wing-beats, and if they glided at all it was for a few moments only, and resulted in loss of height. Most seemed to get away fairly well and were last seen heading for the open sea, but a few came down after 500 yards or so. One such was joined almost at once by one, then two, and finally by four old birds, apparently out of curiosity, as they merely swam round him and did not stay long. This youngster progressed by swimming, interspersed with vigorous but very ineffective bouts of 'rowing' when he lashed the water with flapping wings, obviously trying to take off. Another who made a poor start was 'B', Upper Blue's 1953 youngster: he was a 'blue morph' and so far as we know the first chick of this kind to fledge at a British colony. (A 'blue' chick was also reared on this ledge in 1954.) As he swam out to sea he attempted to rise every few minutes, and although his efforts were a definite improvement on the 'rowing' technique he was unable to get airborne, merely scudding a few yards each time across the wave-tops. His efforts gradually improved until, after a really good scudding effort that took him a hundred yards or more, he cleared the waves and made height, disappearing towards the eastern horizon an hour and a half after leaving his nest.

§

In the majority of cases the youngsters left home of their own accord; in a few, departure was hastened by the interference of adult birds, and in one case another youngster was directly responsible. This was when 'H', trying to move back from the edge after 'looking over', lost his footing and slithered to another ledge below, which was occupied by 'J', who immediately threatened him. Neither then nor five minutes later when 'J' repeated the attack did 'H' retaliate, and indeed on the second occasion he only just managed to cling to the cliff at the very extremity of the ledge. About ten minutes later he made his way back with difficulty, only to be attacked again—this time so fiercely that he fell off the cliff and became airborne. He flew quite capably with occasional glides and loss of height out to sea.

Chick no. 12 very nearly had a similar mishap, falling four feet from his nest on to a grassy slope, and subsequently treating us to a most interesting bit of behaviour. He made several attempts to get back home by clambering with outstretched wings up the steep and narrow gully down which he had slid, and one long and laborious climb looked as though it might end in success. But alas! he tumbled down again. Apparently in a fit of frustration, he then indulged in what I can only describe as 'gardening'. Although incubating adults, and later on well-grown young, frequently nibble and pluck at strands of vegetation, the action is desultory; it is probably an incipient form of nest-building, since in high latitudes the fulmar and its antarctic representative the silver-grey petrel go through similar actions in clearing snow from the ledges before they lay their eggs. This 'gardening' is similar behaviour stepped up to a remarkable pitch of intensity, and is characterised by the impressive quantity of vegetation broken off and tossed aside— so that a patch of partly denuded earth surrounds the bird— and by the astonishing amount of energy this normally subdued species brings to its labours. No. 12 continued 'gardening' for fully twenty minutes, scattering leaves and roots to right and left with vigorous shakes of the head, before it lapsed into repose. The unconsummated drive to regain its own nest found a useful outlet in an instinctive behaviour pattern which enabled the young bird to fashion a new home where he spent the next two days before taking his maiden flight.

The last chick to leave in 1953 was 'E' on 6th September, and his was fairly typical of the deliberate type of departure. I watched him throughout his final hour ashore. His ledge was a fairly long one, and when I began watching it held three adult fulmars, probably non-breeders, which 'E' kept at a distance, though he joined them in head-waving and cackling from time to time. At ten o'clock only one of these visitors remained, a short distance from 'E', and the two exchanged the usual pleasantries; then 'E' lost interest in the other, and shuffled to the brink to 'look over'. He waved his head from side to side and even half-spread his wings, but his nerve failed and he retired. Half a minute later he tried again, twice spreading his wings wide as though about to jump, and I thought, "Here he goes at last!" But no! He retreated from the edge and gave vent to mounting nervous tension by shuffling along towards the visitor he had hitherto tolerated, 'spitting' so aggressively that the bird left at once. At five past ten, and again a minute later, he went to the edge and spread his wings, but again withdrew and did a little 'habit-preening', turning his head and flicking at his feathers almost absent-mindedly. And then quite suddenly, at eight minutes past, he went to the brink and took off without so much as a glance at the sea below.

Both 'L' and 'G' flew as the result of adult interference on 25th August. They were taking wing-flapping exercise, facing inwards, when adults flew within a couple of feet of them; turning quickly to 'spit' they lost their balance, and after a few tentative wing-beats flew steadily out to sea. These happenings, and the fact that flying fulmars quite often approached wing-flapping chicks in this way, made us think that the parents were eager to see their young leave so that the ledges could be reclaimed. There was plenty of evidence that ledges were re-claimed, but of course there was no way of telling whether the adults concerned were the parents or non-breeders, or a com-bination of both. An adult settled on 'G's ledge three minutes after his precipitate departure; two other ledges were claimed after five and seven minutes respectively, and Upper Blue's was occupied by a normal adult (whether or not the normal parent we couldn't say, as this bird had no distinguishing features) ninety minutes after the chick left on its maiden flight on 29th August. In other cases the reoccupation took longer—sometimes a matter of days. Our thinking at this time, early on in our study, was also coloured by the general belief, stated in most works which deal with the fulmar, that the parents desert their chick when it is five or six weeks old, leaving it to last out the remaining three weeks or so on its stored reserves of body-fat.

§

However, the more we thought about what we had recorded, the less attractive this 'starvation theory' seemed. We saw a number of young ones being fed in late August 1953, but could be reasonably certain of the interval between the last feed and first flight in three cases only. 'E' was fed most often— once on the 24th, no fewer than three times next day, and for the last time (so far as we know) on the 27th: he flew ten days later, and his case seemed to support the theory. 'G' was visited and fed on the 23rd and fell from his ledge on the 25th; but, as his departure was enforced and therefore in a sense premature, his case is not significant. 'X', also fed on the 23rd, disappeared between the late evening and early morning checks of the 27th/28th.

Another fact which made us more than a little suspicious of the validity of this 'starvation theory' was the high weight of young birds when they take their first flight. On leaving the cliff they fly into the wind, and if the wind is blowing off the land they are just as likely to finish up on the moor as on the sea. Strong winds in late August always resulted in a few strandings of this kind, and when we succoured the young birds we always ringed and weighed them at the observatory before launching them from a suitable cliff. Our heaviest bird in 1952, on 24th August (early in the departure period), weighed 1,036 gm., and two on 2nd September (late in the period) weighed 900 and 920 gm. The average weight of six of these waifs and strays was 945 gm., which compares more than favourably with an average of 760 gm. for seven adults which I had caught in a Faeroe fowling-net as they flew along the cliff-top in Mavers Geo. Clearly, we required much more information on the parent-young relationship at this late stage of the breeding cycle, so we decided to concentrate on this in 1954.

The belief in a 'starvation period' originated with reference to the wandering albatross about 1865, and seems to have been applied to the fulmar and some of its relatives, by analogy, at a much later date. It is a shining example of how a statement made by one writer can be freely copied by others (who do not bother to check it) until it assumes such a weight of authority as to command general acceptance. The history of the theory in so far as the albatrosses are concerned has been given by L. E. Richdale, who has shown beyond doubt that it is not valid for either the royal albatross or the sooty shearwater. When we returned to our watching at Johnny's Peats in 1954 many more feeds were recorded than in the previous year, and we undoubtedly missed others, since we were not at the cliff between about seven o'clock in the evening and nine o'clock next morning. Nevertheless, we got enough evidence to satisfy us that no such phenomenon as a period of deliberate starvation of the young bird exists.

A few words should be said in explanation of the table on p. 120 summarising this evidence. Only those chicks are included for which we recorded at least one feed. Sometimes, when a youngster accepted a visitor to its ledge, it would beg, but its pleading would go unheeded: recorded instances of unrequited begging are shown by the letter 'b'. While there seemed to be a marked reluctance on the part of some adults to satisfy the chick (nest 'A' gives a good example of this), there were cases in which the opposite was true and no amount of parental caressing would stimulate the youngster to take food. Generally speaking, however, the young one begged with the harsh rasping noise as soon as the parent settled beside it, and feeding took place. It was seldom protracted, and most parents were ashore for a few minutes only. All observed feeds are shown in the table as 'f' and the subsequent departure of the chick on its maiden flight is indicated by 'd'. Each day is divided into forenoon and afternoon.

Summarising the table, we find that chick 'F' departed within half a day of receiving food, 'A' and 'V' one day later, 'B' two days later, and several others after three to four and a half days. There are longer periods ranging from six to nine days, but in these instances we may have missed one or more feeding-visits. Perhaps it is essential that the parents slow down the feeding-rate when the chick is fully fledged, or it might never develop the urge to fly at all! The last to leave in 1954 was 'W', on 8th September, and he was fed more frequently than any other during the end of August watch. In any event, one is left wondering if a spell of up to a week without food can be said to constitute a 'starvation period' in a species which can sit uninterruptedly for that length of time during the incubation period.

In 1954 all the departures we witnessed were deliberate; although flying adults often made passes at exercising youngsters we saw no case of one being dislodged by such interference. Again we saw that most of the ledges were reclaimed, some very shortly after the departure of the chick, but we now believe that in most cases at any rate the claimants are wandering non-

TABLE 4

INTERVAL BETWEEN LAST RECORDED FEED AND DEPARTURE FROM NEST OF YOUNG FULMARS AT FAIR ISLE, 1954

Each day is divided into morning and afternoon observation periods. f = feeding visit; b = unsuccessful begging; d = departure

Nest	Aug 24	25	26	27	28	29	30	31	Sep 1	2	3	4	5	6	7	8	Interval in days
2		f			d												3½
9		f		f		f		d									3½
11		f	f	ff													3½
12																	4½
13							d										8
16		f	f			d											3½
A				b b	b	d											3
B		b		b	b	f						d					1
D				f		d											2
F		f		f	d												3½
G			f			f		f	d								6
P			f	f			d										9
Q				f		ff		f		d							6½
R				f f	d	ff								d			3
T																	4
V		ff	f	f													1
W		f		f f f	d												8
Y										d	d						7½
Z		f	f								d					d	8½

breeders. These birds would show little interest in the ledge as such, merely using it as a perch from which to cackle and display to other fulmars, which would frequently land and return the compliment. Sometimes there would be up to half a dozen on one ledge. However, some adults would go through a distinctive kind of behaviour on alighting, peering about the ledge, shaking their heads from side to side as they did so, and frequently shuffling along it to examine the recesses and corners. They gave the watcher the strong impression of looking for something—that they expected to find the ledge occupied and were a little nonplussed and bewildered because it was bare. Were these, we wondered, parent birds which had come to visit, and perhaps to feed, their truant young? Perhaps so— but at that point we had to leave our fulmars, and it is up to someone else to provide the answer!

Part II

MIGRATION

CHAPTER IX

THE BIRD OBSERVATORY

T HE bird observatory idea is very much a post-war
development, and there is no doubt that it is one of
Britain's major contributions to the science of ornithology.
It owes its inception to R. M. Lockley who, before the war,
combined farming with bird-watching on the small Pembrokeshire island of Skokholm, where he built traps for catching and
ringing birds. The first co-operatively run bird observatory was
on the Isle of May in the entrance to the Firth of Forth, where
Misses L. J. Rintoul and E. V. Baxter had already studied
migration between the wars. Here a group of young men, who
had banded together as the Midlothian Ornithological Club
while still scholars at Edinburgh Academy, set up a trapping
station in 1936, aided and abetted by Lockley and W. B.
Alexander, then the director of the Edward Grey Institute of
Field Ornithology at Oxford, and with the support of the
Northern Lights Commissioners who own the island and
supplied the accommodation. One of the young men was
George Waterston, who was later to transfer a large part of his
attention—and some of his allegiance—to Fair Isle.

During the war the offshore islands, quite naturally, were
sacrosanct to the Royal Navy; but Skokholm and 'the May'
started again in 1945, to be joined soon afterwards by the first
mainland observatory, at Spurn Point on the Yorkshire bank
of the Humber. Under the inspiration and leadership of the
late Ralph Chislett this field-station has prospered, and he and
G. H. Ainsworth have put its early achievements on record;
while, more recently, Dr W. J. Eggeling has set down the story
of the Isle of May Observatory against the wider background of
the island's history and Dr Eric Ennion has written entertain-
ingly of his own observatory in *The House on the Shore*. Two

125

more islands joined the small band in 1948—Lundy off the North Devon coast, and our own Fair Isle.

Hardly a year has passed during the last decade without one or more recruits, so that today well over a score of localities are manned each season. The most important are also shown on the map (fig. 10). It has become the habit of small groups of bird-watchers to keep observatory-type records when visiting other islands and remote headlands—sometimes primarily for other purposes, but often enough with the express intention of exploring the migration picture at a new place. Foula in Shetland, North Rona of the Outer Hebrides, and Rathlin Island off the Antrim coast were kept going for a few years while enthusiasts had the opportunity. Other localities have attracted individuals or small groups over short periods, and indeed several of the established observatories—for example, Cape Clear Island and Malin Head at opposite ends of Ireland —began in this humble way.

It will be gathered that bird observatories are amateur and not professional institutions, and the very considerable contribution they have made to science has been due almost entirely to the devotion of men and women with boundless zeal and energy, but a limited amount of spare time and ready cash. All the observatories are autonomous, each being responsible for its own finance, manning, documentation and domestic arrangements. Though observatories are primarily concerned with birds, they welcome and encourage students of other aspects of biology, and the hostel and laboratory facilities are readily made available. These services are often rugged but generally adequate, for the observatories are run on a shoe-string budget and few among them can afford even the luxury (one ought to say necessity) of a trained warden to ensure a smooth-working organisation and continuity of research.

Poverty, however, has done one thing that no amount of money could buy—it has welded the bird observatories together in what is possibly the most fraternal band in any of the field sciences, under the avuncular care of the British Trust for Ornithology. This happy arrangement, the inspiration of W. B. Alexander, began as a small committee which met to discuss matters of mutual interest once a year, and has evolved into a two-days' conference bursting at the seams—though nobody minds this so long as there is a big enough college in Oxford to contain it.

At its 1957 meeting this conference asked the B.T.O. to make efforts to obtain funds to finance co-operative research, together with analysis and publication of the results. Through the generosity of the Nuffield Foundation the B.T.O. was able to supply this long-felt need. I left Fair Isle to become the Trust's Migration Research Officer, based at Oxford, but visiting the various observatories from time to time to advise on their research and other problems. Standard methods of recording the day-to-day observations and laboratory data were devised, and reports and analyses, together with short papers of interest to observatory workers, were published after the spring and autumn seasons in a new journal called *Bird Migration*. Identification guides dealing with the difficult warbler genera were produced as an aid to observatory workers and bird-ringers in general, and an interest in moult, bird-weights, ectoparasites and other aspects of 'field-taxonomy' was fostered.

The Nuffield Foundation grant expired in the summer of 1963, but happily the Trust is still able to carry on this migration work, though on a somewhat reduced scale, *Bird Migration* having ceased separate publication and the seasonal summary and analysis now taking the form of an article in the Trust's own journal *Bird Study*.

§

Bird observatory work falls into two categories—the study of migrants (to which the second half of this book is devoted), and the study of the local breeding birds, which naturally vary from place to place. The first can again be subdivided into field and laboratory work. The chief aim of the former is a day-by-day assessment of the numbers of each species present in the area, and in order to secure this a good deal of time needs to be spent in observing and noting down names and numbers. Usually the visitors work independently or in small groups, the better to cover the ground, and the final record is made at 'call-over' after the evening meal, when the day's events are discussed and agreement is sought on the figure to be entered for each species in the Migration Schedule. As a general rule this figure is an estimate only, since it is impossible to achieve strict accuracy even with the rarer birds; but sampling of this kind does produce results with a comparative value at the same station from one day to the next, or between different stations on the same day. Since the adoption of a standard record-keeping system in 1958 comparison and a full analysis have been greatly facilitated.

There is also the Migration Log, a diary in which weather notes, a ringing summary, and any important changes in the bird population since the previous day are recorded: it is really a detailed extension of the factual day-to-day Migration Schedule. Some observatories keep an informal document known affectionately as the 'chatty log', wherein visitors may write about the place, the people, or any of the day's events which particularly appeals to them. The record need not concern birds, and indeed the choicest entries seldom do. To those who revel in this carefree kind of life the 'chatty log' makes splendid reading on a wet afternoon, or pleasant fireside relaxation in the evening when serious things have been put aside. W. J. Eggeling's book about the Isle of May contains a good many witty extracts from the observatory's log.

The field-work has another important side—looking for and identifying the rarer birds, observing their behaviour and choice of habitat, and noting down field-characters which will help to make identification so much easier for others who may come across the bird at a later date. This problem of correct identification did not worry the migration students of an earlier generation, for to them the gun was a far more powerful instrument than the field-glass. That it is no longer regarded as an essential tool of bird study is a compliment to the methods of the older school, for without collecting they would not have been able to produce the plumage descriptions, age and sex marks, wing and tail measurements, and much other data which are the basis of the modern handbooks and field-guides. The observatories' concern is with the attributes of the living bird—its changes in weight, progress in moult, its ectoparasites, and the slim chance that it may carry a numbered aluminium ring to a distant corner of the earth. In an earlier epoch the visitor to Fair Isle and any similar place had no need to trouble himself overmuch about a rare bird's identity until he had leisure to examine it in detail, and compare it with 'skins' of other collected birds, in a museum. Today, correct identification is a matter of urgency if the chance is to be taken that additional knowledge might be gained.

I went to Fair Isle fresh from a spell at a museum, and perhaps not unnaturally my early leanings were towards the older technique; it was unexciting but it was sure. Indeed, I took a gun to the first critical rarity (an eastern race of the redstart) that came my way in the autumn of 1948. Fortunately (or unfortunately, depending upon where your sympathies lie) I am a wretched shot, and when the bird disappeared over the back of Ward Hill I could only shrug my shoulders and repeat the words of wisdom which had once fallen from Seebohm's lips—"What's hit is history, what's missed is mystery!" I doubt whether it occurred to me at the time that circumstances might ever permit of a modification of this resounding maxim, but I was completely won over by the next really difficult bird a year later.

It was a 'small brown job' as so many of them are, in a turnip field at Lower Leogh on 8th October. There were eight of us, all experienced bird-watchers. We found the bird hard to observe well because of its skulking behaviour; it would run along the drills like a mouse, and then fly quickly over or round us and pitch into cover some way behind. This went on for several hours during quite lengthy periods spread over a couple of days before everyone had seen the few elusive characteristics and was completely satisfied about its name. We had all collected a large sheaf of notes, and it was a matter of no little satisfaction to each of us personally that these substantially agreed, and that the bird was still there for ourselves to look at again if we wished, and for the next party of visitors to study when they arrived on the morrow. It was a Pallas's grasshopper-warbler from somewhere in central Siberia, only once previously recorded in western Europe when a bird was found dead at Rockabill Lighthouse, Co. Dublin, on 25th September 1908.

FIB I

The aesthetic attitude was so succinctly expressed by one of the party (Major R. F. Ruttledge, who founded Great Saltee Bird Observatory a year later) that I cannot do better than quote from the letter he wrote to me on his return home. He said: "Perhaps the thing that struck me most of all was the wonderful opportunity one gets to practise making field identifications, and the chance of making rapid notes of essential characters. That Pallas's grasshopper-warbler could surely be held up as the finest example of the care and perseverance necessary to make a 100 per cent identification. I know that both Wilhelm Biermann and I (and others too, I think) were overjoyed that never for an instant was there any thought that the bird should be shot. Why should one kill to satisfy one's curiosity, or to make a name over a record?"

Why indeed? Bird study is a sport as well as a science, and where is the challenge when you stand behind a gun? Our experience with this little bird drove home what I believe to be one of the most fruitful lessons of bird observatory work as practised in this country, namely the training value of a team-effort of this kind for the experienced and inexperienced alike. I have seen many rare birds in Britain, both in company with others and alone—and when alone I have always felt cheated and frustrated that I was not able to share the experience. Nevertheless, Seebohm's dictum dies hard in some quarters—especially abroad, where the general standard of field-identification has not yet risen to the same heights as in the British Isles. It may be less satisfactory that a record should rest on the deposition of a few observers than on a feathered sarcophagus in a museum, but against this must be set the important gains that have accumulated from hundreds of similar events at the bird observatories, reservoirs, estuaries, sewage-farms and other haunts of birds and their watchers over the years. One could not ask for a stricter exercise in acuity of observation, in patient and careful synthesis of the obscure or little-known characters which are essential for correct identification, in teamwork directed towards a single goal, and in greater love and understanding of the bird. Such occasions have helped in no small way to foster the Briton's present-day zeal for wise protection and conservation of nature on the widest scale.

§

This brings us to the threshold of that other side of bird
observatory work which is conducted for the most part in the
laboratory. The gun may be out, but the trap and the snare
are most definitely in, for one of the vital needs of the observatory is a variety of apparatus for catching birds so that they can
be examined in the hand, and then sent on their way with a
ring. This Pallas's grasshopper-warbler (but not a second one
which we caught in the Haa Trap on 2nd October 1956)
escaped the indignity of a visit to the lab, since we had no
mist-nets as in later years, and it was far from any of the
permanent traps. These traps are large wire-netting structures
modelled on a type first used on the North Sea island of
Heligoland; they are wide and fairly high at the entrance
(where bushes, bait and a drinking-pool provide an attraction

Fig. 8. The Gully Trap from the 'business end', showing the
funnel and catching-box.

for the birds), but narrow down to a funnel which turns sharply away from the main axis of the trap, and terminates in a glass-fronted catching-box. The birds are urged or 'driven' from the shrubbery into the funnel, where seemingly the only escape lies towards the small square of open sky at the box. We had two Heligolands on the classic model, one at the observatory itself, and the other at the laird's house, The Haa, close to South Harbour.

Cover of the right kind does not grow readily at Fair Isle because of the acid soil and the blighting salt spray carried on the winds. So we had to improvise. We found it expedient to modify the design and construction to suit the terrain, and exploit to the fullest advantage the natural behaviour of the migrant birds. The best was undoubtedly the Gully Trap, closing off the final narrow portion of a ravine which carries the Gill o' Finniquoy. Here the coast funnels the birds from north and east into the deep, sheltered defile, and they come up in their hundreds on good autumn days. All we had to do

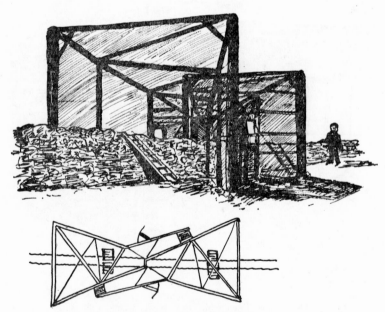

Fig. 9. The Double-Dyke Trap

was bridge the head of the ravine with 20-foot wooden beams to carry a wire-netting roof, and build a funnel and catching-box at the landward end. We were able to extend the trap considerably in our third year by laying 30-foot iron girders across the rocky cleft; they were derelict after the rebuilding of part of the South Lighthouse (bombed during the war), and I still do not know how we managed to manhandle them into position. Driving the Gully was always something of a commando course, for after negotiating the full length of the steep-sided ravine (and its stream, always swollen after heavy rain), one had a couple of iron ladders to climb at the double, else many of the birds which had gone on ahead would escape. But very often the results made any amount of physical effort well worth while, and I maintain that this is the most exciting bird-trap in Britain.

Not only do many migrants move up on to the island's heath and fields from the cliff slopes in this way, but, once on the top, they tend to concentrate along the course of the dry-stone walls, or 'dykes' as they are called in Shetland, which divide different portions of the scathald or outmark grazing. Some birds keep to the walls for shelter and protection from birds of prey, but many use them as 'guiding-lines' or 'leading-lines' to assist them on their way to the crofting land in the south, as described on p. 211. We adapted the Heligoland principle to this situation too, and ultimately had two double-ended and one single traps of this kind (fig. 9). The original Double-Dyke had long spars of 6×4 inch timber for its four corners, until two of them snapped in twain during a nor'west gale: so we rebuilt the trap using telegraph poles from the hill, and it has stood four-square to all the winds of heaven since. Despite their prominence in the landscape (which many people thought would be a disadvantage), the Dyke Traps catch a large number of birds each year.

Ancillary to these are the Ditch Traps: they are small structures placed at various points where a natural hollow or ditch runs alongside the wall, and they are especially good for blackbirds, which tend to keep low. The most successful one in our time was designed as a two-way trap. Since Ditch Traps do not span the wall, being of equal height, they catch fewer birds than the Dyke Traps, but save a good deal in labour and materials.

The little valley of Vaadal half a mile inland from the Gully has a similar trap, the roof in this case being slung on wire cables; and in the first two years we also had a small Heligoland below the summit of Ward Hill, the 'shrubbery' in this case comprising a heap of rusty rolls of Dannert wire and odds and ends of junk from the war-time Ward Hill camp. The birds liked it, but the winds did not: they did not actually blow it down, but one wild autumn night a nearby Nissen Hut alighted on the trap after a brief but hilarious flight.

In the middle fifties trapping birds for ringing was revolutionised as a result of the introduction of mist-nets from Japan, where the peasantry use them for catching birds for the pot. They are large nets (some are 40 or even 60 feet long and about 10 feet high) of thin silk or nylon thread, spread between guyed bamboo uprights. Shelf-strings run across the net, dividing it into two-foot high panels; and when a bird strikes, its weight and the force of impact make a pocket or 'bag' behind the shelf-string immediately below, so that it is well and truly imprisoned. We began to use mist-nets, sent to me by an American friend Alexander Bergstrom, in the autumn of 1956; and although they afford a wonderful means of taking birds in sheltered localities where a background of trees and bushes makes the nets well-nigh invisible, they were not so successful in the exposed and windy fields of Fair Isle. They were so conspicuous in the stubbles (where we set them to catch skylarks) that the birds could easily see and avoid them, and indeed the local twites often sat in an impudent twittering row along the topmost strand.

Usually there was too much wind for the effective working of the nets, so that such birds as did strike bounced off because the shelf-strings and mesh were kept too taut, and the impact did not therefore make a proper 'bag'. Another disadvantage, compared with the permanent traps, is that mist-netting restricts one's movements (and therefore observations), since the nets cannot be left unattended lest the birds become too entangled. It was obvious even in those early days, however, that here at last was the answer to the rare and difficult skulker in the crops—birds like our Pallas's grasshopper-warbler of 1949. Since that time many desirable birds, at Fair Isle and elsewhere, have been captured by this technique, often in a modified single-shelf version of the original net.

Mist-netting had its pleasant side on the calmer days. My diary for 26th September 1956 reminds me of this. "Yesterday and again today, as we sat watching in the lee of the Busta garden wall, Jerry Stout came from the house bearing a refreshing brew of tea and a selection of Ellen's cakes all nicely laid out on a tray. A welcome interlude followed as we ate and drank and chatted with our hosts, who afterwards joined us in one or two drives. But we failed to catch the bird which excited their admiration most—a piebald member of the starling flock with a completely white head and white feathers in mantle and wings." But we did catch, by way of consolation, a seven years' old starling first ringed on Christmas Day of 1949.

§

The only justification for trapping birds at all is to learn more about them. There are two ways of achieving this end. By putting a numbered metal ring on a bird's leg you have a potential recovery, either in your own area or a distant one, and from this you stand to learn something of its habits, its migration, its life-expectation, or the manner of its death. The returns from this source, however, are exceedingly small—much less than 1 per cent in the case of small passerines—but in the aggregate a scheme as extensive and well-conducted as the one organised by the British Trust for Ornithology yields invaluable data which could not be achieved by any other means.

The other method is a careful examination of the bird in the hand, and this of course has the great advantage of producing immediate results. There are many things one can look for—plumage and structural abnormalities, sex and age marks, geographical characteristics, measurements of certain features, weight, evidence of moult, infestation by ectoparasites, and so on. The bird observatory, through handling hundreds of birds every year, is in a unique position to accumulate information on all these points. In 1948, when F.I.B.O. was founded, our knowledge of some of these aspects of the bird was woefully incomplete, simply because nobody had ever had the great opportunities which trapping on this scale present for study of the living bird. To be honest, there was also too great a dependence on the first source of information—and 'ring and fling', while loading the dice in favour of more recoveries, was extremely wasteful of opportunity.

We had to decide whether to 'ring and fling', or sacrifice mere numbers to a more intensive quest for a variety of knowledge which could be gained only in the lab—for to examine each bird thoroughly takes time, and therefore restricts the number that can be handled during a busy day. So we decided to ring only as many birds as we could handle consistent with the need for a thorough individual examination. There grew up what we liked to think of as a new technique of 'field-taxonomy', in which one studied not only the attributes of the individual bird, but also those of the population as a whole. If there were any differences, of whatever nature, between merlins or redwings from Iceland and Scandinavia, or between the wheatear populations of Greenland, Iceland, the Continent and our own island, then it would be of manifest value to migration studies to know about them. Some aspects of this situation are dealt with more fully in chapters XIII and XIV.

The beam-balance very soon produced evidence that migrant birds lose a lot of weight during their flights, but in many cases make up the loss in a remarkably short time once they have settled down to a normal routine. (One of the earlier cases which we found impressive was a Continental dunnock which came in on 3rd October at 16·8 gm., and subsequently increased its weight by 30 per cent in a fortnight and 45 per cent in just under a month.) It is now known that, in preparation for migration, small birds lay down a store of body-fat which, together with the glycogen contained in the liver and muscles, can be converted into energy during their flights; and American work has shown that in long-distance flyers this store may be equivalent to more than 40 per cent of normal body-weight. After a bird has used up the glycogen and fats, energy for life and movement has to come from the protein of muscle fibre, and exhaustion rapidly sets in, death following when the heart tissues are diminished. If enough were known about normal and pre-migratory weights, the mean of a sample taken in the traps would give a very useful indication of the distance covered during the previous night's flight. The trouble we were up against at Fair Isle was that practically nothing was known about normal weight changes and pre-migration gains, and for many years most of the available data on bird weights concerned birds actually on migration. More discussion on this subject, including the correlation of weight with wing and tail measurements, will be found in chapters XIII and XIV.

Similarly the importance of racial segregation of trapped birds, and the elucidation of age and sex characters, will become abundantly clear in the second part of this book. For a time we used a colorimeter in an attempt to measure and record the fine plumage differences between geographical races, and between different phases of plumage within the same species; but this did not prove very satisfactory because of the rather wide individual variation, often due to wear. One subject which is not dealt with later, and should be mentioned briefly here, is moult. Many birds have a complete change of plumage directly after breeding; others have only a partial post-nuptial moult, retaining their wing and tail feathers until they reach winter quarters. Prior to 1948 the only information on moult for the majority of species had been gathered from museum skins, and as most collectors prefer to take birds in fresh plumage rather than those whose feathers are bleached and frayed, the material available from this source is not very large. Much of what was put on record years ago we now know to be partly or wholly incorrect, which is hardly surprising in view of the poverty of the museum material.

Live material has obvious advantages for this purpose, and by trapping and often retrapping the local starlings, house-sparrows, twites, wheatears, rock and meadow pipits throughout the late summer, we were able to elucidate the pattern of moult, determine its timing and duration, draw comparisons between different species, and between different age-groups within a species. The resident starlings, for example, had a much more leisurely and protracted moult than the migratory wheatears, which had to change their complete plumage in a matter of five or six weeks before leaving for the south; in the sparrow and starling, moreover, young as well as old have a complete change in the autumn, but not so young pipits, wheatears and twites, which retain their first wing and tail feathers for over a year. When the crossbills came in 1953 we found that, despite their early nesting season (often over in March), they do not start to moult until August—an adaptation, perhaps, which enables them to lead a nomadic midsummer life as described in chapter XII.

§

Finally, though it was less strictly ornithology, we became very interested in the many and various ectoparasites of birds—feather-lice, mites, fleas, blood-sucking flies of the order *Hippoboscidae*, and ticks. We quickly appreciated that bird observatory work afforded a golden opportunity for quantitative as well as qualitative research into the relationship between these hangers-on and their hosts. A well-known entomologist once defined a bird as "a flying zoological gardens", and although it is perhaps not quite so all-embracing as the correct definition that a bird is a feathered biped, it is near enough to the truth.

The pinhead-size *Mallophaga* or feather-lice are obligatory parasites, and in an evolutionary sense have grown up with the birds. Each population survives only so long as its particular host survives—though individuals will transfer to young in the nest, and even (in a rather curious manner described below) to other free-flying birds. They will sometimes transfer to birds of prey which kill their host, and may cross over from one bird to another in the confined space of a catching-box. It is doubtful if many of these adventurous ones survive, since most *Mallophaga* are host-specific. Some birds are virtually 'clean', while others may harbour a population which runs into thousands—waders, crows and starlings seem particularly badly affected, and someone has claimed a world record of over 7,000 from an African cormorant! When the infestation is heavy feather-lice may deplume the bird and bring about its death, but a normal healthy bird keeps its parasites under control by frequent preening, washing and dust-bathing. It is usually when a bird is sickly or has a deformed bill that mites and *Mallophaga* get out of hand.

Because they are host-specific there are very many species, divided into two major groups—one feeding on downy parts of the feathers (and provided with special enzymes to break down the strongly resistant kerotin), and the other feeding on blood, serum and mucus of various kinds. One of the latter lives attached to the inner walls of the pouches of pelicans, and the nymphs of another are said to feed on liquid secretions from the eyes of swifts. There may be as many as four or more different species of *Mallophaga* on a single host, competition between them for living-space being reduced by a preference for different parts of its anatomy. One lot might live among the flight-feathers, another lot on the body, and a third confined to the head. When the young arctic skuas were hatching on the moorland we would find that examples of the skuas' head-louse, *Saemundssonia cephalus*, had transferred from the brooding parent to the chick within a matter of hours, and had begun to lay their eggs round the baby bird's eyes and gape. The feather-lice lose no time in setting up new colonies.

A great deal was already known about *Mallophaga*, but very little about the life-history of the various bird-fleas and parasitic flies, and these provided the main challenge. First, however, we had to devise some means of collecting *all* the fleas and flies from any given bird without harming the host itself. At first we used a 2-lb. jam-jar with a piece of white blotting-paper in the bottom, on which was put a small piece of cotton-wool soaked in chloroform. The bird was then held with its body inside the jar and only its head outside, this being protected from the chloroform vapour by an oiled silk 'cape' with a hole in the middle just large enough to slip over its head. The asphyxiated flies and fleas soon dropped to the bottom of the jar, and could be lifted out with tweezers and put into labelled specimen tubes.

The method was primitive but efficient, though rather tedious to work with and very wasteful of chloroform. With the help of a visitor, Dr W. Timperley, we soon had a design for a much-improved apparatus in which a hollow perspex cylinder rests on a white tile, and the chloroform vapour is pumped into the cylinder from storage-tubes clamped to the sides. This was certainly 100 per cent efficient for collecting fleas and flies, though much less so for *Mallophaga*, which have hooked processes on their legs, enabling them to keep a tight grip on the feathers.

We found that each of these major parasites had its particular season. We began to take the first fleas from trapped birds in the early spring, as soon as the weather warmed up, and a peak of infestation was reached about the middle of May, the number dropping away quickly afterwards. In mid-June, when the first broods were leaving their nests, we began to get flatflies instead of fleas, and these continued in abundance throughout the summer, declining rapidly in September, and almost disappearing by the end of October.

Birds are important to the fleas as a means of transport to a nest, where they disembark and make their home. When the fleas' eggs hatch the larvae feed in cosy warmth on the refuse from the meals brought to the young birds, and when the young birds fledge the flea larvae pupate, usually hibernating in the nest-lining until the following spring. Then, on warm April days, the new generation of adult fleas emerges, leaves the nest, and Fair Isle is hopping mad with them as they look around for a bird. Some (we have no means of knowing how many or how few) find a host and stay with it until they are taken to a nest, when the cycle begins anew. Roughly half of the birds we examined in spring had been 'found', and often we examined a retrapped bird we had thoroughly 'cleaned' a day or two before, to find that it had been reinfested in the meantime.

There are only a few different species—very few indeed compared with the *Mallophaga*—and they are not host-specific, though the house-martin does have a flea of its own. Some species have a preference for dry nests in trees and bushes, while others flourish in the more humid microclimate of the ground nests of marsh and water-birds. One of the characteristic fleas of Fair Isle is *Ceratophyllus borealis*, an island form in the north and west of a flea *C. garei* which, though common on the mainland, was only brought to us very rarely by some passing migrant. This *C. borealis* is very much a wheatear flea, with a definite preference for the burrow nests of that bird, though sometimes specimens came to hand from pipits, twites and others.

The only flea with a double peak at Fair Isle is *Dasypsyllus gallinulae*, common on the local starlings, which usually make damp nests at the base of a stone wall. These would have a second period of abundance in late July and early August, correlated with the second broods which starlings not infrequently reared in the same nests.

There is no doubt that many of the migrants picked up their fleas after arrival at Fair Isle, and some may have carried them hundreds of miles to a distant part of Europe. The distribution of the various fleas on these birds of passage was probably dictated largely by environmental factors. Thus the Greenland and Iceland wheatears (which have a habit of exploring burrows even during their migration) picked up a number of *C. borealis*, as did also birds which tended to haunt the drystone dykes, like whitethroats and redstarts. On the other hand, the ditch-haunting birds like the bluethroat, sedge- and grasshopper-warblers, had *D. gallinulae*, which likes damp situations, almost exclusively. One day we found eleven specimens of this flea on a wryneck—not a record, since a young starling of a second brood, captured just after leaving its nest on 12th August, dropped twenty-two fleas into the jar!

Identifying bird-fleas is a specialist's job; we merely collected them and kept the records, the Hon. Miriam Rothschild making the identifications and publishing the results. Sometimes we took old nests and examined them for fleas: we had a Burlese funnel for this purpose, the warm water jacket providing just the right temperature to induce the pupal fleas to emerge. Three wheatear nests examined in this way gave us totals of 336, 150 and 129 fleas, mainly *C. borealis*, so there would be that many fewer to indulge in speculative jumping about the island the following spring.

§

Gordon Corbet took charge of the flatflies, and we found

these no less interesting. They are about the size of a house-fly and rather flat-bodied, and run crabwise among the feathers with a rapid, sideways gait, so that they are extremely difficult to catch. They have a disconcerting habit of suddenly leaving their host and zooming towards your eyes. They can fly well, though some of their relatives (the ones which infest swifts and swallows, for instance) are wingless. We had only one species, *Ornithomyia lagopodis** resident at the isle, though another, *O. avicularia*, turned up on migrants occasionally, and once we got an African fly *Lynchia falcinelli* from a tree pipit in spring. Some birds might have a dozen or even more flies at the height of the season, though in the late summer and autumn you would find them in numbers only on predators such as the merlin, sparrowhawk and kestrel, which accumulated a stock from their prey.

The flatflies' chief enemy was undoubtedly the bird itself, for by constant preening it managed to keep them under control, and eventually killed them off. Any fly caught late in the season was sure to be minus one or two legs and to have torn and tattered wings, and many looked as though they had led a charmed life. Maimed flies increased, in fact, from only 2 per cent at the beginning of July to over 40 per cent at the end of August. However, they are nimble and it must be very difficult for a bird to rid itself of this encumbrance. They show a predilection for juvenile birds, perhaps because the young are less competent at preening than the experienced adults. The flies are viviparous, and the single egg develops in a purse-like protuberance at the hind end which eventually becomes a shiny red-brown in colour, and drops away from the adult insect. This puparium (we found a female could produce ripe ones about every five days) presumably falls to the ground and lies dormant until late in the following spring.

In order to learn more about their movements and habits we started marking the anaesthetised flies with a few dabs of cellulose paint: as they have six legs and two wings it was

* Named *O. fringillina* in Fair Isle publications; but recently Dennis S. Hill has shown that two species are involved, of which *O. fringillina* occurs in south and east England, being largely replaced by *O. lagopodis* in the north and west (*Proc. R. Ent. Soc. Lond.* (B) 31: 11-18 (1962)).

possible to arrange a very large number of permutations with just a few different colours—and indeed 582 individually marked flies were set free in the summer of 1954. Usually we put them, one at a time, on another bird than the one which provided them, of either the same or a different species—and some we released without a host at all, out of the lab window. We got a surprisingly large number of 'recoveries' (in fact, 92 or 15½ per cent of the total releases), usually from the same bird, which shows they have no species preference but are quite happy to remain on any host given to them. Some of the ones set free without a host lost no time in finding one, and were back in the lab with a new bird after a few days.

There is a famous adage that bigger fleas have smaller fleas upon their backs to bite 'em, and so on—*ad infinitum*. The flatflies were no exception to this, and on many we found gravid females of an epidermal parasite of birds, *Microlichus*, attached by their mouth-parts to veins in the flies' wings, often amid a cluster of eggs. Also, the flies were not infrequently host to *Mallophaga* (one had a population of 4 *Mallophaga* and 100 mites!), but these were not really parasitic and were merely intent on using the fly as a means of conveyance to a new host.

This phenomenon, known as phoresy, was most frequent in the case of flies taken from starlings, and the main cause of such infestation is probably over-population on the 'home' bird. One particularly lousy starling on 24th August had 4 flies with 30 feather-lice distributed among them! This method of transportation must have risks for the *Mallophaga* since, as we have seen, they are host-specific, and the flies are not particular as to their choice of bird. However, the risks may not be very great, since starlings are highly sociable in late summer, feeding in flocks and roosting together on ledges inside coastal caves.

The most repulsive of all the ectoparasites were the bloated, pea-size ticks which we sometimes removed from our birds. Almost the first we took was a new British record on the back of a rose-coloured starling from south-east Europe—a creature rejoicing in the name of *Hyalomma marginatum* var. *balcanicum*. When we trapped an American gray-cheeked thrush on 6th October 1953 we found attached to it a larva of the tick *Haemophysalis leporis-palustris*, which spends its adult life infesting the snow-shoe hare; both were 'first records' for Britain.

An example of the adventitious way some parasites find a host was provided by two crossbills during the invasion of July 1953 (chapter XII). They had specimens of the tick *Ceratixoides uriae*, which had previously been reported only from sea-birds, and it seems clear they must have got them whilst roosting on the cliffs. Nymphs of the ordinary cattle or sheep-tick, *Ixodes reduvius*, were the most common, occurring on a variety of migrant birds, but especially on blackbirds and redwings in the autumn. They were attached to the soft fleshy parts round the birds' eyes and gape. An interesting case was a newly-arrived Lapland bunting on 5th September 1953 which had ten larvae and four nymphs of this tick on its head, having almost certainly brought them from the sheep-farming districts of the interior fjord country of south-west Greenland.

Another Greenland bird, a tired wheatear captured on 1st October 1956, had an even more curious group of passengers— four small snails of the species *Vitrina pellucida* sticking to its flank and under-tail feathers; they had probably climbed aboard while the bird was at roost, since the snail is active at night. There are now a number of records of this snail being found on birds (I have collected it from meadow pipit, chaffinch and hooded crow, and it has been taken from an American waterthrush in the Scillies), and it is no wonder it has an extremely wide distribution from North America, through Greenland, Iceland and Spitsbergen, to northern Europe and Asia.

BIRD OBSERVATORIES IN GREAT BRITAIN AND IRELAND

The observatories are numbered as on the map (fig. 10), clockwise from North round to West. Those with an asterisk employ a warden and have facilities for the accommodation and instruction of visitors. Addresses of secretaries etc. can be obtained from the Migration Research Officer, British Trust for Ornithology, Beech Grove, Tring, Hertfordshire.

1. FAIR ISLE*   Between Orkney and Shetland. 1948. Fair Isle Bird Observatory Trust ("Friends of Fair Isle").

Fig. 10. Map showing the location of the British Bird Observatories: see the list on pp. 144-7.

FIB K

2. ISLE OF MAY — Entrance to Firth of Forth (Fife). 1934. Midlothian Ornithological Club.

3. MONKS' HOUSE — Northumberland coast opposite the Farne Islands. Formerly a private venture of Dr E. A. R. Ennion, 1951-60.

4. HARTLEPOOL — Teesmouth, Co. Durham. 1961. Local Committee.

5. SPURN POINT* — Humber Estuary, E. Yorkshire. 1945. Ornithological Section of Yorkshire Naturalists' Union and Yorkshire Naturalists' Trust.

6. GIBRALTAR POINT* — N. E. coast of the Wash, Lindsey, Lincolnshire. 1949. Lincolnshire Naturalists' Trust, Lindsey County Council, and Skegness Urban District Council.

7. CLEY AND BLAKENEY* — N. Norfolk coast. 1948-64. Local Committee.

8. BRADWELL — Essex. 1955. Local Committee.

9. SANDWICH BAY — N. Kent. 1957. Local Committee.

10. DUNGENESS* — S. Kent. 1952. Kent Ornithological Society, Hastings Natural History Society, and London Natural History Society.

11. SELSEY BILL — Sussex. 1959. Local Committee.

12. PORTLAND BILL* — Dorset. 1954. Local Committee.

13. ST OUEN — Jersey, Channel Islands. 1951. Société Jersiaise.

14. SLAPTON LEY — S. Devon. 1960. Local Committee.

15. ST AGNES — Isles of Scilly. 1957. Local Committee.

16. LUNDY* — Bristol Channel off N. Devon. 1947. Lundy Field Society.

17. SKOKHOLM* — Off Pembrokeshire coast. Formerly a private venture of R. M. Lockley, 1934-39; since 1945 run by West Wales Naturalists' Trust, and Field Studies Council.

18. CAPE CLEAR ISLAND — Co. Cork. 1959. Cape Clear Bird Observatory ("Friends of Cape Clear").

19. GREAT SALTEE — Off Carnsore Point, Co. Wexford. 1951-64. Private venture of Major R. F. Ruttledge and John Weaving.

20. BARDSEY* — Off Lleyn Peninsula, Caernarvonshire. 1953. "Friends of Bardsey Observatory".

21. HILBRE   Dee Estuary, Cheshire. 1957. Local Com-
                    mittee.

22. CALF OF MAN*   Off southern tip of Isle of Man. 1959. Manx
                    Museum and National Trust, Douglas, Man.

23. COPELAND ISLANDS Outside Belfast Lough, Co. Down. 1955.
                    Local Committee.

24. MALIN HEAD   Co. Donegal. 1961. Local Committee.

25. TORY ISLAND   Off Co. Donegal. 1959. Local Committee.

26. ST KILDA   Outer Hebrides. 1957. The Nature Conser-
                    vancy, Edinburgh.

Other localities where observations have been conducted on bird observa-
tory lines over less extensive periods are: coastal localities north of the
Tyne, Northumberland; Yorkshire coastal localities from Flamborough
Head to Hornsea Mere; Holme, N. Norfolk; Minsmere R.S.P.B. Reserve,
Suffolk; Walberswick, Suffolk; Beachy Head, Sussex; Gilkicker Point and
Christchurch Harbour, Hampshire; St Catherine's Lighthouse, Isle of
Wight; Steepholm and Flatholm in the Bristol Channel, Somerset; Laver-
nock Point, Glamorgan; Skomer off the Pembrokeshire coast; Grune Point
on the Solway, Cumberland; Rathlin Island off Co. Antrim; Walney Island,
N. Lancashire; Handa off the Sutherland coast; North Rona, Outer
Hebrides; and Foula, Shetland.

Inland bird observatories are few and the only long-established ones are
in the Home Counties, viz. Rye Meads Ringing Group in the Lea Valley,
Hertfordshire; Regent's Park, London N.W.7; Romford Sewage Farm,
Essex.

CHAPTER X

MIGRATION IN GENERAL

TRUE migration is the seasonal coming and going of animals, guaranteed to secure them the best environmental conditions throughout the year. Whilst it is by no means the prerogative of birds, it has been most closely studied in relation to these abundant, ubiquitous and exceedingly mobile creatures. Nevertheless, we should not forget that regular migrations of considerable extent are shown by many other animals, among them seals, whales, fishes and man himself. The Norwegian *bondir* who moves his household from the fjord to the mountain *saeter* in order to exploit the summer grazing, returning before the onset of the winter snows, performs a migration in much the same sense as the swallows which nest under the roof of his byre and fly at the summer's end to Africa. Similarly with the 'booleying' of Irish folk and the Highlander's permutation between the lowland township and the summer 'shieling' in the hills.

These alternating movements may be between regions of the ocean affording an abundant food supply and an area of land suitable for breeding, as in the case of fur-seals and phalaropes and many sea-birds; or they may be between fresh-water streams and oceanic spawning-grounds, as with eels—or ·the reverse, as with salmon. It is the regularity of such movements which distinguishes true migration from the periodic mass exodus from the breeding area of certain mammals, such as the lemming; and certain insects, such as the monarch butterfly of North America and the painted lady butterfly of the same Continent, Africa and Europe. The classic example of 'irregular migration' of this kind is provided by the vast hordes of desert locusts which move between East Africa and Arabia down-wind, in search not of food but of regions of atmospheric convergence, where conditions are humid enough to permit their successful propagation, as shown by Dr R. Rainey. The whole pattern of their life has been evolved to this end, for without it the species could not exist. The spur to such irregular wanderings is serious overcrowding in the home area, and the complexity of the responses to this situation has been discussed recently by Wynne-Edwards (1962).

Birds show a similar eruptive dispersal when the population is at a high level, and although such dispersion may occur in any species when circumstances enable the numbers to increase (and may confuse the true migration picture when it does), the most striking examples in Europe are the sporadic excursions of crossbills and waxwings. Unlike true migrants, which are in quest of a known summer or winter home, the irruption species are primarily searching for new food resources, which they exploit until exhaustion of the crop forces them to move on. Nothing definite is known of their navigational powers, and indeed it seems likely that the dispersal is a random one, though in Europe certain climatic factors combine to give it an apparent westwards flow. It is a feature of wanderings of this kind that many birds are absorbed by new areas where life-conditions are suitable, so that colonisation (sometimes only temporary) occurs, and there is seldom a return movement on any appreciable scale.

Migration in birds is primarily related to securing the best available food supply at a given time, and there can be little doubt that the behaviour originated to meet this vital need. That this is the ultimate cause does not necessarily mean that it remains the proximate factor stimulating each fresh outburst of migratory activity; and, indeed, it is a commonplace observation that in most cases birds begin their journeys long before the food shortage becomes acute. The great precision in the timing of true migration can be better understood when one realises that the behaviour is an intrinsic part of the seasonal cycle of the bird's life, and, like courtship, nest-building and the moult, can be prosecuted only when physiological changes have prepared the bird for the experience. Sir Landsborough Thomson has put forward the concept of an annual physiological cycle, established as an inherent rhythm, controlling the timing of these major activities, and deriving their immediate stimuli from environmental changes. The exact nature of these stimuli is not fully understood: decreasing day-length in autumn (reducing the available feeding-time), temperature changes (rising in spring, falling in autumn), and changes in barometric pressure may, separately or cumulatively, influence migration. Much recent work suggests that the last of these phenomena may play the most important rôle, but indirectly through its effect on wind-strength and visibility. This is a point to which we shall return.

§

Migration may be manifested in remarkably different ways even among closely related birds. Thus among the leaf-warblers of the genus *Phylloscopus* the arctic warbler journeys from Lapland across Siberia, then southwards through China to the islands of Indonesia, while the East Siberian race of the willow-warbler travels a virtually opposite route from the Kolyma region to the Kenya highlands. Individuals may cover between seven and eight thousand miles twice a year. In contrast, many of the Himalayan leaf-warblers migrate up and down (like the Norwegian *bondir*), finding their seasonal habitats at different levels on the foothills and steep mountain-sides. There are a few of the genus, such as the Canary Islands races of the chiffchaff, which are entirely sedentary, though European chiffchaffs go to Africa, Siberian ones to India, while in the Pamirs and the Caucasus there are forms with an altitudinal migration.

Wild geese travel in tribal flocks and remain together throughout the winter, the survivors returning in flock to their nesting grounds in Greenland, Spitsbergen and northern Europe. When the Icelandic whooper swans reach Shetland in October we find they come, and stay on the lochs, in discrete family parties, so that a late autumn count gives a good indication of how successful their breeding season has been. The young need the leadership and experience of their elders, and the few whooper swans we managed to catch and ring at Fair Isle were cygnets which had somehow become separated from their parents: deprived of wise counsel, they allowed themselves to be manoeuvred into positions where their large bodies could not get airborne quickly enough to avoid a well-timed 'rugby tackle'! No such filial bond exists among the ducks: in this group pairing takes place in winter quarters, and this often gives rise to a peculiar movement known as 'abmigration', when local birds pair with visiting drakes from far afield, and may travel hundreds of miles from their native heath to breed.

Although the geese and swans show their young the way, this is the exception rather than the rule in the bird-world. There are sea-birds such as the gannet in which the young begin their first migration by swimming solitarily away from the cliffs; the migration habit is strong in the first two years, but declines so that the bird is a mere wanderer when adult. Once or twice we intercepted young gannets which, swimming out to sea from the Noss colony fifty miles away, were borne by wind and tide into North Haven; having ringed them, we launched them across the causeway on the South Haven shore, and watched them continue on their way!

The young cuckoo, which can never know its real parents, must find a way to Africa entirely on its own. Two New Zealand cuckoos have an even more miraculous pathfinding to perform; one, *Chalcites lucidus*, is known to winter only in the Solomon Islands and Bismarck Archipelago, while the other, *Urodynamis taitensis*, has a rather wider winter range based on the Fiji, Samoa and Society Islands. Both cross ocean gaps over two thousand miles wide, leaving New Zealand at a time when there are helpful south-easterly winds; but, as we shall see in chapter XIII, some of our own passage-migrants also make spectacular oceanic flights.

There are many other astonishing journeys, such as the trans-Pacific flights from Alaska to the Hawaiian Islands and beyond of the bristle-thighed curlew and the wandering tattler. The arctic terns nesting on the eastern seaboard of America first cross the North Atlantic to Europe, along the fringe of the colder waters where their food is most abundant, before turning south to cross the equator and continue to the antarctic pack-ice. Their's is the longest regular journey so far revealed by bird-marking, for there are recoveries of West Greenland birds over 9,000 and 11,000 miles distant in South Africa. This completely dwarfs the longest journey yet recorded for a land-bird from Fair Isle—a bar-tailed godwit caught on the North Haven shore in September 1956 and recovered at Noril'sk near the mouth of the River Yenesei in central Siberia in June 1960. This is not more than 3,000 miles distant, but there is no guessing what vast distances the bird must have covered between the two dates.

Some movements arise from the fact that migration is a 'back-tracking' of the route of immigration to a new area, and indeed the arctic terns' migration may reflect a relatively recent colonisation of North America. Thus also the Greenland wheatear, which has now penetrated to the Canadian arctic, still journeys to and from West Africa by way of the British Isles. Siberian species which have forced the Bering Straits and now nest in Alaska—bluethroat, yellow wagtail, arctic warbler and wheatear—retrace their immigration route at the end of each breeding season; while two American songbirds— gray-cheeked thrush and northern waterthrush—which have colonised the Anadyr region of north-east Siberia, cross to the New World for the winter.

Among sea-birds, the great shearwaters which roam the Atlantic as far north as Greenland in the summer months, passing south through British seas, have no difficulty in finding that pin-point of land where they breed, Tristan da Cunha, in February and March. Similarly the short-tailed shearwaters which nest on islands in the Bass Strait between Australia and Tasmania 'home' accurately at the beginning of each new breeding-season after a vast figure-of-eight migration which takes them successively across the waters of New Zealand, Japan, Kamchatka and the Aleutian Islands, Alaska and back across the Pacific to Western Australia. Coming nearer home, we have seen that the same colour-ringed individuals of the arctic skua rendezvous with their mates on precisely the same moorland territories of Fair Isle year after year, after eight months of wandering in the southern oceans. These, and a thousand other cases, postulate an accurate navigational skill in migratory birds.

One of the most remarkable features of this twice-yearly

coming and going of immense numbers of birds is that so many make their journeys during the hours of darkness, because it is necessary for them to reserve the daylight for finding food and replenishing lost strength. Generally speaking, the insect-eating birds such as thrushes, warblers and flycatchers are night-migrants, while the seed-eating finches and buntings move by day. The swallow-kind and swifts, which are able to feed on aerial plankton as they go, and also most birds of prey, many of which use the rising air-currents or 'thermals' beneath cumulus clouds to assist their flights, are also day movers. However, no hard and fast line can be drawn, and some typical night-migrants frequently move by day and vice versa, much depending upon local conditions of weather and food supply. The diurnal migrants have the distinct advantage of being able to use sea-coasts, river-valleys and similar topo-graphical features as 'leading-lines' to help them on their way, but it seems unlikely that nocturnal travellers can do this except on bright moonlit nights.

The returns from ringing birds show that different species, and sometimes different populations within a species, have a different route-preference or 'standard direction' between summer and winter homes. The 'standard direction' of lesser whitethroat, red-backed shrike and wood-warbler is south-east from Britain in autumn; most of the European blackcaps and spotted flycatchers follow suit but the British stocks of these species move south-west towards western France and the Iberian Peninsula, agreeing in this respect with the 'standard direction' of the majority of migrant European songbirds.

Research by Dr G. V. T. Matthews in England and by the late Gustav Kramer in Germany has shown that day flyers are able to orient their flight by observation of the position of the sun, while Sauer and his associates have shown that night-migrants use a form of stellar navigation. This implies that birds must have some sensitive timing mechanism which takes note of the apparent movement of sun and stars across the sky, so that they can fix their position on the earth's surface, and the nature of this 'internal clock' is a mystery which students of navigation are still trying to probe. A prerequisite of successful navigation is that the cloud-amount must be small and not obscure the sun's position, or too much of the night sky; if there is heavy overcast, or precipitation in the form of rain, fog or drizzle, the experiments of these workers suggest that the bird's navigational mechanism is impaired.

§

Soon after our work at Fair Isle began it became clear to me that a knowledge of the properties and behaviour of air-masses, and the ability to apply such knowledge to the reading of a synoptic chart or weather-map (such as the *Daily Weather Report* issued by the Meteorological Office of the Air Ministry) are essential to a full understanding of bird movements. That bird migration is closely bound up with the weather nobody has ever seriously doubted, but there is still no general agreement as to what aspect or aspects of weather influence migration most.

In consequence, fundamental questions such as the nature of the external factors which either promote or inhibit migratory movements, remain a fertile field for controversy. One basic fact is paramount—the bird on the wing is essentially a part of the medium in which it moves; its freedom of action is dependent upon circumstances of time, place and atmospheric phenomena, and these do not always combine to give the optimum conditions for a successful long-distance flight. We have seen that the migrant has an inborn faculty for accurate navigation between summer and winter resorts (indeed, its very existence is implicit in the survival of migratory stocks), but this faculty cannot function properly when the environmental conditions fall below a certain threshold. Under adverse circumstances, which may develop suddenly and change the bird's situation materially in the course of a single migratory flight, its powers of pathfinding may be eclipsed, and its behaviour at such times is likely to become very much the behaviour of the air-mass in which it is borne.

Our studies at Fair Isle were not concerned with the nature of the bird's ability to find its way—that is the sphere of the experimental biologist—but with the conditions of the environment which either stimulate or inhibit its movement, and with what happens to the bird when the efficiency of the navigational mechanism is reduced. A good many papers have appeared in which these problems are discussed in the light of experience at Fair Isle, and in which the dominant theme is the concept of 'migrational drift'—in effect, the displacement of large numbers of birds by adverse winds. The concept is a development and refinement of views first put forward over forty years ago by two Scottish ornithologists, Misses E. V. Baxter and L. J. Rintoul, who had studied migration at the Isle of May in the entrance to the Firth of Forth. Somewhat similar views were expressed at a later date by Dr Finn Salomonsen (1935) and Professor James Ritchie (1940), and were confirmed in the late fifties by Dr David Lack and others who were able to study the echoes made on radar screens by migrating birds.

'Migrational drift' in its usual form is represented by the new track imposed on a bird when a beam wind acts upon its movement in a given heading or 'standard direction', and this drift is bound to occur with an airborne bird even though the conditions for navigation are excellent, unless the bird is following a 'leading-line' or has some other point of reference on the earth's surface below, which will enable it to observe and make corrections for displacement due to the wind. Birds flying over a uniform environment such as the sea or a desert will be much worse off in this respect than those with a coastline or varied countryside beneath them. Theoretically the extent of this drift or lateral displacement from the preferred heading could be assessed by applying the triangle of velocities if the speed and heading of the bird and the force and direction of the wind were known.

The fundamental difference between this interpretation and my own is that I consider there are a number of situations in which the drift is not a lateral deflection of this type, but essentially a down-wind movement. Such a movement can be either active, as I believe it must be in the case of American birds blown across the Atlantic to Britain, and the 'cyclonic approach' to this country of Greenland and Iceland birds (both of which are more fully discussed in chapters XIV and XVI) or passive, as may well be the case with birds engaged in dispersion rather than true migration. In the first case the bird, appreciating the direction of the wind by observing its own progress in relation to the waves, adds wind-speed to its own flight-speed and so covers the greatest possible distance in the shortest time, and with the most economic expenditure of energy. In the second case, the bird is probably not oriented on any given heading and may fly for short spells in different directions at different times, the net result being that it is borne along by the wind.

The earlier drift theory (and it was an inspired theory, considering the poor state of knowledge of synoptic meteorology just after the first world war) was entirely at variance with the orthodox views then held by the majority of students, who agreed with the findings of Dr William Eagle Clarke, whose *Studies in Bird Migration* (based largely on his field-work at Fair Isle) was published in Edinburgh in 1912. He thought the British Isles formed a stage on a well-defined route or 'trunk-line' linking Norway with France and the Iberian Peninsula—a route along which millions of birds travelled unerringly season after season, with a fairly wide sea-crossing to negotiate at either end of the British Isles. So strongly entrenched was this view that the alternative, put so convincingly by Baxter and Rintoul, seems never to have been seriously considered, with the result that the beliefs of the orthodox school held sway down to quite recent years. ("We were young at the time and easily discouraged!" Dr Baxter told me, a little sadly, one evening in 1955.) The drift theory denies the existence of any such trunk-line, or of a direct and purposeful journeying of Continental birds at either season through the length and breadth of the British Isles, and shows that many of the big influxes which occur in Britain are entirely fortuitous—the outcome of a massive displacement by easterly winds from the real fly-lines across the Continent between southern Scandinavia and France, Portugal and Spain.

§

At Fair Isle we found a number of phenomena which adherence to orthodoxy entirely failed to explain. The most obvious (and most indicative of the overriding importance of wind direction) was that impressive falls of migrants, in both spring and autumn, took place with the wind in an easterly quarter. In other words, the same winds were responsible for bringing both northbound and southbound migrants. When we compared our Fair Isle observations with contemporary data from other east coast observatories, such as the Isle of May, and Spurn Point in Yorkshire, we found that such falls were often very local in weather of low pressure type. The reason for this will become clear when we examine the meteorology of such events. Sometimes the falls were confined to Shetland and Fair Isle with no suggestion of a corresponding movement farther south; and at other times a noticeable movement in the Humber Estuary or the Firth of Forth had no parallel in the north.

There were days, however, when a vast invasion was widespread along the full length of the eastern seaboard, arrivals coinciding at all the observation points from Cley on the Norfolk coast north to Shetland, usually with different species dominant in different areas. These falls were sometimes phenomenal not only in extent but also in the vast multitude of birds involved: one such, the great 'robin rush' at the beginning of October 1951, will long be remembered by those who were engaged upon bird observatory work at the time. Thousands of robins suddenly appeared on the Norfolk and Lincolnshire coasts, and although the birds were relatively fewer at the Isle of May and fewer still at Fair Isle, this remained a dominant species everywhere for the best part of a week. There have been similar invasions, of redstarts, pied flycatchers and other species, since. Such falls occur in anticyclonic weather with a light to moderate easterly wind; and, as conditions on both sides of the North Sea are usually favourable for oriented migration, it seems probable that such invasions are made up largely of young birds still moving randomly on post-breeding dispersal.

During the course of a migration season we had other movements in quiet, clear weather, with calm airs or at most a light variable breeze. In some years, always towards the end of August, a big invasion of wheatears would develop with a light northerly or north-west breeze following such conditions. This

weather often brought passage of meadow pipits, white wagtails and other species which breed in the Faeroe Islands, Iceland and southern Greenland. Often, too, there was a pronounced double peak in the appearance of certain Continental
species, the first coinciding with easterly weather and therefore
due to drift or drift-aided dispersal, and the second following a
few days later as soon as fine, quiet weather of the type just
mentioned was restored. This appeared to be a 'redetermined
passage' southwards of birds carried to Shetland and Faeroe
in the original movement, and not infrequently during such
spells we would have birds of both Continental and Icelandic
origin passing through together—sometimes different geographical races of the same species, such as Scandinavian and
Icelandic redwings.

Finally, we had to find some explanation for a feature of the
migration seasons which has made Fair Isle justly famous in
ornithological circles—as famous as the German isle of Heligoland had been in an earlier epoch. This was the occurrence of
extra-limital species which we accept as 'British' on the strength
of one or a few records—and even, on great occasions, birds
which were not until then on the British list at all. These
rarities, much sought after by our visitors and undeniably a big
part of Fair Isle's strong attraction for bird-watchers, might
come from regions as far apart as north-west Russia and the
Mediterranean, or Siberia and eastern North America—regions
up to 8,000 miles apart. All are species whose normal migration routes take them in a direction entirely away from Fair
Isle, at no point approaching it within hundreds or even thousands of miles. Yet some of these extra-limital birds appear there
so regularly that we dubbed them 'sub-rarities'—birds like the
scarlet grosbeak, little bunting, Richard's pipit, red-breasted
flycatcher and yellow-browed warbler. Why do they appear
so frequently in Britain; and why do the more distant ones, like
the American and east Siberian species, come here at all? The
answers to these questions must be deferred for fuller consideration in chapter XVI.

It will be appreciated how utterly impossible it was to
interpret all these phenomena using as a basis the simple idea
of a north – south traffic. If such a trunk-line existed we should

surely expect that a big spring movement at observation-points farther south would be succeeded a day or two later by a similar influx at Fair Isle; but this never happened on anything except the most insignificant scale. We should surely find that a big autumn rush would first strike Fair Isle, and not (as we observed) make its impact simultaneously along the length of, or at isolated points on, the eastern seaboard. Indeed, the most spectacular movements suggested an entry into Britain on a front extending from north to south, rather than one aligned from east to west as would be expected on the trunk-line theory. There was certainly evidence of some direct passage taking place through the British Isles in calm, quiet weather at either season, but this was a very small part of the whole, and apparently a quite subsidiary phenomenon as far as Continental species were concerned. With birds from countries to the north-west—the Faeroe Islands, Iceland and Greenland—such passage appeared to be regular enough.

All our observations pointed to the strong probability that the major factor concerned was the wind. It appeared to have much more to do with ordering the character of bird movement in general through the British Isles (and Fair Isle in particular) than had been appreciated in the past. When we began to organise our data as separate migration 'mosaics', so to speak, analysing each movement in relation to its meteorological environment, all the apparent anomalies fell neatly into place like the bits of a jigsaw puzzle if the concept of 'migrational drift' was applied. The close agreement we found, then and in subsequent years, between the behaviour of birds as visualised by this concept, and the behaviour of air-masses as postulated by the 'polar front' theory of modern meteorology, convinced us that much of the bird movement into Britain is accidental, and due either to a lateral deflection from the migrants' true heading, or to a down-wind displacement in thick weather when orientation was not possible, and in fine weather when the birds concerned were merely dispersing at random from their breeding haunts.

CHAPTER XI

WEATHER FOR MIGRATION WATCHERS

THE observational results of our work at Fair Isle, therefore, were indicative of a close bond between certain kinds of movement and the flow of the wind. In trying to establish a correlation it has to be borne in mind that the feature of weather which we call 'wind' is a property of the distribution of barometric pressure. The movement of air is stronger where there are inequalities in the pressure distribution than in areas where the changes are gradual and small. Any examination of the effects of wind on migrating birds must therefore begin with a consideration of the pattern of change in atmospheric pressure over the region likely to have been encompassed by their flight. As a preliminary we must learn something of the theory of weather—of the structure and behaviour of the different kinds of pressure system we are likely to encounter in our investigations.

When air of substantially the same homogeneous composition covers a vast area it is referred to as an air-mass, and the area in which it originates is known as its source-region. Air-masses, since they are continually on the move and their characteristics of pressure, temperature and humidity are subject to change as they go from place to place, are best classified by their source-regions. At the outset we may concern ourselves only with two very broad divisions—equatorial air, warm and moist, derived from the subtropical high pressure belt; and polar air, cold and dry, derived from the arctic ice-cap. Subdivisions are possible and indeed desirable when we come to consider the control which air-masses exert over the movement of birds.

In order to become endowed with the properties characteristic of its environment an air-mass requires to hang around in

The Bird Observatory from Landberg, with the island boat beside
the Stack o' North Haven.

The visitor's first view of the Observatory as *The Good Shepherd*
comes to her mooring.

Sheep Craig, misty in the flying spume of an autumn day.

The precipitous southern face of 'the Rock', whitewashed with guillemot and kittiwake ledges.

its source-region for several days before prowling about the atmosphere. We find that the major source-regions are where the pressure gradient is least marked—i.e. where the isobars joining points of equal pressure (like the contours joining equal heights on a map) lie furthest apart. These conditions tend towards inertia. Here we have the permanent high pressure systems such as the subtropical belts north and south of the equator, the arctic and antarctic polar highs, and the Continental anticyclones of North America and Siberia which are in the ascendant during the winter months, at a time when the subtropical belt has undergone some recession.

So far as our own part of the globe is concerned the main source-regions include the subtropical zone from which we sometimes have incursions of air, generally warm and dry, from the Mediterranean; and of maritime air, warm and moist, from the Azores region of the Atlantic. There are also the cold polar highs of which the most important to us are the vast winter anticyclone of Siberia, which begins to develop in the late summer and may spread right across Europe in mid-winter; and the high which frequently slips down from the polar ice into Scandinavia, and may merge with the Siberian one in the winter time. Greenland has a large enough ice-cap to support a small polar anticyclone of its own, which extends sometimes as far south-east as the British Isles; and there are rarer occasions when outbreaks of polar air originating in the Canadian arctic get across the Atlantic to the eastern side.

Adjacent anticyclones, the 'highs' of the weather-charts, may have very different physical attributes, depending partly upon their place of origin, and partly upon their history since leaving the source-region. Thus, one which has spent a long time over the Continent in the late summer will consist of warmer and dryer air than an Azores high which has roamed about in mid-Atlantic for several days, taking up moisture from the sea. The shallow high which sits on Greenland's icy mountains, occasionally thrusting out ridges into adjacent parts of the Atlantic, is a good deal colder, dryer and denser than either of these.

Although air is volatile, air-masses at different temperatures and densities do not mix readily when they meet—each

FIB L

preserves its own individuality, and along their common frontier they keep a somewhat troubled truce. This narrow zone is called the 'polar front', and in our hemisphere it separates the south-westwards flowing polar air from the north-eastwards flowing equatorial air. Along the polar front where two such air-masses maintain contact their differing physical properties may interact in such a way as to give rise to the 'lows' or depressions which are a dominant feature of the weather of middle latitudes.

The situation at the polar front is constantly changing, partly due to the varying speed of movement of the air-masses in relation to the west-to-east spin of the earth. Short-term changes are caused in a large measure by the nature of the low pressure disturbances which arise at points along the polar front and shift large bodies of unquiet air from place to place. Long-term changes result from the seasonal growth and re-gression of certain source-regions, or from variations in the strength and dominance of the several air-masses from year to year.

One of the most important attributes of an anticyclone from the bird-watcher's point of view is the stability or instability of the air it contains. A maritime air-mass invading a Continent in the summer is warmed unequally by features of the land-scape, so that convection currents are set up, and the rising air in them may be forced to jettison some of the moisture gathered by the high when it was over the sea. Local insta-bility showers may result. Such unstable air, in which the lapse-rate or loss of temperature with height is gradual and fairly even, is associated with excellent visibility, and apart from occasional light showers the condensing moisture takes the form of a sparse cloud cover of cumulus type at the tops of the thermals. The conditions are therefore perfect for bird movement, and indeed certain kinds of birds—particularly storks, buzzards and eagles—actually use these thermals as a means of conserving energy on migration, soaring effortlessly upwards on outspread wings, allowing the rising air to lift them to a great height. Having reached the top of the thermal they descend, equally without effort, in a long shallow glide to the base of another thermal, and repeat the procedure as often and for as long as they can. Migrating birds of prey regularly cross narrow water-gaps such as the Kattegat and Straits of Gibraltar in this way.

If, on the other hand, the warm air of an Azores high passes over a part of the ocean where the currents are cold, then the air is cooled at the surface and its moisture condenses into droplets of mist or fog. Since the lower layers are being progressively cooled and made denser than the warmer layers above, there can be no convection to dissipate the mist, and in stable air of this type visibility is very poor. At places such as St Kilda and Fair Isle, the weather may stay like this for days on end. Sometimes, however, the difference in temperature is slight, and when the islanders say that the fog will probably clear with the turn of the tide, they recognise the possibility that the new flow will raise the surface temperature by the small amount necessary to induce instability. When that happens at Fair Isle a number of birds, prevented from making an earlier start because of the fog, get on the move in Shetland, and an hour or so later wheatears, white wagtails and meadow pipits appear on the hill and the North Haven shore; and often there is a late sprinkling of warblers and flycatchers in the traps, for although these are generally regarded as night-migrants they are by no means averse to travelling by day if the atmospheric conditions are good.

Since the air cools more quickly than either the land or the sea when the sun's warming influence is removed, convection may arise at night giving clear skies for nocturnal migrants, though stability may return later, causing the birds to be grounded at dawn. In winter highs convection may go on through the lower part of the atmosphere until the gradually cooling air meets an upper crust of warmer air at a lower density which it is unable to penetrate. The droplets condensing from the rising air then form an overall layer of cloud, creating that unpleasantly dull situation often referred to as anti-cyclonic gloom. As this effectively shuts off the sun and stars, there are manifest dangers to navigation during a cold spell when birds are forced by frost or snow to seek new wintering grounds.

The British Isles are situated on the border of the Continental and Maritime regions, and are therefore never very far removed from polar front developments. The differences between opposing air-masses jousting in our vicinity not only make our weather a good deal more changeable than in most parts of the world, but also very substantially affect the quality and quantity of our visitations of migratory birds. Indeed, the pattern of bird movement through Britain is just as fickle as British weather, and if the latter did not have this quality of changeableness which we so often deplore, bird-watching would be a dull pastime outside the breeding season.

§

The polar-front theory visualises the formation of cyclonic disturbances in that narrow zone of discontinuity of temperature, humidity and pressure between air-masses. If a vortex is created by the shearing action of the wind at any point where the front makes a sharp bend or wave, then a cyclone or depression develops. The physics of this situation are outside the scope of this discussion—any appetite with leanings in that direction can be satisfied by reference to one of the good standard text-books on meteorology. The theory, which is all that need concern us here, can also be studied in greater detail in such works, among which the books by Brunt, Petterson, Sutton and Scorer can be warmly recommended. Only the bare outline, sufficient I hope for our present purpose, follows.

In the newly-formed depression or low the colder air forms a vast segment embracing the warmer tropical air, and—since it is denser—forcing this warmer air off the surface. At the leading-edge of the warm sector of the low the lighter tropical air mounts gradually above the cold mass; it is cooled in so doing, and is less able to hold the water vapour it contains, so that this condenses as cloud, and eventually descends as precipitation. This leading-edge is the 'warm front' shown on weather-charts by the convention of a line of black semicircles, facing the direction in which the front is moving. (If a front is stationary, then the symbols are placed in pairs on either side of the line.) The approach of a depression is generally marked by feathery cirrus clouds which may extend some hundreds of miles ahead of the warm front: it is ice-cloud trailing its long and picturesque 'mare's tails' in the jet-stream of upper winds blowing parallel to the front. The Shetlander calls it the 'weather-head' and knows by observation the direction from which the storm is approaching—invaluable foreknowledge for one whose activities are so intimately concerned with the sea. Closer to the front the cloud is heavier and of cumulo-nimbus type, giving way to heavy nimbus within the rain-belt. The rain is usually light or drizzly, or the precipitation may take the form of fog if the front is weak.

Behind the warm sector the advancing body of cold air, being denser, drives a wedge beneath the warm air, lifting it sharply to a higher level. The process of condensation is much more rapid and this too is a zone of precipitation, with the rain coming suddenly after the clearer skies of the warm sector. Although the rain-belt here is relatively narrow, the rain is of a more vigorous kind because of the steeper and more rapid ascent of the tropical air; so a cold front may be characterised by a brief but heavy downpour, by a thunderstorm, or by a sharp line-squall. Its position on the weather-map is indicated by a line of dog-tooth symbols facing the direction of movement of the front.

We may pause here to comment that even summer thunder-storms have a considerable ornithological interest. The heavy rain creates a cold down-draught which scoops up the warm air ahead of the storm, and a large amount of air-borne insect life is carried aloft by the vigorous convection set up. Study-ing the structure of thunderstorms by means of radar and telescope, W. G. Harper showed that hundreds—probably thousands—of swifts are attracted to this section of the storm, and travel immense distances with it, feeding on the concen-trated insect harvest near the cloud-base.

As the depression grows the cold air gradually overtakes the warm front at the ground level, from the centre of the de-pression outwards, so that the warm sector gradually diminishes and eventually disappears. During this occlusion the region of contact of the cold and warm air is well above the surface. A depression may continue to deepen and may remain vigorous for some time after occlusion has begun. The line of occlusion is depicted on the charts by alternately placed semicircle and dog-tooth symbols.

By reason of the kinetic energy produced in a cyclone of this kind, winds at gale and even hurricane force are developed in the early stages, and the movement of the low (which often tends to follow the line of the polar front) may be very rapid in its early life. As occlusion proceeds the low weakens, and gradually slows down, beginning to fill, the barometric pressure rising in the centre. Precipitation may continue for a time along the line of occlusion, but its character will depend much on the history of the depression—i.e. on whether or not the polar air has undergone any marked change in temperature due to its new environment. By this time the low may be several days old and may have covered hundreds of miles, and it is unlikely that the cold air which thrusts up the warm air at the rear of the depression will have the same properties of temperature and humidity as the air at the forefront of the low. If the overtaking air is colder than the mass ahead, then we have a 'cold occlusion' with behaviour not dissimilar from that of a cold front; if the overtaking air is warmer (perhaps due to passage across warm ocean currents) then any precipitation is likely to be light.

Before the low fills and dies a natural death, a kink or wave of the kind which started the whole thing off at the polar front may occur again along the line of occlusion separating these two unequal air-masses, so that a new satellite depression is born. Or a new low pressure cell may develop in a trough or V-shaped extension of the primary depression, with the result in either case that a 'secondary low' appears on the scene. Such secondaries move counter-clockwise about their parent systems, and, if they are at all vigorous, outlive and eventually replace them on the weather maps. Many of the small depressions which sweep northwards through the North Sea are secondaries belonging to lows centred on the Iceland region. Though they may be born over the land, they seem to have a predilection for moving offshore and continuing their journey by sea; and occasionally they are detained by orographical features such as the mountains of the Scandinavian peninsula, so that they remain in the Skagerrak for a day or two or even swing eastwards into the Baltic.

Just as there are regions of high pressure in the earth's atmosphere, so there are regions of low pressure, but apart from the equatorial doldrums the low centres are less permanent, and the annual cycle of oscillation goes largely in favour of the great highs. When the Siberian anticyclone retreats in summer the equally famous monsoons, the huge lows of India and the South China Sea, take over. The Aleutian low comes into its own in winter, but virtually disappears before the midsummer spread of the Pacific high. Only the Icelandic low, like the poor, is always with us (though it did disappear for a short spell in the early months of 1963), a region of minimum pressure filling a little in summer, and usually deepening a lot in winter. It is the terminal of the vast majority of the depressions which are born in endless succession along the polar front, the tempestuous children of that eternal conflict between arctic and equatorial air.

§

Buys Ballot's law—about the only incontrovertible law of weather science—states that if you stand with your back to the wind in the northern hemisphere, then you will have high pressure on your right hand, and low pressure on your left. Across the equator, it is the other way round. In our own hemisphere the movement of air round a centre of high pressure is in a clockwise direction, since highs tend to lag somewhat behind the earth's rotation. As anticyclones are regions of divergence—i.e. of subsiding air—the wind flows roughly parallel with the isobars but with a slight deviation outwards from the centre; and because subsiding air undergoes compression and warming, which tends to evaporate cloud, highs usually bring warm days with bright sunny skies. Because the pressure-gradient is gradual, so that the isobars lie far apart, such wind as exists is very light near the centre, gradually increasing in strength farther out.

In the northern hemisphere the movement of air in the much more vigorous cyclonic disturbances is counter-clockwise (the reverse being true south of the equator), and, since a low pressure system is a region of convergence, the wind-system is drawn inwards towards the central vortex. For all practical purposes we can say that in the lower levels of the atmosphere, where the great majority of migrants fly, the wind blows anti-clockwise about the centre with an inwards deviation of some 15 degrees from the run of the isobars, though this angle varies according to the intensity of the system and in extreme cases may attain 40 degrees. In an active depression the pressure gradient is steep, the isobars lying close together, and the wind in consequence is strong.

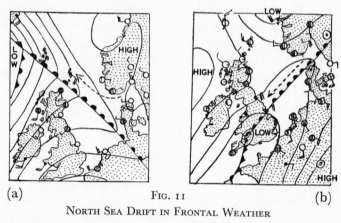

(a)   Fig. 11   (b)

North Sea Drift in Frontal Weather

Fig. (a) shows the type of weather situation which brings migrants to Shetland and Fair Isle but nowhere else on Britain's eastern seaboard. The warm front of a cyclone moving north-east towards Iceland has brought rain at sea and a good deal of cloud to southern Norway, where we can expect migration to be in progress because the weather inland is fine and clear. Birds leaving the anticyclonic region and coming into contact with the murky conditions will be disoriented, and will drift down-wind in the south-east airstream blowing along the front, arriving in the northern isles. Adverse west winds preclude the arrival of migrants at places behind the front.

Fig. (b) shows an occasion when the position of the front was such that the immigration was localised in parts of Yorkshire and Lincolnshire on either side of the Humber estuary. Here the wind was north-east, blowing from the Skagerrak where so many migrants run into a change of weather when leaving Norway by night. Farther north in Britain the wind was from the west and inimical to drift. On both occasions Redwings, with Blackbirds and Fieldfares, were the main immigrants.

In an active low of the kind we have been considering the fronts are usually lines of discontinuity in wind direction, due to the changing pressure distribution before and behind the front. The passing of the front through a given spot is therefore marked by a sudden veer or westwards shift of wind. From the point of view of migration study this is a most important property of a depression, as we shall see, and is of vital importance to a clear understanding of the effects of migrational drift.

Two other pressure patterns must be mentioned, since there is good evidence that they have a direct bearing on migration. They are the col and cyclonic variable situations. A col is a kind of no-man's-land surrounded by active systems, with highs on two opposite sides and lows on the other two. It is therefore a region of light winds, belonging to opposing systems and tending to blow in contrary directions, so that in effect they cancel each other out, leaving the region relatively calm. The winds may be of different humidity and temperature, however, so that there is plenty of scope for the formation of mist and fog, especially in the winter months. Cols seldom persist for long, the lower pressure separating the two anti-cyclones proving an irresistible attraction to the quickly moving depressions.

Sometimes a large depression, especially if nearing the end of its active life, develops two adjacent low pressure centres, each with closed isobars and a ridge of relatively high pressure separating them. The winds flowing about their centres meet from opposite directions on this ridge and the result is the same as in a col—the mixing of the airstreams reduces their strength to light variable or calm. This situation also does not normally persist for long, at any rate in any given area, the cyclonic variable region moving on with the depression or disappearing as one or other of the centres continues to fill. A region of calm air or very light variable breezes, comparatively small in geographical extent, may also exist at the heart of an old depression.

It will be readily understood that the depression, with its fronts and their associated heavy cloud-cover and precipitation, its rapid movement in the early stages and its strong internal wind system, creates a kind of weather which would not seem to be favourable for migration. Indeed, there is plenty of evidence that under these circumstances the migration urge is temporarily inhibited, birds remaining 'off-passage' until the weather improves. Quite apart from the dangers to navigation, contact with an active front would quickly distress a travelling bird, wetting the plumage and lowering its efficacy as an insulation against loss of body-heat, resulting in a more rapid combustion of glycogen and fats and a serious reduction in its cruising range. If the urge to go is very strong, birds will sometimes get under way as soon as the cold front has passed by and the cold polar air coming in behind clears the sky and increases the pressure, reducing the strength of the wind.

Contrast with this the attributes of an anticyclonic situation. Normally a region of high barometric pressure affects a vast land-area; its movement is relatively slow, so that it may be effective over the same region for a long period; the air within it is homogeneous and the distribution of temperature and humidity are more even; winds are non-existent or light, except on the periphery, where they may be moderate to fresh; and because of the subsiding air there is very little cloud. Thus an anticyclone would seem to offer the birds over a very large region the optimum conditions for undertaking a migratory flight.

There is very strong evidence that some property or properties of anticyclonic weather are indeed a powerful stimulus to bird movement of several different kinds. There does not seem to be any physiological evidence to support the view that a bird is able to appreciate changes or trends in either temperature or barometric pressure, or both. It seems more likely that birds must recognise an anticyclone by the two factors which are always constant in a system of this kind in spring and autumn, and which we know to be all-important to their well-being—namely, the continuance of calm or nearly calm air conditions, and the absence of heavy cloud.

CHAPTER XII

BIRDS IN SPRING AND SUMMER

D A VOOAR', as the Shetlander terms his spring labours, is finished at Fair Isle by the end of April if the weather has been reasonably dry. It is a big 'if' in these northern isles, but the people are diligent crofters, and by that time few tractors disturb the quiet air—quiet, that is, except for the subdued, eternal roar of the waves upon the coast, so familiar that we were hardly ever aware of it.

The turned black soil, seed-bed of the season's oats, potatoes and turnips, was a rewarding habitat for birds. Skylarks, wheatears and twites, which would nest at the isle, predominated but drew scant attention. We were usually in search of more exciting game, and our field-glasses scanned the plots in the hope of picking up some scarce and colourful species which had overshot its Continental range, or was paying a brief call *en route* to Scandinavia—like the cuckoo which was found at Bergen within three days of entering one of our traps. Colour was the keynote of the spring, making it aesthetically preferable to autumn, when most of the small birds have exchanged their bright breeding plumage for a dowdy out-of-season dress. Usually (but by no means always) bright sunshine enhanced these colours, while the warm air made bird-watching a joy.

Perhaps we would find a small party of reed-buntings, the males with jet black heads and bibs, and collars as clean as the Fair Isle men wear to kirk on Sunday. Or we might come across a couple of yellowhammers, canary-bright in the strong sunlight, or a little group of pink-breasted linnets. All these were good to watch, for although common on the Scottish mainland, they are infrequent enough at Fair Isle to attract interest. We always looked carefully among the twites for the

reed-bunting's scarcer and slightly smaller relative, the little
bunting with his warm rufous cheeks and crown-stripe, and
a ticking call reminiscent of a robin, but lacking the reed-
bunting's curious mannerism of shivering his tail. Later, when
the first blue-green shoots of the corn had appeared, we scanned
the fields with extra diligence, for the rare but always delightful
ortolan buntings whose grey-blue overtones matched this
background so well could be easily overlooked.

One or other of the crofts would have a few late bramblings,
the cocks inky-headed and white-rumped, the rest of their
livery dominated by bright terracotta; and somewhere, with
luck, we might chance upon a few Lapland buntings, the ebony
heads and breasts of the males highlighted by a russet band
across the nape. There was an occasional shorelark, sandy-
grey with a yellow-striped face and pointed black ear-tufts; or a
red-throated pipit with the whole of his head and throat a
blushing pink. One year we had a short-toed lark, a visitor
from the Mediterranean, among the young shoots at Kennaby;
he kept company with the skylarks, and so afforded good
opportunities for an instructive comparison. The rare bird
stood out at once by virtue of his reddish-sandy plumage,
whereas the darkly-streaked brown backs of the skylarks merged
so well with the soil-colour that it was difficult to spot them
unless they moved. Its creamy underside was almost immaculate
save for twin dark spots at the sides of the neck; the wing-
coverts and crown were brighter rufous, as though it wore a
russet waistcoat and cap.

Like many of our spring rarities the short-toed lark had
overshot its breeding range by several hundred miles. A more
handsome vagrant of this kind, also south European, was the
subalpine warbler we found creeping unobtrusively about a
heap of rusty iron girders on Smirri Geo beach on 20th May
1951—the first of two which visited us that year. Compared
with most of the birds that came our way its plumage was
exotic in splendour—dove-grey back and head, rich dark
chestnut breast, delicate pinkish-buff flush at the sides of the
belly and flanks. The tail, darker than the back, had a white
border, and the grey head and chestnut front were separated
by clear white moustachial streaks. The little bird had startling

red-rimmed eyes—"eyes like a miniature oystercatcher", one of the watchers remarked.

We caught it in a small movable trap consisting of a light aluminium catching-box and a small-meshed net which we draped over the girders; and when we had finished our examination we returned it to the scrap-heap, since it was obviously faring well on the column of gnats attracted to the sun-warmed metal for their aerial dance. During the following week it often flew across the geo to a low cliff to hunt among the rough grey-green lichen and cushions of sea-pinks for other insect fare. A fulmar had her egg in a grassy alcove there, and to see the two together was as exciting as the rainbow and cuckoo's song had been to the poet—a bizarre juxtaposition one might never find again, for the natural ranges of the two birds are many hundreds of miles apart.

We were made aware of this spring overshooting quite early in the observatory's career, when on 14th May 1949 a Kentish plover (the first to be recorded in Scotland) turned up on the beach at Mid Geo. This delightful aristocrat of a wader ought to have come down in Denmark or Holland, not 500 miles north-west at Fair Isle. It had to compete for our attentions with another 'first for Scotland', an immature albatross (perhaps a black-browed), which was seen off Sheep Craig in the morning, was later being mobbed by inquisitive gulls off Malcolm's Head, and later still was chased by the ravens at Milens Houllan. A week later another southern bird, the nightingale, a great rarity in Scotland and previously un-recorded at Fair Isle, was trapped at the Haa to make this first spring a memorable one.

§

So far as Fair Isle is concerned, this overshooting phenom-enon tends to bring birds of a south-eastern rather than a strictly southern distribution, the latter element (birds like the hoopoe, bee-eater and golden oriole) being more prone to turn up in the southern counties of England and the Irish Sea region when the urgency of spring flight carries them beyond their homes. This is neatly illustrated by the scatter of the nineteen subalpine warblers found in the British Isles up to 1964. Remarkably for a Mediterranean species, nine have occurred in Scotland (five of them at Fair Isle), all in spring, while there have been two in north Norfolk at the same season. This strongly suggests an approach from the south-east rather than the south; indeed, at least two of the Fair Isle birds had plumage characteristics of the south-east European race *Sylvia cantillans albistriata*, and other east coast birds may also have belonged to this population. The few which have crossed the English Channel or entered the Irish Sea in spring, however, are more likely to represent overshooting of the typical race *S. c. cantillans* of France and the Iberian Peninsula.

There are several species which have a south-east heading across Europe in autumn, entering Africa via the Lebanon and Egypt, or in a few cases going even farther, to India, and they reverse this route in spring. If the weather over central Europe proves markedly anticyclonic, strongly stimulating the birds' migratory urge, then it seems that their homeward trek is not halted as it ought to be when they reach the breeding area; instead, they overfly their homes, sometimes for several hundred miles, odd ones crossing the North Sea to the British Isles. This phenomenon explains why the lesser whitethroat is commoner than the common whitethroat at Fair Isle in spring, why the regular member of the yellow wagtail fraternity in Scotland at that season is the northern *Motacilla flava thunbergi*, and why spotted flycatchers and red-backed shrikes are less rare in spring than in autumn—for all are south-east oriented migrants over most of their European range, and anticyclonic weather in spring encourages returning birds to keep going. For this reason 1951 was a good year for red-backed shrikes, and between 17th May and 2nd June they appeared in better numbers than before or since.

Usually we saw them perching on the wire fences of the crofting area, on the look-out for insect prey; and although most appeared to be content with such fare, a few killed and ate small warblers, twites, and one a robin. The head was always the first part of the victim to be attacked, the shrike breaking open the back of the skull and eating the brain, leaving the beak and frontal portion untouched, and usually taking very little of the body. The shrike does not appear to form 'larders' in the spring as it does in autumn, when young birds on dispersal collect the red Shetland bees *Bombus smithianus* and impale them on the points of barbed wire fences. There may be a good reason for this difference: true migrants would have no need of 'larders' since they would not remain in the area longer than a few hours, but most autumn occurrences are of young birds windblown during dispersal, and more likely to stay around because they have yet to develop a strong migratory urge, as discussed in chapter xv.

Shrikes disturbed when eating a bird they had killed would always come back to it when we moved away, and this trait enabled us to catch several with the help of spring-nets baited *in situ* with their prey. A shrike would also come to prey that was not of its own killing if the spring-net was set close to the particular fence it was working; but they are not carrion eaters, and we found that the meat had to be fresh. Another and larger bird with similar habits was caught by much the same technique in early June 1955; it was the first red-footed falcon to appear at Fair Isle—another south-east European species which overshoots in some numbers into England in occasional years. In this case we used a clap-net baited with a dead field-mouse, operated from a hide twenty feet away, and sited close to a fence which the handsome little falcon used as a vantage-point. It always paid dividends to watch one's birds closely for a short while, and consider how best to take advantage of their feeding behaviour with the limited means of trapping at one's disposal.

Yet another overshooter of some importance is the greenish warbler, a small chiffchaff-like bird (but with a better superciliary stripe and a small whitish wing-bar) which is gradually spreading westwards through Europe from Siberia, probably helped by the generally higher summer temperatures over the past thirty years. Jack Peterson and I spent the morning of 2nd June 1949 trying to persuade our first to forsake the shelter of the stream banks in the Gill o' Finniquoy and go up to the Gully Trap. So intent were we on this occupation that we paid scant attention to a buzzard, and later a pomarine skua, which flew overhead, though both are rarely enough seen at Fair Isle.

We captured a second greenish warbler in early July 1955, and there have also been a few young birds in autumn seasons.

This warbler colonised a few places in eastern Germany in the 1920's; it had spread west to Lake Müritz by 1935, and had penetrated well into Finland by the end of the decade. Nesting was not confirmed in Sweden till 1953, and there was a small incursion of these birds the following spring; so its spread has been gradual, but sooner or later, one feels, it may well reach Britain as a breeding bird. It has become an almost regular wanderer to our bird observatories since 1949, mostly young birds in autumn, but sometimes as a result of overshooting in summer. It is a late returning migrant from India, reaching western Russia during the last week of May and Scandinavia in early June.

Another handsome bird which has appeared on several occasions at the height of summer is the red-headed bunting—brilliant yellow beneath, rich brown above, and golden-bronze on the rump in flight. Its head is like burnished copper and the face and throat are usually darker, almost chocolate, this hue extending downwards to form a patch on the breast. One turned up on a day when we were all busy celebrating the festival of St Coalboat, and was first recognised by a few of the islanders on the back of the lorry as they were delivering a load to the village. It became the main topic of conversation at the quay, and needless to say I was an eager volunteer for the next run!

This beautiful bird is something of a mystery; as with the greenish warbler, its appearances in Britain have become increasingly regular in late years, usually in the summer, always adult males, and very often at remote islands like Fair Isle, North Rona, St Kilda and Lundy. But the reasons for its appearance are probably very different: although a few have turned up in the company of other south-eastern species under weather conditions suggestive of a long drift from Turkestan, this is now perhaps the most commonly imported cage-bird in Britain and on the Continent, and the great majority of the records are doubtless due to escape from captivity.

Fair Isle yoals drawn up on the shingle of Kirki Geo, their winter
noosts fashioned from the escarpment behind.

The play of tidal streams in South Harbour.

The burial ground overlooking Kirki Geo, and the summit of
Ward Hill away to the north-west.

A Fulmar on her nest at the base of a dry-stane dyke.

§

Invariably the wheatear was the first summer migrant to appear, though we seldom got one in March. The local birds came in strength in mid-April, and the bigger north-western wheatears arrived from the beginning of May, with a peak passage during the last days of the month. It was clear from the proportions of age and sex groups among trapped birds that the adult males led the way. In 1956, a good anticyclonic season with fairly continuous arrival and passage, the proportion of adult males dropped to only a few per cent between 5th-9th May, while first-summer males (44 per cent) and females (48 per cent) made up the bulk in nearly equal numbers. Many of the adult males, in fact, had already chosen their territories and were in full song, often imitating the calls of migrant redshanks, turnstones and other birds.

When the long-winged Iceland and Greenland birds came in strength between 12th-20th May there were 24 per cent adult males, 32 per cent first-summer males, and 44 per cent females; but over the ensuing week the adult males dropped to only a few (as with our own stock some three weeks before) while females increased steadily from about half the total to reach 70 per cent in the first week of June.

This same eagerness on the part of mature males to be first home was also to be seen in other species, particularly blackbird and chaffinch. With blackbirds in 1950, for example, the first big fall between 7th-16th March gave us 69 per cent adult and 27 per cent first-summer males, and very few of the opposite sex; but after 17th March there were 27 per cent of each age-group among the males, showing a considerable decline in mature birds, while in the remaining 46 per cent young females outnumbered older ones by three to one. In the following year return blackbird migration to Scandinavia was much later at the isle, and was concentrated in a shorter period; during the first five days of April our trappings comprised 72 per cent males (with the age-groups about equal) and only 28 per cent females, but the sex-ratio was more even afterwards. At the same time there was a bigger chaffinch arrival than usual and of thirty-nine taken during the following fortnight

FIB M

all but six were males. So far as blackbirds are concerned the reverse applies in autumn, the majority of the earlier trappings being of young birds with the sexes about equal; but after the end of October adults preponderate, especially females, mature males being the least in evidence throughout the whole period.

Although bird migration reaches its fullest intensity during the spring months of April and May, and again from mid-August to mid-November, there is hardly a week of the year when movement of some kind is not in progress. One evening at the beginning of July when mist lay like a thick grey blanket over the hill, magnifying everything, four great shapes rose from a pool on the Mire of Vatnagard. They were greylag geese, and they stayed at the isle for four days, an unprecedented event at that season. At this time the young starlings were forming noisy, quarrelsome flocks on the hill, wandering in search of insects and crowberries, and it was with some surprise that I saw in their midst the shell-pink plumage and rakishly-crested head of an adult rose-coloured starling, a wanderer from the Near East. The common starlings made much of this exotic companion, following him whenever he chose to change his ground, and showing a rare submissiveness when he bullied them for some titbit whose ownership was in dispute. Turtle dove, great northern diver and quail were other mid-summer visitors in some years, the last breeding in the rye-grass fields occasionally, their whistled *wet-my-lips*, *wet-my-lips* enlivening the twilight hours, and providing a pleasant change from the corncrakes' infuriatingly monotonous song.

Midsummer migratory movements were sometimes strong, as with the curlews in July 1955. The species breeds in Shetland (though not at Fair Isle), so there is a thin trickle throughout June in most years, accelerating from mid-July when southwards passage begins; but this invasion was altogether too early and too large to have had its origin in the local population. The first big party turned up at the end of June, and a single very tired bird sought 'assisted passage' on the deck of *The Good Shepherd* when she was crossing Sumburgh Roost, in thick fog. At the peak three days later well over a hundred curlews were at the isle, and there were black-tailed godwits and summer-plumaged ruffs on the airfield at Sumburgh, clearly a part of the same movement and hinting that it was in all probability composed of failed breeders and non-breeding adults which had begun to flock and move south while the main body of the species was still occupied with domestic affairs. It was a drift influx aided by a south-east airstream blowing across the North Sea ahead of an occluded front which stretched from the Faeroe Islands to the Hook of Holland; pivoting on a centre a little way south of Fair Isle, this occlusion took its belt of drizzle northwards across Heligoland Bight during the night, disorienting the wader flocks and deflecting them on a down-wind track to Shetland and Fair Isle.

§

High summer is the slack season for bird movement, but there are exceptional summers like 1953, the first during the life of the observatory when crossbills came to Fair Isle. They were cheerful company as they flew about with their musical *twink, twink* conversation, and the flocks were always colourful with their liberal sprinkling of pink males and green and golden-yellow females, though the majority of the birds were in the dark brown, blackish-streaked plumage of young of the year. Their presence met with opposition from one quarter, for the skuas never lost an opportunity of giving chase to the flocks, and we fear that many a laggard made a half-digested meal for the growing chicks.

These birds of the northern spruce forests do not visit western Europe every year, but only irregularly. Recently they have turned up in the British Isles about every three years —1953, 1956, 1958-59, in great strength in 1962 (when an invasion during July was succeeded by another in October) and again in 1963. The intervening period may be much longer than this, and earlier in the century when Fair Isle was well-watched by Dr Eagle Clarke and Surgeon Rear-Admiral Stenhouse and their helpers, irruptions were recorded in 1909, 1910 (much smaller), 1911 (also small), 1927, 1930 and 1935. Thus they may take place in successive years, though this is rare, or may be a decade or more apart.

A Finnish worker, Antti Reinikainen, has shown that the

crossbill really has no fixed abode; he is a nomad, occurring plentifully in areas where there is a rich spruce seed yield, and moving elsewhere in years of cone failure. A Swedish naturalist, Gunnar Svärdson, has pointed out that the northern forest trees do not have two fruitful years in succession—a season of rich flowering and fruitfulness saps their energy, so that the next year's crop is poor. Thus the crossbill population is constantly wandering from one part of the total range to another. What, then, causes these tremendous outbursts of restlessness when hundreds of thousands of crossbills travel far from their native area?

The problem has been studied by many workers, especially on the Continent, where eruption* movements of this and other northern forest birds are far more frequent and spectacular than in Britain. Svärdson's contribution is a most valuable one: he shows how a warm, fine summer can bring about a prolific flowering of the trees—spruce, pine, rowan, birch and others on which the forest birds rely for their food—and at the same time enable more young birds to survive than would do so in an inclement season. Such weather also permits the successful rearing of second broods in many cases. The net result is a big upsurge in numbers, but as there are plenty of seeds and berries no great stress is put upon the population, and there may be no cause for exceptional movement. The plentiful food supply means a low winter mortality, so that the population is still high at the onset of the next breeding season, and may become even more greatly inflated if the weather is again congenial. But this time, because of tiredness, the trees do not respond to the good summer, and at the end of the breeding season there are far too many birds for the impoverished yield of seeds and berries.

It is then that nomadism is magnified into eruption, almost explosive in its suddenness and far-reaching in its effects. The flocks invade new areas beyond the normal limits of their range. Unlike true migrants they are not seeking a hereditary winter home, but food resources which will tide them over the bleakest months of the year. The tendency is to settle for a

* Mass departure from the breeding area is 'eruption'; arrival in, or passage through an outside area is 'irruption'.

time whenever they find one, moving on again when they have exhausted it. Consequently, small irruptions are absorbed long before they reach the fringe of the Continent; and, conversely, really big ones may take the flocks west to Ireland and France, and south to the Mediterranean. It is a normal sequel of such irruptions that many birds stay and breed in the countries they visit if their food requirements are met, while those which return north in the spring often cause an expansion of the breeding range within Fenno-Scandia. The events leading up to such movements, and their effects, are succinctly shown in an important study by R. K. Cornwallis of four successive wax-wing invasions of Britain between 1956-60.

There is one aspect of the problem, however, which has not received the attention it deserves, and that is the meteorological one. Where do the big invasions derive their momentum? Dr David Lack, in his book on animal populations, expresses the view that the immediate stimulus for a big eruption is provided by high population density itself, as though increased numbers encouraged greater restlessness among groups and individuals. Some deep-seated behavioural mechanism must be involved (its nature has been discussed at great length by Professor V. C. Wynne-Edwards), but it is not clear what the immediate stimulus is or how it goes to work. In my view much the most powerful proximate influence is anticyclonic weather at the time when the population is ready to move. There can be little doubt that irruption birds require much the same external conditions as true migrants for safe travelling—clear skies, little wind, absence of precipitation, in short the conditions created by anticyclonic weather. I believe such developments act as a stimulus to the flocks, greatly intensifying their nomadic instinct, and keeping more of the population on the move over a longer period. This is the source of the great momentum of invasions.

It is becoming increasingly clear as more and more data from the bird observatories are studied that this applies not only to the nomadic species of the northern forests, but to birds in general, whether migratory or sedentary; and in years when the population density is great the normal dispersion (largely of young birds) which follows the breeding season assumes the character of an eruption under the kindly aegis of anticyclonic weather. This was strongly borne out in the case of several finch species (and even the house-sparrow) in Britain during the splendidly anticyclonic autumn of 1959, after one of the most congenial summers for many years. Normally sedentary species like the dunnock, greenfinch, house and tree sparrows, when they erupt, tend to be concentrated on a lee coast, since they are loath to fly out over the sea.

The dispersion takes place largely within the region of anti-cyclonic development, where the atmospheric environment is favourable for movement, and Continental birds reaching the fringe of the high are liable to be drifted to Britain when caught by east or south-east winds in the North Sea basin. Very often there is an association between the spread to Britain of a Continental high and the arrival, in great strength, of the birds it carries. Redwings, robins, redstarts and others have flooded the east coast in this way in different years. In the early days we thought these spectacular falls were of birds actually on migration, though we were always puzzled by their apparent inability to navigate as true migrants should in the well-nigh perfect weather prevailing over the Continent and North Sea. There seems little doubt that these big incursions, deposited by the Continental anticyclones on our shores, are not oriented migratory movements at all, but the random dispersion within the fine weather system of a species which has enjoyed singular breeding success and has attained a high density of population.

In retrospect, the 1953 crossbill invasion had all the hall-marks of this kind of situation; moreover, the autumn proved that other species had also benefited from the excellent northern summer, for kestrels occurred in unprecedented strength in Shetland and at Fair Isle, and the number of fieldfares passing through in late September and October was greater than in any previous year. The crossbills' breeding season is at an end by April, but although the bird has evolved an early breeding season it has not evolved a correspondingly early moult. This serves the crossbill well, since there are no other calls on its metabolism during the vital period in midsummer when its strength must be devoted to seeking new food resources. So the birds have the late spring in which to feed well and attain the peak of physiological condition, and June and July are the critical months when they are most fit and ready to respond to the stimulus of anticyclonic weather.

In 1953 a polar high reached Scandinavia from the seas around Jan Mayen on 7th June and spread into north-west Russia next day. It remained the controlling factor in north European weather for the whole of the following month, setting the crossbills' eruption from the northern spruce forests in motion. The vanguard of the invasion reached Shetland in mid-June when a high pressure cell developed to the north, uniting this part of Britain with the whole of Fenno-Scandia in one great anticyclonic system. During subsequent days the weather remained calm but there was stable air and a good deal of sea-fog among the northern isles, so dense with us that no proper search for crossbills could be made until the 18th. We then found a flock of over 40 which haunted the slopes of Burrashield by day, feeding avidly on juniper berries, and roosted on the rocky sides of Troila Geo each night.

Though the polar high persisted over northern Europe, British and North Sea weather became cyclonic for a short spell, and the crossbills' invasion was temporarily halted; but when a ridge of the high reached across the sea into Scotland on 22nd June the crossbills came again, a new lot of 60 reaching Fair Isle and many others entering Shetland. The westwards expansion of the high embraced the Faeroe Islands, where Esther—at home on holiday—found birds in a small conifer plantation at Tórshavn. Some got as far to the north-west as Iceland at this time.

Subsequently many of these birds moved south on fine days, and the fluctuating numbers at Fair Isle (up to 150 on some days in early July) bore evidence of continual passage. The 6th was a notable day because we succeeded in trapping 32 birds, mostly in two batches from a big flock which obligingly decided that the best roosting-place on the island was in the Gully Trap. At this period too there was a noticeable change in the crossbills' feeding habits, for whereas the earlier ones had given their whole attention to the juniper on the hill, these later arrivals concentrated on the seeding heads of thrift along the 'banks'. There is little juniper in Shetland and none at all in

Faeroe, and perhaps the southward-moving birds were already conditioned to sea-pinks when they got to Fair Isle.

A new major wave of invasion took place in mid-August when the Continental and Azores highs affected Britain and the North Sea crossing. This time the crossbills were widely dispersed about the cultivated parts of the isle and fed mostly on thistle seeds and the centres of the partly withered ragwort blooms. It is an interesting reflection on the lack of purpose in crossbill movement that one of the birds we ringed from the Gully on 6th July was found dead at Bergamo in northern Italy on 25th August, while another ringed a week earlier was killed and eaten on 17th September by the Upper Stoneybrake cat!

CHAPTER XIII

MIGRANTS FROM THE NORTH-WEST

Ask an ornithologist to name his favourite bird, and he will probably give you the one he happens to be studying at the time. A good many species—oystercatcher, whimbrel, arctic skua, wheatear, wren—have figured at the head of my list at different times, and for two or three seasons in the middle fifties the merlin held pride of place. Not infrequently merlins were lured into our traps in pursuit of small birds whose guile they sorely underestimated, finding themselves floundering in the funnel whilst their would-be prey looked on from some secure last-ditch retreat in the cover at the mouth. Sometimes they would even catch one another. One morning I brought five home from the pre-breakfast round, three of them taken from the catching-boxes of the Double Dyke. And there were still three birds chasing each other playfully with strident *kee-kee-kee* conversation around the framework!

There were times when this fine little falcon was a not uncommon bird at Fair Isle: it did not nest with us, as it does in Shetland, and this period of abundance was confined to the autumn migration between mid-August and the end of October. Making sure of a trapped merlin was always a ticklish operation, for unless you grasped him firmly first time across the back and wings he would be on his back striking with lightning speed—and a merlin's talons sink a long way into flesh. Even in the lab we had fun and games. I recall one occasion when a particularly aggressive falcon, caught late in the day, had submitted with a notable lack of grace to the admiration of half-a-dozen seasoned ornithologists, and was at last ready to have her freedom. It was dark and the electric light was burning when I opened the window and put her out into the night. In a split-second she made a magnificent reentry, and swept round the lighted room scattering papers, specimen-tubes and people in all directions. Three of my companions disappeared under the lab bench, two ducked under the table, and I (being nearest) fled through the door. She stood imperiously on top of the beam-balance while we gathered our wits and crept away, dowsing the light so that she could find her own way into the night.

Fondness for the merlin, therefore, derived partly from a deep respect for this cavalier creature, but also from the fact that the species provided our first serious essay into field-taxonomy. Taxonomy, the study of the relationship of living forms, is largely the province of the museum worker with ample time and opportunity to make critical comparisons between 'series' of specimens collected in various parts of an animal's range. It seemed to me that the bird observatory, which also handles 'series' of specimens, could make good use of taxonomic methods for the identification of different stocks among its migrant birds; and (since it would of course be dealing with living examples) could also increase our knowledge of the variation within species in a way denied to the museum worker, whose studies are limited to dead and preserved material. With the aid of ringing, for instance, we might hope to learn if there are differences in the migration times, migration routes and winter quarters of the separate population groups, once we had mastered the problem of recognising them. Moreover, we should be in a position to learn a good deal about the respective variations in measurements and weights.

With some species all this was relatively plain sailing, either because the text-books gave a good enough outline of the differences between populations, or because we could sort these out for ourselves with the aid of specimens borrowed from a museum. In this respect we were fortunate to enjoy splendid co-operation from the Royal Scottish Museum. In the case of the merlin, the text-books gave us to understand that the considerable passage through the northern isles came from the Continent, but we soon found that the wing and tail measurements of the majority of our trapped birds were considerably in excess of the upper limits given by the authorities for Continental merlins. An Icelandic race *Falco columbarius subaesalon* had been described many years before but had not found general acceptance, and we suspected that these bigger birds must belong to it. A colleague, Alec Butterfield, did some statistical tests on about three hundred merlins which I measured one winter in a number of museums, and showed that the Icelandic race was indeed larger, sex for sex, than the Continental. Having got thus far, we could examine the meteorological background against which arrivals of our birds took place, and see how the picture compared with that given by other north-western species, and also by Continental birds.

The migration of the Icelandic merlin begins about 17th-19th August in most years, coinciding with the early passage of white wagtails and meadow pipits (which one is tempted to think of as the merlins' haversack-rations!) from the same source. There is a bigger influx at the end of the month, and its frequency at the isle increases gradually during September to reach a peak during the first week of October—by which time most of its food supply has also emigrated. By the end of October all but a few have left Fair Isle, though occasionally a merlin is seen in the winter. As a spring migrant it is scarce and the birds clearly return to Iceland by some other route. Many merlins stay 'off-passage' at the island for a period, which is hardly surprising in view of the almost continuous flow of small birds. Two of the merlins whose playmates trapped them in the Double Dyke for me on 18th August 1953 were recaptured on 9th September and 1st October respectively, having stayed for 23 and 45 days. A meteorologist friend Ivor McLean, whose work took him aboard the weather-ships to 'Station India' in the Atlantic 300 miles south of Iceland and 500 miles west of Faeroe, sometimes saw these birds on their way south, and one stayed a week with the ship at the end of September 1956, chasing other migrants by day and roosting in the rigging at night.

Sometimes the merlins travelled south on the outskirts of depressions as these retreated from Iceland towards Jan Mayen or northern Norway; they then had a backing north-westerly wind to aid them. Most of the arrivals, however, took place either with anticyclones to the west (and therefore a light north-west breeze between Iceland and Scotland), or with

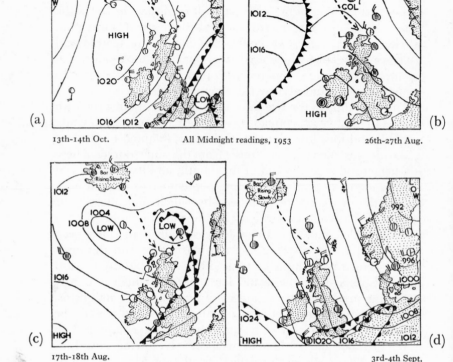

(a) 13th-14th Oct.   All Midnight readings, 1953   26th-27th Aug. (b)

(c) 17th-18th Aug.   3rd-4th Sept. (d)

FIG. 12

HOW ICELANDIC MERLINS REACH FAIR ISLE

The four maps illustrate typical weather situations under which Icelandic
Merlins (as well as other birds from this quarter) reach Fair Isle. Common
in early autumn, before the recession of the Azores high pressure system, is
an anticyclonic approach in which the north-westerly airflow between
Iceland and Scotland helps the south-east-oriented birds (a). They may
also pass unimpeded through cols between separate depressions (b) or
between the twin centres of a filling low (c): in either case the opposing
winds are light and variable, giving a calm 'bridge' between the two
countries for direct passage. Late in the season when the weather is more
stormy, the Merlins may have to wait for a depression to pass Iceland
before clearing skies and a lessening wind give them their cue to leave;
they will then make a cyclonic approach to Fair Isle (d).

quiet col weather over the sea between the two countries. Such birds travelled south-east through a region of the atmosphere in which light opposing winds belonging to the low pressure systems on either side tended to cancel each other out. The arrivals of 18th August 1953 came in this way, between the twin centres of an old depression. In the col and anticyclonic situations the departure conditions in Iceland, and those along the route, are dominated by clear skies and relatively calm air—the conditions which one would expect to be most favourable for a long migratory journey. Except for a stronger (but following) wind, similar circumstances attend the start of the cyclonic type of movement, since the cold polar air behind the retreating depression soon clears the skies, and this is probably a sufficient stimulus to get on the way when the migratory urge has been thwarted by several days of unsuitable weather.

Unfortunately the merlin is less loved and respected by gamekeepers than by ornithologists, and there was a time when the recovery rate of our ringed birds was as high as 40 per cent. These recoveries show that the steep decline during October is caused by birds moving on to winter quarters in Scotland, though occasionally one would make yet another long sea-crossing and turn up on the Continent.

§

There was another species in respect of whose status and movements authoritative works were misinformed, and which provided a pleasant exercise in field-taxonomy. This was the Lapland bunting. It is a small brown bird, a little bigger than a sparrow, inconspicuous enough in autumn and easily overlooked; but, if you are lucky enough to find a good male, it is one of the joys of the spring season. Then, the jet-black head and throat contrasting with creamy-white under parts, and offset by a chestnut band across the nape, combine to make the cock Lapland bunting one of the handsomest of small birds. The females are much plainer and in autumn the males resemble them, their spring glories being obscured by buff and brown feather-tips which wear off late in the winter. The best characters in autumn are the wine-coloured conical bill (which turns yellow in spring) and an unmistakable call-note that begins as a tuneless *tik-tik-a-tik* and ends with a lilting, high-pitched *tew*. So distinctive is this call that ears were more effective than eyes during our hill quests for these birds.

Like the merlins, they were supposed to come from northern Europe. Some, especially those which winter in small groups on estuarine salt-marshes of the east coast (especially in East Anglia), almost certainly do so, but we soon found that those which arrived at Fair Isle came in the wrong kind of weather for Continental birds. Moreover, their companions were the big Greenland wheatears, low-arctic redpolls, and snow buntings. When I examined museum specimens collected years ago at Fair Isle, the Flannans and St Kilda by Dr W. Eagle Clarke, I found they matched the Greenland buntings better than the European: the former are a trifle darker, and slightly bigger in the bill, but there is a good deal of inter-mediacy since Lapland is half-way along a 'cline' of gradual change from the darkest birds in the west to the palest in the Yenesei district of Siberia and beyond.

It was generally assumed that this Greenland stock went to America for the winter, since the Lapland longspur (as it is called there) is a common bird in some years in the central United States. We now know that every year a part of the population—probably from the south-east of Greenland—crosses the Atlantic in the opposite direction to winter in western Europe, 4,000 miles away from the winter haunt of their West Greenland neighbours. Not much is known about its winter quarters on this side: there is some evidence that birds arriving in the north and west cross England and leave for the Continent from points along the east coast. Certainly the few known flocks wintering in Britain do not add up to anything like the numbers which stream into Scotland and Ireland in a good year.

There are good years and bad: sometimes the Lapland bunting is a rather scarce passage-migrant with fewer than a score or so on one or at the most two peak days, and sometimes veritable invasions take place. We know that these invasions are not confined to Fair Isle because other places in the west have also been well-watched in recent years—Inishtrahull and Malin Head off Co. Donegal, St Kilda and Tory Island, and Lundy in the Bristol Channel. In 1953 the first Lapland buntings were spotted at Fair Isle, Lundy and two of the Co. Donegal stations on 3rd September; Fair Isle had a few and Lundy a score on the 5th; Fair Isle and Inishtrahull had 75 and 26 respectively on the 9th, and 55 and 20 on the 16th; while Fair Isle and Malin Head had 60 and 30 respectively on the 19th. Between the 9th and 12th inclusive the number rose to over 80 at Fair Isle—a record high number which was not exceeded until September 1960.

Three important features of the month-long 1953 invasion pointed to Greenland and not Scandinavia as the source. Firstly, the main arrival days coincided at two or more of these widely separated watch-points, the Irish stations roughly 380 miles south-west of Fair Isle and Lundy 320 miles farther on. Meanwhile, only insignificant numbers appeared at observatories on the North Sea coast. Secondly, the weather in Greenland, being anticyclonic, was much more suitable for emigration on most days than the weather in Scandinavia, which was troubled by a succession of depressions, often with adverse winds too strong for small birds to have flown across the North Sea. Thirdly, the main arrival days were dominated by westerly winds, sometimes anticyclonic on the northern edge of the Azores high, at others cyclonic on the rim of a depression centred on or near Iceland.

A fourth body of evidence might eventually accrue from the weights of birds caught on passage, but this species is not easily trapped, so at present our knowledge of the variation is slight. But this variation is very wide, consistent with a long and arduous sea-crossing burning up glycogen and fats, followed by an 'off-passage' period of rest and recuperation. Most of the dozen or so weights fall between 25 and 30 gm., and probably include rested birds as well as new arrivals. There are two striking exceptions, one at 17·5 gm. which must be near the absolute minimum, since the bird had died from exhaustion; and the other at 40·3 gm., a bird which we knew had spent several days feeding on turnip seed scattered around a small trap. Normal departure weight may well be near this figure, and if so the loss sustained during the ocean flight may be of the order of 30 or 40 per cent.

§

At the peak of the invasion, between 9th and 12th September, strong anticyclonic developments in the North Atlantic and low pressure passing eastwards of Iceland combined to give a fresh west to north-west airstream which could have given the small birds a ground-speed of 50 or 60 miles an hour and brought them to Britain in a day and a half. The general meteorological situation was not very dissimilar from that of 10th September 1949 when some 40 Lapland and as many snow buntings appeared at Fair Isle. That also was a good Lapland bunting year, but this bird was completely overshadowed by its more spectacular companion, which came in extraordinary abundance. By the 16th there were some 2,000 snow buntings in large flocks in the crofting area, and I shall never forget the singular beauty of the scene as the massed birds, calling musically, rippled across the stubbles, flashing like an undulating swarm of big white butterflies. So huge a concourse so early in the autumn was quite unprecedented, and has not been equalled since.

There is little doubt that they too came from Greenland, for on the big day of 10th September there was a light north-westerly breeze across the Atlantic between low pressure centres lying to the north of Iceland and far to the south. As with the Lapland bunting, the West Greenland birds cross Davis Straits to Labrador and carry on to southern Canada and the United States, wintering mostly around the Great Lakes; there are many ringing recoveries of birds marked in both Greenland and America to confirm this. There are also a number of recoveries of birds ringed for Dr Finn Salomonsen at Daneborg in north-east Greenland showing an autumn migration in the opposite direction, a flight across the Arctic Ocean to northern Russia. Those from the south of Greenland perhaps go either way, as the wind listeth, for there is an intriguing record of a snow bunting ringed at Fair Isle on 7th April 1959 being found on Fogo Island off Newfoundland on

1st May a year later. This is on the migration route of south-west Greenland birds (one marked at Narssak in Godthåb District at 64° N in July 1958 was taken at Fogo Island only a week before the Fair Isle bird), and while the weather conditions in the North Atlantic may permit travel to America in most years, they may compel numbers to journey to Europe in others.

As a result there appears to be a considerable mixing of snow bunting populations on the shores of the North Sea basin in the winter time, and bird-ringing has revealed movement between English observatories such as Spurn (E. Yorkshire), Gibraltar Point (Lincolnshire), Foulness (Essex), Sandwich Bay (N. Kent) and localities in West Flanders in the same and subsequent seasons. It is known that Fair Isle migrants have moved on to Spurn, and a nice crop of recoveries from the wintering flocks at the Yorkshire observatory has been obtained in spring at such widely separated places as East Lothian, Orkney, Nordland in Norway and Vatnajokul in Iceland.

The snow buntings of Iceland form a distinct race from Greenland and Continental birds, being a darker and richer brown and lacking a white rump in the nesting season. (The only example of a Scottish breeding bird I have been able to examine also belongs to this race, *Plectrophenax nivalis insulae*.) They are said to be sedentary, but occasional specimens have been taken in the Hebrides, and we twice captured examples of *insulae* at Fair Isle. So the Spurn bird may have been an Icelandic native, although the date, 8th May 1959, does not rule out the possibility that it was still on migration to Greenland. Indeed, on this date a year later, Ivor McLean recorded a strong passage of snow buntings at the ocean weather-ship at 'Station Alpha' in Denmark Strait, with birds passing down to the 26th.

The migration picture at Fair Isle supports the conclusion, based on ringing, of an intermingling of populations around the North Sea in the off-season; for although the meteorological environment of the earlier autumn arrivals, from the end of the first week of September, indicates an origin in Greenland with the Lapland buntings and redpolls, heavier arrivals at the end of the month and during October take place largely with

FIB N

easterly weather and in the company of typical Continental immigrants. Moreover, the snow bunting is one of the few small birds which has a regular spring migration through Fair Isle: the fluctuations at this season do not correlate with the east-wind drift conditions which bring the majority of European migrants to the isle, and passage may go on with the wind in the west, south-west and even the north. It is most marked when col and anticyclonic weather suitable for departure exists over Scotland. The best month for spring passage is March, and these are probably the north European birds, the Greenland stock going north in early and mid-April.

This great abundance of snow buntings in 1949, and the periodic big invasions of the Lapland bunting (there was yet another in autumn 1962), set an interesting problem, for there can be little doubt that the high numbers are a function of population pressure and reflect an unusually productive summer on the breeding grounds. At first it seemed possible that the invasions might merely reflect special weather conditions over the Atlantic, favourable for large-scale movement to the eastern side; but as the seasons progressed we found that while the snow buntings never repeated their phenomenal entry of 1949, Lapland buntings had peak years in 1953, 1960 and 1962, and Greenland redpolls visited us in force in 1955 and again four years later. If special weather factors were responsible then it was odd that they should work selectively in favour of one and against the others in any given year. Only in two recorded years, 1925 and 1959, have Lapland buntings and redpolls appeared in large numbers together, while in the buntings' peak seasons the redpolls have often been scarce. Moreover, if the weather were diverting large numbers to Europe in some years we should expect there to be fewer on the American wintering grounds—but 1953 at any rate was also a bumper year in the States. Clearly the difference in numbers must already be apparent in the breeding area, and it seems likely to be due to a combination of good summer weather and a plentiful food supply operating to ensure an unusually high survival rate among the season's young.

§

Another year in which we sustained an invasion of Greenland birds was 1955, and this time it was the turn of the low arctic redpolls. A few of these wholly delightful creatures came our way in most seasons, and were usually to be found in one or other of the cabbage gardens, either alone or with the noisy twites. They are much darker than the Continental mealy redpolls; their dark-brown backs show a varying amount of silver-grey streaking, especially on the rump, which seldom approaches the whiteness of the mealy redpolls. The Greenlanders are bigger, and have bulkier bills, but much the best character for identification is the heavy dark brown striping on their whitish flanks. Their red foreheads, black bibs and portly bearing invest them with a greater charm and personality than have most small birds, and it was always a joy to find and watch them, so that their constant presence in small numbers made 1955 one of the more memorable seasons.

The last recorded invasion had taken place as long before as 1925, and then as now the first-comers appeared towards the end of August. We trapped the second bird we saw, on the 27th, and at 14·4 gm. it was in pretty poor shape and had probably travelled direct from Greenland approximately along latitude 60° N in the westerly airflow between an Icelandic low and a high west of Ireland. The thousand-mile flight had sapped its strength, but these little birds have a marvellous power of recovery, and when it entered another of the traps nine days later the beam-balance registered 20·2 gm.—a 40 per cent gain! An even weaker bird, at 13·8 gm., put on 20 per cent in ten days; and another, better off initially at 16·4 gm., showed a 25 per cent increase to 20·5 gm. after seventeen days.

It is interesting to note that this recovery seems to have a delayed action, and that the intake of food does not apparently overhaul the combustion rate of fat for the first day or two. Thus a bird at 18·6 gm. early on 5th September had dropped 1·5 gm. by the following afternoon; one at 15·3 gm. on the 6th was nearly a gramme lighter early next morning, and another at 17·5 gm. late on the 16th was down to 15·3 gm. early next day and still lighter when recaptured four hours later. Our heaviest recorded weight for this race is just over 21 gm., our lightest only half that figure at 10·7 gm.—yet we feel pretty confident this bird survived, since recuperation had already started on the second day with a gain of 1 gm. These weights are given in some detail because they serve to illustrate not only the tremendous exertions demanded by an overseas migration of this kind, but also the birds' amazing powers of recovery.

About a dozen birds were with us from 2nd to 6th September, having in all likelihood travelled down-wind in the complementary westerly airstream of a low centred on Jan Mayen and the ridge of an Azores high. We had 13 in one flock for several days following the 10th. Foula, which stands 45 miles nearer to Greenland than Fair Isle, had many birds during September: Christopher Mylne, the island's schoolmaster, returning from holiday on the 14th, found 30 among the twites, while the inhabitants told him of a flock of a hundred or so which had been about in their small gardens and enclosures eating the docken seeds. The mid-September birds may well have reached Shetland *via* Iceland and the Faeroe Islands during calm days of col weather.

Other western localities were also getting redpolls from Greenland. Mr O'Sullivan, the Principal Lightkeeper at Tory Island off Co. Donegal, noted a big arrival on 12th-13th September, when a force six west-nor'west wind on the periphery of an Icelandic low would have helped the birds on their way. They became fewer at Fair Isle at the end of the month, though still around the 30 mark at Foula. A bird ringed by Mylne on the 15th turned up, with an unringed companion, at a lighted window at Uyeasound, Unst, 55 miles to the northeast, on the night of 12th October. Quite a few were still moving about Shetland in October, when Jack Peterson had small parties in his garden at Lerwick. There was evidence at Fair Isle of 'onward passage' on fine anticyclonic days: a group of four caught on 24th October, for instance, had an average weight of close on 18 gm., indicating that they had spent time off in Shetland recuperating. Another party of eight appeared in similar weather on the last day of the month; an unusually big flock of thirty was seen on 15th November, and James Stout of Mires told me of another party of five—virtually the last of the invaders—which passed through as late as 2nd December.

§

We have been concerned mainly with the smaller migrants in this study of migration from the countries of the north-west, but we should not neglect the wild geese and whooper swans. The latter were always a magnificent sight, a thrilling manifestation of migration in progress, when your watchful eyes caught them as they came in from the sea, powerful wings holding their ivory bodies a few feet above the waves. Sometimes a family party would put into the North or South Havens and stay there for a while, like lords and ladies among the proletarian gulls. But more usually they were on the move—and although autumn is the season when all birds should be going to the south, our swans were not infrequently flying purposefully in the opposite direction.

There was a good enough reason for this, since Loch Spiggie in the south of Shetland is one of their favourite wintering haunts. Esther and I were cycling home from the village on the afternoon of 1st October 1955 when a couple of swans overtook us as we passed through the Heem Grind, trumpeting musically as they flew on a line which looked as though it would take them to sea past Skroo Lighthouse. The time was 4.57 p.m. We sped after them, and they were shining specks abreast of Mopul when I went into the observatory and put through a telephone call to Tom Henderson, who lives beside the loch, asking him to keep a lookout for the birds. He went out just after six and did not have long to wait, for they came in from south of Fitful and planed down gracefully to the best feeding-area at the northern end of the loch at 6.09 p.m. There can be no doubt that they were the same two birds since only a single swan had reached Spiggie before this date. The 1 hour 12 minutes taken to cover the 29 miles gave them a speed of about 24 m.p.h., a leisurely flight with a light beam wind from the south-west.

The explanation of these northward movements at Fair Isle

seems clearly to be this: the swans reach us by cyclonic approach (as they did on that occasion, together with many snipe
and golden plovers), riding the winds of a depression, and make
a landfall somewhere in the north of Scotland. They then
establish their whereabouts visually (for many of the adults
will have passed through the area in previous winter seasons),
and direct the latter part of their migration over known
territory to their favourite winter quarters—in this case northwards to Loch Spiggie. There are other whooper swan lochs,
such as Loch Stennis in Orkney, and conceivably such southwards passage as we saw may have been due to birds making
their landfall too far to the north, and redirecting their passage
through the islands to this or some other favourite water.

Towards the end of October and early in November the last
of these north-west migrants travel the trans-Atlantic trail to
Britain. They are the geese—greylag and pinkfoot from Iceland, and barnacle, brent and whitefront from Greenland. In
some seasons large skeins overfly Fair Isle, but in most years
their cyclonic journeys bring them to the British area farther
to the south and west—as in 1951, when hundreds of barnacle
geese were observed by the lightkeepers at the Flannans and
Tory Island on 21st-22nd October. A vast depression covered
the eastern side of the Atlantic, and traffic round its perimeter
was heavy: the Loch Spiggie whooper swans built up rapidly
to a peak total of 104 birds, and there were big arrivals of
Greenland whitefronts at their winter haunts in Ireland during
the two days.

In the case of the swans and geese an earlier departure for
the majority is precluded by the long nesting-season and the
need to complete the annual moult, during which the adults
are flightless for a time. Consequently goose passage in anticyclonic weather is rare in autumn, though the departure of
these same species to Greenland and Iceland in spring is invariably triggered off when high pressure builds up over
Scotland in the second half of April. We may assume that the
geese and swans would travel in anticyclonic weather in autumn
if they could, as do many of the small birds earlier in the
season; but at this late period the influence of the Azores high
pressure system has diminished greatly, and there is an almost

constant succession of depressions moving north-east towards the Icelandic low pressure 'minimum'.

This suggests the possibility that natural selection may have played an important part in determining an early migration time among the smaller birds, which in general seem poorly equipped in view of their low weight and lack of energy-building reserves to withstand long cyclonic journeys, with the risk of exposure to frontal disturbances. It is well known that small migrant birds leave their homeland long before the local weather becomes too rigorous, or the food shortage acute, so that in effect their departure anticipates by several weeks the inevitable famine of the northern winter. There has been much discussion as to why they do this, and although no clear reason is apparent (and, indeed, a number of different factors may be cumulatively concerned), it is not unlikely that the rapid deterioration of weather after the autumnal equinox has had some selective effect in adjusting migratory behaviour, bene-fiting those stocks which took advantage of the subtropical anticyclones before their recession.

CHAPTER XIV

WHEATEARS AND REDWINGS

EVERY year the end of August found us profoundly wheat-ear conscious, for during the last ten days of the month the Shetland, Faeroe and Iceland wheatears choose to fly south on the first leg of their long trek to tropical Africa. In 1949 we had this spectacular wheatear 'rush' but few traps to catch the birds; in 1950 it came again and we fared better; and when the 'rush' came a third time in late August of 1951 we began to look upon it as an annual (if slightly movable) festival. The same period in ensuing years found us rising expectantly before dawn for the first hopeful round of the traps, but for some reason not then apparent the wheatears never came in any strength. Experience has taught us that we should not look for this massive passage unless a ridge of the Azores high settles firmly over Shetland and Faeroe, giving fine clear weather for the wheatears' departure, and bringing them to us on a light north-west breeze—preferably with a little sea-fog at dawn to bring the travellers down.

In 1955 it looked as though the wheatears had cheated us yet again by taking a slightly different route—and then, at the end of the month, the 'rush' came. At dawn there were wheat-ears everywhere, their white rumps glinting in the half-light as they fled along the drystone dykes or danced like will-o'-the-wisps against the dark heather of the moor. In three hours' work before breakfast 50 birds had been weighed, measured, ringed and searched for insect parasites. The trapping was brisk all day, and the late afternoon was enlivened by en-thusiastic efforts on the part of all our visitors to set up new 'observatory records'. First we aspired to reach the 500th wheatear for the season; next, it was the 100th wheatear for the day. The last round of the traps saw us safely home and dry, and any danger of anticlimax was averted when one visitor created yet another record by returning at dusk with the first turtle dove to be captured at the isle.

As a migrant the wheatear greatly interested us because the north-western populations of Shetland, the Faeroe Islands, Iceland and Greenland show average differences in measurements of wing and tail, and also weight, which made grand material for field-taxonomy. The more distant their origin the bigger and heavier they are, the size-range culminating in the birds of West Greenland and Baffin Island, which are half as big again as our own Fair Isle breeders. Our birds in turn are noticeably bigger than the Continental ones which sometimes cross the North Sea with other drift-migrants. The wheatear is the only European songbird to have colonised North America, but it has no winter home there, its migration taking it east-

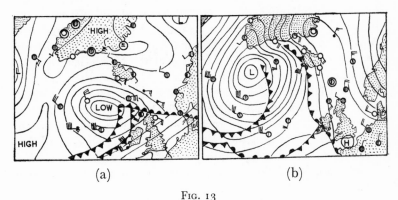

(a)   (b)

Fig. 13

WHEATEAR ARRIVALS FROM WIDELY SEPARATED REGIONS

Between 2nd and 5th September 1953 there were arrivals from three different Wheatear populations. A high over Greenland led to the departure of many of the large Greenland race, and these reached Fair Isle by cyclonic approach (see fig. 14). Simultaneously the warm front of the depression, reaching across the North Sea to the Skagerrak, caused a strong westwards drift of the small Continental birds as they left Norway (a). A few days later, with this low now over Norway and a successor affecting Greenland, emigration from both countries was halted; but the long anticyclonic ridge between the two extended northwards to the Faeroe Islands and Iceland, and stimulated renewed migration in the intermediate race *Oenanthe oe. schiøleri* (b).

wards across the Atlantic to maritime Europe, and then south-wards to West Africa. It is a prodigious migration and the first leg, from southern Greenland to Scotland or Ireland, may call for over a thousand miles in a single hop. There are few birds which regularly undertake so hazardous a trip, and the Green-land wheatear is worthy of any man's admiration.

There was a fascinating period at the beginning of September 1953 when we had a dual arrival of wheatears from both west and east. Most of the local stock had already departed, so our captures were about equally divided between the long-winged, long-tailed Greenland race *Oenanthe oe. leucorrhoa* and small birds of the typical European form—veritable pygmies by comparison. The meteorological setting was provided by a big Atlantic depression moving on a north-east course between Greenland and Britain, with a warm front reaching across Scotland and the North Sea to the Skagerrak. Strong anti-cyclonic developments over both Greenland and Norway gave ideal conditions for departure, and the situation of the low resulted in a cyclonic westerly airstream over the Atlantic and an easterly one ahead of the front over the North Sea. On the 4th the low passed over Norway while another reached southern Greenland, so that in both countries further emigra-tion was inhibited; but between the two depressions a long cigar-shaped anticyclonic ridge forced its way northwards to Iceland, the light airs and clear skies affording good travelling weather for the intermediate population *Oenanthe oe. schiøleri*, which had been held in check by the bad weather of previous days.

These birds, which arrived on the 5th (average wing-length 96 mm., tail-length 55·5 mm.), showed the best weights, with an average of close on 28 gm.; they had come the shortest distance, island-hopping in good weather, and so had used comparatively little energy. Although the thirteen Green-landers captured between the 1st and 4th (wing 103 mm., tail 60 mm.) must have been substantially heavier than this, and the nine Continental birds of the 2nd and 3rd (wing 93 mm., tail 52·5 mm.) substantially lighter at the beginning of their respective journeys, both forms were extremely light and about equal in weight when they reached Fair Isle—the Greenland birds at an average of 22·7 gm. to the others' 22·3 gm. The small birds had had to make a fortuitous sea-crossing of some 300-400 miles in the easterly airstream ahead of the warm front, while the big ones (whose loss was proportionately much greater) had circled the other side of the depression, covering a distance which seems likely to have been three times as great.

I was paying a visit to Fair Isle in the autumn of 1960 when the best series of Greenland wheatear arrivals I have seen took place, and we managed to sample a few of each day's birds. The story was much the same. There was a big influx on 9th

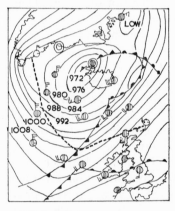

10th Sept., 1960   11th Sept., 1960

FIG. 14

CYCLONIC APPROACH OF GREENLAND WHEATEARS

The Wheatears, Redpolls, Snow and Lapland Buntings of Greenland often travel round depressions to the British Isles (see chapter XIV). A protracted invasion of Greenland Wheatears took place between 9th and 13th September 1960: the Atlantic weather was similar prior to all the arrival days except the 12th. The maps show the situation at midday on the days preceding arrivals, when the birds concerned were far from any land. The dotted line is an approximation to the birds' track, assuming a departure oriented south-east from southern Greenland, and a north-easterly displacement due to the backing winds after passing through the fronts. Birds arriving on the 9th, 11th and 13th probably had a 30-hours' non-stop flight of about 1,600 miles, and lost 35-40 per cent of their body-weight. Those of the 12th had a more direct journey of little more than 1,000 miles in perhaps 24 hours, and lost only about 20 per cent of their body-weight.

September (extending as far south as Tory Island) at a low average weight of 25 gm. Others on the 11th showed an even lower average, 23·2 gm. A peak on the 12th of over 300 birds at Fair Isle only (in company with 90 Lapland buntings) gave a higher value of 30·8 gm., but the next day's arrivals had declined to 26·5 gm. With the exception of the third wave all these birds appear to have made a cyclonic approach in the backing winds of big Atlantic depressions centred near Iceland. Assuming they set off with a south-east orientation they must have had a following wind for part of the way, but in the later stages would have passed through the warm sector of the depression, a cloudy region of west or even south-west wind strong enough to deflect them from their course. Effectively their journey was with the wind round the low pressure system—a circuitous route, but a fast one—and cyclonic approach of this kind may take the birds across 1,500 miles of ocean, the actual distance depending of course on the size of the depression. The conditions on the 11th-12th, when the birds arrived in much better trim, offered a more direct flight of probably not much more than a thousand miles, with a filling low to the north of Iceland and col weather in mid-Atlantic.

Cyclonic approach is not just an occasional phenomenon— it is a regular pattern of trans-oceanic migration for these north-western birds, whether they be Greenland geese, wheatears, redpolls and buntings, or Icelandic swans, merlins, redwings, white wagtails and meadow pipits. The Iceland low pressure 'minimum' is a quasi-permanent feature of the atmosphere: it does not fill much even in summer, and is already deepening when the time comes for these birds to leave their homeland. Throughout the autumn it attracts a constant succession of Atlantic depressions, most of which form along the 'polar front' separating the cold, dry arctic air from the warm, moist subtropical air. In the nature of things, therefore, the majority of Atlantic lows pursue a north-eastwards course, and as they pass southern Greenland clear and relatively calm polar air pours in from the north-west and gives the migrants their cue to move.

Once they have left these good conditions behind, the birds soon pass into the sphere of influence of the depression proper out over the ocean. At first the wind is north-west, and as they are oriented south-east towards Britain, their path is effectively down-wind. Farther on, in the southern sector of the retreating low, the winds back progressively, and in the final approach to Britain and Ireland may be blowing from the south-west. The persistence of a south-east orientation may depend upon whether or not the birds must pass through a cloudy warm sector, with frontal rain and drizzle; conditions of this kind must impair their navigation, but even if they are forced to drift the winds are still helpful, and bring them to land somewhere in western Europe between south-west Norway and north-west France.

§

One of the commonest and most spectacular migrants to pass through Fair Isle is that handsome north European thrush the redwing; and because it has fairly distinctive geographical races on the Continent and in Iceland, it is perhaps the best species of all for a study of the ways in which the weather affects bird movements. The Icelandic race, *Turdus iliacus coburni*, is larger and heavier on average than its Continental counterpart, *T. i. iliacus*, for reasons discussed at the end of this chapter. It is also more heavily saturated with dusky olive on the underside and flanks, while the eyestripe, cheeks, breast and under tail-coverts are strongly suffused with buff. Odd birds are sometimes difficult to place, but when they arrive *en masse* and one can get a representative sample from the traps, there is no trouble at all in deciding which is which.

A few European redwings appear at Fair Isle during the last week or so of September, but October has opened before they come in any strength. The biggest arrivals normally take place in the second and third weeks of the month, when the flocks come in company with other European thrushes (mainly fieldfares and blackbirds), big falls of woodcocks, and lesser numbers of robins, goldcrests, bramblings and other small birds. These arrivals usually coincide with easterly winds, sometimes anticyclonic, at other times associated with the movement of frontal disturbances over the North Sea.

Interspersed with them are smaller flocks which reach the isle with westerly weather, and whose fellow travellers are wild geese, golden plovers, and a few late wheatears and merlins. They can be confidently placed with the Icelandic race on plumage features. Since their migration time is six weeks later than the main merlin and wheatear passage the birds have less opportunity for a direct, island-hopping journey in col or anticyclonic weather, for by mid-October the Azores high pressure belt has retreated and the Atlantic depressions have grown more active, so that most of them are obliged to enter Britain by 'cyclonic approach'. Their numbers are generally small, and never to be compared with the sometimes immense influx of Continental birds.

Because the conditions for resting and feeding are good at Fair Isle there is a sprinkling of both kinds in the fields on many days in October, though the Icelanders tend to keep to themselves and seem to favour the root-crops rather than the open fields and moors. There are also fine, quiet days when birds of both kinds pass through—Icelanders from Faeroe and Shetland on continuing migration, and Continental birds on 'redetermined passage' after a drift to the northern isles.

The ringing of young birds has shown that redwings from Scandinavia and Finland pass the winter in large numbers in the British Isles, France and Spain, but many birds also winter in Italy and countries farther east in the Mediterranean region. Whether or not different population-groups prefer distinct wintering areas is not yet known, and indeed it does not seem very likely on such evidence as we have from the recoveries of marked birds. There are some records of birds returning to the same winter quarters in successive, or subsequent, years; but a greater number ringed when on passage or wintering in western Europe have turned up in later years in Italy and parts of the U.S.S.R., thus giving the impression that many redwings are not tied to a particular migration route and winter home as are so many European species, but wander rather untidily within a vast area. M. J. Ashmole has suggested that this apparent nomadism may be an adaptation enabling the species to seek out regions with good berry crops, their staple winter food—and this at once puts us in mind of the chief difference between the true migrants and 'invasion species' such as the waxwing and crossbill, discussed in chapter XII. This wide scatter of returns from our ringed birds would be more easily understandable if we could show that redwing movements, like those of so many other northern species, suggest eruptive outbreaks at times of over-population.

To examine the possibilities of this view we need to turn back the pages of the years and look closely at some of the really big redwing arrivals recorded at Fair Isle. We have seen that surpluses are exported when great anticyclonic systems develop and excite the birds to far-ranging movement, often transporting vast numbers far to the west of their home range. The most spectacular invasion during our stay took place on the morning of 8th October 1954, when at a conservative estimate some 5,000 birds were scattered in flocks about the moorland, fields and 'banks' above the western cliffs. The weather was anticyclonic with a vengeance—there were separate high pressure cells over Scandinavia and England, though Scotland lay on the rim of an Atlantic depression. The movement provided a splendid illustration of drift, for the fall of birds was heavy only in the north where the wind below the Scandinavian high was blowing from the south-east. Elsewhere along the coast of Scotland and north-east England the complementary airstream between the English high and the Atlantic low was from the south-west, inimical to drift, and no birds appeared. Moreover, the wind was very light and the weather stations in southern Norway and on the east side of Britain reported cloudless skies, so that there was nothing to deter true migrants from making an oriented journey across the North Sea and a purposeful entry into England. The fact that this large number of redwings was carried to Fair Isle, while no comparable movements were witnessed farther south, suggests that dispersion was an important feature of this situation.

Peter Davis recorded an invasion of double this scale on 4th October 1962, an unprecedentedly early date for so massive an arrival. Again the conditions over Fenno-Scandia and the North Sea were markedly anticyclonic, except in the far north of Scotland, where the wind was southerly on the perimeter of an Atlantic low. It is worth noting that 1962 was an invasion year for several other species, particularly crossbills and greater spotted woodpeckers. I was staying at the Isle of May at the time, and although many redwings halted there they numbered hundreds, not thousands, and again it looks as though the cyclonic wind in the north must have whisked the 10,000 wandering birds out of the anticyclone and flung them like a tidal wave upon Fair Isle.

There have been similar occasions in other years, less spectacular but involving large numbers nevertheless. Some 5,000 appeared on 22nd October 1950 after a high had moved across the North Sea from Britain, embracing the whole of Scandinavia; again the sky conditions on both sides of the North Sea were favourable for oriented movement, and there was virtually no wind to create drift of oriented birds. An Azores high crossed Britain during 10th-11th October 1952 and settled over Norway; the 800-plus recorded on the 12th were merely the precursors of a rush of over 2,000 birds on each of the two following days, with the high firmly uniting Fenno-Scandia and

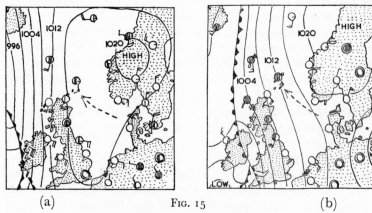

(a)   Fig. 15   (b)

REDWING MIGRATION SET IN MOTION
BY AN ATLANTIC HIGH

During the night of 11th-12th October 1952 an Atlantic anticyclone, moving eastwards into Scandinavia, set in motion a migratory movement of redwings, of which some 800 drifted across the North Sea to Fair Isle (a). The high intensified, and next night emigration was on a much larger scale, over 2,000 birds reaching Fair Isle on the morning of the 13th (b).

Britain. Bad weather intervened and reduced the numbers, but when the anticyclone reasserted its superiority movement got under way again, and the invasion culminated in a further 2,000 on each of the 20th and 21st. The great 'robin-rush' of the first week of October 1951 also brought early redwings to Fair Isle, in hundreds not thousands, but a steady flow extending over six days. This high had moved from the eastern Mediterranean through Russia before swinging westwards across Fenno-Scandia and finally to the British Isles (fig. 17).

Redwings are so abundant and familiar a feature of the English winter scene that we have perhaps been too easily lulled into accepting them all as intentional immigrants, oriented south-west from Finland and Scandinavia. No doubt many thousands are purposeful immigrants of this kind; there is, indeed, indisputable evidence from radar studies that immense numbers of the thrush kind enter Britain on a south-west bearing every autumn. Nevertheless, this well-established fact does not preclude the possibility that large numbers may come in certain years because they are brought willy-nilly by anticyclonic winds during post-breeding dispersal in which oriented movement plays no part—and that they may sometimes come in such quantity as to give the strong impression of a huge population surplus somewhere in the breeding range.

Many of these wanderers may have been reared in Russia or even Siberia, among groups which normally winter in Italy and the eastern part of the Mediterranean basin. A bird I ringed on 9th October 1954—a big anticyclonic occasion mentioned above—was at Meleski in the Estonian S.S.R. on spring passage in April 1960. The more fortunate may eventually 'home' to their native region, and travel as normal migrants to the traditional winter area of their group in subsequent years. This could be the explanation of the nine recoveries, after more than a year's interval, of British-ringed redwings in Italy, to which must be added a bird in Cyprus, two in Georgia on the eastern shore of the Black Sea, and one at 60° 30′E in the Chelyabinsk Nature Reserve, Ilmensk, U.S.S.R.—the farthest east for any passerine yet ringed in the British Isles.

§

If the redwing in northern Europe behaves as a typical irruption species in certain years, what of the redwing of Iceland? We have seen that some birds from similar latitudes in Greenland, notably the Lapland bunting and low-arctic redpoll, invade the British Isles in large numbers in some years, and the same thing happened with the Icelandic redwing in 1956 and again in 1959. The redwing has been greatly favoured by the climatic amelioration during the past half-century, and is now a very common Icelandic bird; large numbers leave the country in autumn, though many attempt to stay in the mildest part, around Reykjavík in the south-west. Before 1956 we caught only a few *coburni* each year, about 20 per cent of the hundred or so redwings taken in the traps; in 1955 the proportion was better at 25 per cent, and then in 1956 it rose steeply to 60 per cent—just over 200 of the 333 birds caught.

They came in several waves, the first big one lasting throughout the afternoon and night of 11th October, so that more than 500 were present by dawn on the 12th. The 28 trapped had an average weight of 71·3 gm.—an interesting comparison with the 64 to 66 gm. for Continental birds which covered the much shorter journey from Norway on 9th and 15th October. (Spring weights of *coburni* fresh from Scotland may be close on 90 gm.) Then on the afternoon, of the 18th, with cyclonic westerly weather over the Atlantic, the biggest rush of *coburni* we had ever seen descended on the isle, bringing well over 1,000 birds.

It was a fantastic movement, the more compelling because it came so suddenly to a virtually empty isle, and we saw the numbers swell as the afternoon wore on. Usually the big rushes of Continental birds are already in at dawn, and the *fait accompli*, while marvellous enough, lacks the tremendous thrill of migration in progress before one's very eyes. The traps were unprofitable and the moorland bare that morning; and then, shortly after noon, the first birds appeared at Vatstrass and Eas Brecks, and I chased a few obvious Icelanders into the Single and Double Dyke Traps. Very soon afterwards flocks of birds began to pour down off the hill and sweep along the stone dyke which runs from Dutfield towards the village. It was as though this long, straight wall exerted a powerful—almost magnetic—influence upon them, so strong that dozens found themselves in trouble with the traps along its length. It was still blowing pretty hard from the west and the birds were wild and restless, yet the way they hugged the dyke made them so easy to catch. I think the explanation must be that the long wall acted as a useful 'leading-line'—a point of reference which enabled them to assess and offset the strong drifting effect of the wind that had swept them across a thousand miles of ocean waste.

I spent a hectic afternoon, ushering birds into the boxes, removing them, and taking the carrier bags to the observatory, where Esther weighed and measured and ringed with quiet efficiency while I grabbed such empty bags as were available and dashed out to take whatever the traps had to offer. Each time I reached the beginning of the wall a newly arrived flock fled ahead of me and the Double Dyke became a whirling mass of redwings, of which many escaped and went on, leaving a dozen or so to serve the demands of science. I was still going to and fro at dusk, and the last captures were dealt with by lamp-light and put away in roosting-boxes, to be released at dawn. We dealt with 59 birds at an average weight of 71 gm., while 'mopping-up' operations next morning added another 15 at an even lower weight, doubtless because the later arrivals had had no chance to feed before darkness imposed upon them the necessity for finding a safe roosting-place. We had so enjoyed this lively afternoon that we wished we could have it all over again—and we did, with another wave of over 500 birds which began after midday on 24th October.

There was one feature of the arrivals which was very puzzling. Whereas the arrival of Icelandic redwings in previous years had taken place either with anticyclonic weather to the west, or under the typical 'cyclonic approach' situation so familiar to us from our studies of merlin and wheatear, these big waves of 1956 had as their background a strong westerly wind linking southern Greenland and the northern isles. Only once before had redwings come under such conditions, on 11th October 1954; then, as with the first wave exactly two years later, the weather-maps showed a system of nearly straight isobars west-to-east across the ocean between the subtropical high pressure belt and a double-centred depression north of Iceland. With west winds at or near gale force all the way, any birds leaving Iceland would have done so under wretched conditions, and could not have avoided a strong lateral drift to the Norwegian coast. It would have been a physical impossibility for them to have gained Fair Isle. The situation was similar on 18th October, and not much different on the 24th, except that on these occasions the depressions were situated over Iceland and the winds between there and Scotland were even more adverse, being slightly south of west.

Knowing what we do of the effects of wind-drift on birds travelling over a featureless sea with no aids to navigation, the only reasonable conclusion is that the three waves originated not in Iceland, but in southern Greenland between 50° and 60° N, where the aftermath of the depressions had left the skies calm and clear. Assuming they left about dusk from the south-east coast and travelled down-wind, their journey of from 1,100 to 1,400 miles at a flight-speed of 30-35 miles per hour doubled by the prevailing wind-speed, would have brought them to Fair Isle after about 20 hours on the wing—a schedule consistent with an early afternoon arrival. The Icelandic red-wing is not known to breed in Greenland; it is said to be of casual occurrence in autumn, but ornithological observations in this vast country are so sparse that nobody really knows its status there. It could be that in some years, when *coburni* does unusually well in its native land, post-breeding dispersal in local anticyclonic weather carries large numbers across Denmark Strait in the first phase of autumn movement. There had been opportunities for such dispersal in the fortnight preceding the big immigration at Fair Isle.

The reality of 'cyclonic approach' could hardly have been better illustrated than it was in mid-November 1959 when a number of Icelandic redwings which had stayed late in that country were forced to leave during a cold anticyclonic spell. Before the winter of 1959-60 the only redwings ringed in Iceland and recovered abroad were five wintering birds in Ireland and the Hebrides. Then, between 15th and 17th November inclusive, three birds with Icelandic rings were found dead in southern France and Spain; later another was

reported from France, and a fifth from Portugal. This remarkable crop of recoveries, twice as far south from Iceland
as the normal winter quarters, and the first three of which were
so close together in time as to suggest exhaustion, indicates an
enormous displacement due to some stress of weather at the
time. Immediately prior to 15th November a huge depression
was centred over the British Isles, its circular wind system extending north to Iceland and south to Spain; and it looks as
though the redwings were borne across the eastern Atlantic,
far out of reach of Ireland, by the strong peripheral winds, to
make a landfall on the Biscay coast after an overseas flight of
not less than 1,600 miles.

§

There is an 'ecogeographical rule' familiar to biologists,
called Bergmann's Rule, which states that in any warm-blooded
species the body-size tends to increase with the decreasing
mean temperature of the habitat. Thus, the farther north one
goes in the total range, or the higher up a mountainside, the
bigger the organism becomes. In birds this increase in size is
customarily expressed by the linear measurements of wing and
tail, and of course it is also apparent in weight. The effect is
widely thought to be an adaptation for conserving body-heat,
and therefore energy, since a large body-surface radiates
relatively less heat to its surroundings than a small one.

Many species accord with Bergmann's Rule, and in some
cases this need to conserve body-heat may be important. The
Icelandic wren is very nearly twice the weight of an English
wren, and the Faeroe starling is noticeably more robust than
its Continental counterpart: both are resident birds, and have
to contend with rigorous winter conditions. But many of the
north-western species which exhibit this 'latitude effect' remain in the north only during the warm summer months, when
they are no worse off than their Continental relatives, and take
pains to avoid the cold season by migrating to a more congenial climate. In these cases there must be some other reason,
or reasons, for adherence to Bergmann's Rule.

Dr Finn Salomonsen has shown that the climate in the winter

home may be equally important in this respect, and indeed may contribute towards an opposite effect. For instance, one of the notable exceptions to Bergmann's Rule is the ringed plover, the arctic form *Charadrius hiaticula tundrae* being smaller than British and middle European birds. He suggests that this is because *tundrae* has a 'leap-frog' migration which takes it beyond their wintering range into tropical Africa, where it enjoys a far warmer off-season climate than they do and has had no need to evolve a larger size. A similar situation exists among European populations of the redshank. This may also provide a reason why the white wagtails of Iceland do not appear to be larger than the related pied wagtails of the British Isles. As we shall see below, a larger body-size would be expected in the north-western bird, but it also has a 'leap-frog' migration to a warmer winter range, so the two effects are in conflict, as it were, and cancel each other out.

We have seen that a species showing a marked increase in body-size with latitude in the north-west is the wheatear, the Greenland population being about half as big again as the English and Continental ones. We have also seen that the Icelandic merlin is noticeably larger, sex for sex, than the European merlin, and that the same is true for Greenland *versus* mealy redpolls, and Icelandic *versus* Scandinavian redwings. If the larger size is due solely to the effects postulated by Bergmann, a difficulty at once arises in that the north European element of all these species extends as far, or farther, into high latitudes as the Icelandic, and yet does not approach the north-western groups in either measurements or weight.

There is one important difference between the two groups which does not appear to have been critically considered. Whereas the birds of northern Europe have a migratory journey that is almost entirely overland (barring the accident of drift across the North Sea) and can therefore be made in short stages with frequent halts for resting and feeding, the north-western birds are obliged to make a long overseas flight. They have no way of circumventing this: the entire stock, young and old, must make this hazardous crossing in one hop, season after season, generation after generation, if the race is to survive. Such are the climatic conditions over the eastern

Atlantic Ocean that even small birds like the redpolls, buntings and wheatears may have to fly non-stop for the best part of 30 hours, covering up to 1,500 miles. We have noted that their weight-loss on such journeys is very considerable, and may be so severe that some die of exhaustion at the end of it, though most show remarkable powers of recuperation once they are able to rest and feed.

Dr Ernst Mayr has emphasised that the working of natural selection is particularly efficient during periods of great environmental stress; this surely is one such period, and there would seem to be little reasonable doubt that the selective influences which have contributed most strongly to the 'Bergmann effect' operate during these brief but recurring migratory experiences. Down the long centuries survival has favoured those birds which were able to call upon the greatest reserves of strength, having the highest capacity to store the all-important glycogen and fats, and these would rear the most offspring and make the greatest contribution to the peculiar characteristics of their race. To this end Nature has given the north-western populations a more robust frame, with longer wings and tail to help support the extra pay-load of fuel, so that they are better able to withstand the tremendous strain of a mandatory overseas migration.

CHAPTER XV

AUTUMN BIRD MOVEMENTS

A DAY which promised to be dull enough ornithologically was 4th September 1956, for there was hardly a migrant to be seen when I made my early round of the traps. The morning was fine and clear, and after breakfast I set off for the south end, hoping to find something of interest among the crops. A vast black cloud, menacing and oppressive, loomed above the southern horizon, and I turned back at the Heem Grind. It looked as though we were in for a line squall or worse—and sure enough the wind rose ominously as the dark pall spread overhead. I was hardly indoors before torrential rain poured out of the Stygian sky.

After less than an hour the rain slackened and patches of blue reappeared. Going outside, I noted with some satisfaction that with the passing of the front—now frowning on Shetland —the wind had veered from north-east to south-east, always a promising direction for birds. But I was not prepared for the veritable 'avalanche' of small birds which had in fact descended on the isle: there were redstarts, whinchats, wheatears, pied flycatchers and willow-warblers all the way from Mavers Geo to the Gully, and beyond to Vaadal and Tarryfield. The number of redstarts was fantastic, and although we put a figure of 1,000 in the log that night it was a wild 'guesstimate' and I am sure an ultra-conservative one. The drystone dykes were dotted with these colourful birds, and although we took many from the traps during the next few hours the catching-boxes were soon replenished by others which came up off the cliffs, or down from the hill. Later I walked across the moorland to the western cliffs. The coils of rusty Dannert wire, legacy of war-time days below the Ward Hill camp and radar installations, were festooned with small birds, and whenever I stood and looked over the edge of the land I could see redstarts, pied flycatchers and tiny leaf-warblers flitting among the rocks, down almost to the breaking sea.

The whinchats, though abundant enough, were concentrated mostly in the crofting area; I counted no fewer than 35 in and around a half-acre field of oats at Kennaby, clinging to the ripe ears and perching along the wire fence. Willow-warblers were fewer but nevertheless exceedingly common, and next in order of merit came pied flycatchers and garden warblers. Somebody trapped a bluethroat (they were to build up to a dozen by the 7th and over a score by the 9th, and I don't think Fair Isle has had a bluethroat week like this before or since). There were a dozen or so spotted flycatchers and a few lesser whitethroats; a barred warbler and wryneck were seen, and I had the luck to find an ortolan bunting and a grey-headed wagtail.

Some little time after the cessation of the rain, while I was still going helter-skelter from trap to trap, tree pipits began falling from the sky by the score, calling continuously. Once when I stopped to watch a flock as it flew in over Wick o' South Haven, a small party of crossbills flew over my head towards the village with tinkling, musical calls. By mid-afternoon tree pipits were about as common as whinchats with certainly not fewer than 500 birds. Small wheatears, with an average wing-length and weight less than our own local stock (and therefore Continental immigrants), also took part, becoming commoner than redstarts in the trapping area by mid-afternoon. It was a wonderful day, but in a sense frustrating: it was far too brief a day for the amount of watching one wanted to do and the ground one wanted to cover, and it was galling that one couldn't be in half-a-dozen places at once. We were thoroughly embarrassed by the multitude of birds, and had the feeling we might be missing any number of interesting rarities because far too many common birds got in the way.

This was one of the most spectacular falls during our eight years at Fair Isle, and a classic example of how frontal weather can affect the migration picture. It was a movement—or, rather, one of a series of movements—we shared with all the east coast observatories as far south as Dungeness in Kent, 700 miles away. As happens when frontal weather is the cause, bringing heavy cloud and rain to hamper the birds' navigation, and east or south-east winds to drift them off their course, the falls occurred on different days at different places. They were, moreover, of brief duration, because immediately the front had passed through any given point the wind there veered to the south-west and so excluded any further drift arrivals.

The big day at Dungeness was 2nd September, after the warm front of a depression centred over Finistère had crossed the English Channel and swept through Kent and East Anglia. The host of birds may well have been moving through Denmark and western Germany when the clear conditions gave way to north-east wind and rain, and the fall on the morning of 2nd extended through Norfolk to Gibraltar Point on the northern side of the Wash, with fewer birds at Spurn Point at the Humber mouth. By nightfall the front lay athwart the North Sea between Denmark and Northumberland; there were easterly squalls during the dark hours but the wind had dropped by dawn, when whinchats, pied flycatchers, redstarts and others littered the coastal area and the nearby Farne Islands. A very big arrival also took place at the Isle of May in the Forth, but driving rain marred the day and little bird-watching was done. By this time the wind farther south had veered and there were no fresh arrivals, though 'mopping up' operations continued for some days. Our turn came on the morning of the 4th with the front forging northwards past Orkney and Shetland.

§

Exactly two years later there was another series of falls along the east coast in which large numbers of much the same species were concerned, but this time the influx was due to the extension of an anticyclonic system from Europe to the British Isles. The falls were not phased as they are when frontal weather intervenes, the birds keeping step (as it were) with the northwards swing of the rain-belt, but were synchronised from Norfolk north to Fair Isle, with different species dominant at different places on different days. On this occasion more eastern species, carried westwards by the great anticyclonic system, were involved—birds such as barred and icterine warblers, and especially red-breasted flycatchers. It is very doubtful if any of these birds were migrants in the generally accepted sense of the word (though the majority of the September 1956 birds almost certainly were), since in 1958 the weather over the Continent and North Sea was generally fine and clear and not such as would cause a mass displacement of migrants oriented south-west from Fenno-Scandia.

These big anticyclonic falls (there have been others in other years) seem likely to be composed for the most part of an entirely different class of birds—those unready for true oriented migration and still engaged in post-breeding dispersion; and when large numbers of any one species are concerned in anticyclonic invasions of this kind, the fact is probably associated with high population density following an extremely good breeding season over the European range. The populations of most species fluctuate widely from year to year, and east coast falls in anticyclonic weather are probably a good 'barometer' of such changes, whereas falls in frontal weather are a much less sensitive indicator because disoriented true migrants are also concerned and one cannot dissociate the two kinds.

The anticyclonic invasions, whether of common migratory species like the redstart and pied flycatcher, or of eastern rarities such as the icterine warbler and red-breasted flycatcher, have therefore much of the irruption character we have already discussed in relation to the crossbill in chapter XII. There seems no reason why normally migratory species should not react in the same way as the nomadic crossbill to conditions of high population density in the breeding area, and show similar eruptive behaviour under the aegis of anticyclonic weather. Nor is there any good reason to suppose that the same pattern of dispersion should not also apply to sedentary and partially migratory species, such as the dunnocks, song thrushes and several finch species in our own country.

If this is so, then we should expect that in any normally migratory species, until quite late in the autumn if the nesting season has been long and successful, the population will consist partly of birds which have attained readiness for oriented migration (perhaps the majority of the adults), and partly of birds still unready or still with the urge to disperse at random (mainly the young). In any given species it is likely that the latter class will be dominant in a year of high fertility, so that in favourable weather both oriented migration and random dispersal will go on side by side. The birds carried to outside regions will not be the true migrants (unless frontal weather intervenes to impede their navigation as in 1956), but the 'unready' birds wandering vigorously within the anticyclonic system.

When a system of this kind moves westwards from the Continent to envelop the British Isles the dispersing birds are borne along with it, and the resultant falls on the east coast are frequently spectacular. Because anticyclones are relatively inert air-masses they tend to lag behind the earth's west-to-east spin, so that Continental highs frequently have an apparent westwards movement. Thus we in Britain have exciting opportunities in most years to measure the success achieved by common European species, and also to see representatives of other species whose homes lie hundreds—even thousands—of miles away.

§

Our first full season at Fair Isle, 1949, was one of big anticyclonic developments over the Eurasian continent; the autumn brought a large number of greater spotted woodpeckers, an 'irruption' species which overflowed the vast northern forests, many finding their way across the North Sea into Scotland. The first wave on 21st September was shared by the Isle of May, Fair Isle and the Faeroe Islands, and in addition to the woodpeckers there were several yellow-browed warblers whose breeding range lies beyond the Ural Mountains. The North Sea flight on the night of the 20th-21st took place in the complementary airstreams of a weak low over Denmark and a high pressure region around the Faeroes, while another wave followed under anticyclonic conditions on the night of 23rd-24th.

Cyclonic weather clamped down and a 'hold-up' ensued on the Continent while a series of active depressions chased each other across Scandinavia and the Baltic Sea: the last was replaced by a small anticyclone on 5th October, and bird-movement began again in the calm clear weather. The yellow-browed warblers now arrived farther south, but Fair Isle had one great rarity, a Pallas's grasshopper-warbler from south-east Siberia, as well as more woodpeckers. It was they who gave character to this 1949 season. All those seen at Fair Isle were young of the year, distinguished from adults by their crimson crowns, and it was an odd experience to see such highly specialised birds struggling to wrest a living from so hostile an environment. One saw them digging for insects on

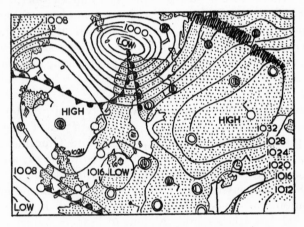

Fig. 16

YELLOW-BROWED WARBLER WEATHER

One of the best seasons for yellow-browed warblers, wanderers from Siberia, was 1949—an autumn of strong anticyclonic developments over Europe and western Asia, with light easterly breezes to carry the birds hundreds of miles across the Continent. The wind was so light and the sky generally so clear that true migrants are unlikely to have been displaced, and the drifted birds were probably young on dispersal. The chart shows the situation early on 21st September when the first three yellow-brows were recorded at Fair Isle, together with young greater spotted woodpeckers (an 'invasion' species from the northern forests) and other interesting rarities—red-breasted flycatchers, Siberian lesser whitethroats, blue-headed wagtails, an ortolan bunting and three dotterels. There was a col with clear sky over southern Scandinavia between Continental and Atlantic highs, and an easterly airstream was maintained by a weak low over Denmark and North Germany.

the grassy cliffs, often within a few inches of such unlikely companions as the fulmar; one saw them spiralling up the telephone poles, or hammering at the fencing-posts in an un-rewarded search for food. A number grew weak and died, others became grain-eaters and survived, at least for a time. They attacked the stooked oats in the fields, and later took up their abode in the stackyards, where a few remained until well into the winter, the last being seen on 4th January. Wood-peckers did not come again in comparable strength until the autumn of 1962, when hundreds of thousands swamped the Swedish spruce forests during September and October, coming from Finland and farther east with vast numbers of common and parrot crossbills. A number filtered through to the northern isles and east coast of Britain, the biggest single influx taking place on 11th October with an anticyclonic set-up which was almost a replica of the peak day, 6th October, of thirteen years before.

A classic example of the anticyclonic type of invasion took place at the beginning of October 1951, when tens of thousands of robins flooded the east coast. Spurn and Gibraltar Point Bird Observatories each ringed over 500 in the week, and 300 were caught at the Isle of May. The few winter recoveries from these birds suggest that an eastern rather than Scandinavian population was concerned, for two were found in Italy, two in the Balearic Islands, and only one in France. When a more restricted drift of robins occurred in south-east England at roughly the same period in 1959 all the winter recoveries were from the south-west corner of the Iberian Peninsula; two on the return spring migration were found in northern Germany, and a summer recovery at the head of Oslofjord showed that in this case a south-west oriented Scandinavian stock had been dis-placed to England by the prevailing easterly wind.

During the 1951 'rush' robins were many fewer at Fair Isle than farther south; nevertheless, far more were present on the island than on any previous occasion, and with them were numbers of song thrushes and dunnocks, big flocks of redwings, unusually early goldcrests and fieldfares, and a small passage of chiffchaffs belonging to a rather drab north-eastern form. The last were particularly interesting, for they also appeared at a

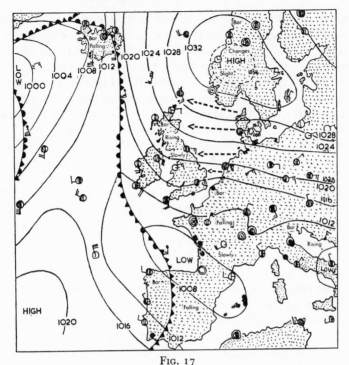

FIG. 17

THE GREAT 'ROBIN RUSH' OF 1ST OCTOBER 1951

A vast anticyclonic system, having moved north through Russia in late September, swung westwards across Finland and lay centred on southern Scandinavia on the last day of the month. There was a belt of light east wind across all of Europe south of the high pressure centre, with overcast sky near the coasts at night. A veritable 'avalanche' of birds, mostly robins, descended in eastern Britain at dawn on 1st October, from Fair Isle south to Kent. Only five of the hundreds ringed at the east coast observatories that day were subsequently recovered, one at Piombino in Italy 42 days later, and two in the island of Minorca early and late in the winter. They were much farther to the east than the recoveries of Scandinavian birds, which winter in south-west Spain and Portugal. Their reorientation suggests an origin in some east European population whose winter quarters are in the central Mediterranean. Probably many Scandinavian birds were also caught in the drift, since robins ringed on the 3rd, 4th and 13th were reported from France, near the mouth of the Gironde (one in winter three years later), while another marked on the 5th eventually reached Sardoal in Portugal. The two others of the five ringed on the 1st were recovered at Oldenburg in Schleswig-Holstein on 28th March 1952 (probably returning to Scandinavia), and in Pas de Calais, France, in January 1953.

number of other places on subsequent days, and as the weather
remained delightfully anticyclonic over the whole country,
their peak movement at various points gave some idea of their
onward progress under the best conditions. The peak at Fair
Isle was on 2nd October; at Little Ross Light in the Solway,
350 miles to the south, the best night was the 4th-5th; while at
Great Saltee, off Co. Wexford, and at Portland Bill on the
Dorset coast, they were most in evidence on the 6th. This
suggests that a good deal of the onward passage was down the
west coast, five days being needed to travel roughly 750 miles.

The year 1953, also markedly anticyclonic, had quite a
different character. It was our first big crossbill year since the
war, and a regular migrant which exhibited an irruption-like
movement into Shetland and Fair Isle in mid-September was
the kestrel. A few appear in most years, but in 1953 kestrels
were hovering in the upcurrents over the stubbles, the moorland, the wrack-strewn beaches, and especially the steep
western cliffs. A moderate wind blew steadily from the south-
east, and as the sky conditions all over the Continent were
excellent for oriented migration one can only suppose that this
big passage of kestrels (for the most part birds of the year)
reflected an abnormally high breeding success. One or two
recent years have been equally good for kestrels at Fair Isle,
and also at Spurn, and as there is good evidence that big
numbers at the Yorkshire observatory coincide with vole
plagues on the Yorkshire moors, it is not unlikely that Fair Isle
invasions reflect a similar link between the kestrel and its food
supply over a large area of the Continent. As with the woodpeckers, a number languished and died, for food at Fair Isle
was scarce, but a few took to preying on small birds and these
appeared to flourish.

§

One of the best-known winter visitors to Britain and Ireland
is the chaffinch, and as a migrant it has received much attention—though not at Fair Isle, for in most seasons only a hand-
ful of the vast numbers which leave Scandinavia at the beginning of October came our way. The reason for its scarcity

Arctic Skuas: a pale morph settling on her eggs.

A dark morph bird incubating.

Bonxies: a parent lifts her wings in display above her egg and newly-hatched chick.

The chick crouches in the heather when about four weeks old.

among the northern isles lies in its habits, for the chaffinch is a
day-migrant, and diurnal migrants are much less exposed to
the dangers of drift than those which must fly blind at night.
The chaffinch is able to gauge the amount of wind-drift, and
correct for it, by following 'leading-lines', and it is along the
coastal highways of the Netherlands, where the birds sometimes concentrate in vast numbers awaiting favourable weather
for the short sea-crossing to eastern England, that its migratory
behaviour has been most closely studied.

Nevertheless, there are occasional seasons when much larger
numbers than usual reach Fair Isle, such as autumn 1950.
Over two hundred came in overnight on 22nd-23rd October,
and with them were the first bramblings and jackdaws—also
normally diurnal migrants, and scarce at Fair Isle. As chaffinches were also entering the country at Spurn and Gibraltar
Point at this time, and the peak was a day earlier at these
observatories, it looks as though the birds sustained a long
drift down the full extent of the North Sea. Perhaps, under the
influence of the anticyclonic weather prevailing on the 22nd,
many began the short sea-crossing late in the day, and drifted
northwards during the hours of darkness. Their arrival-weight
was low, consistent with a long journey, and several recaptured
subsequently showed good gains.

Another big invasion, in 1961, preceded by almost a fortnight the usual time of chaffinch immigration into eastern
England. The weather over Scandinavia and the North Sea
was again anticyclonic, and if they were true migrants bent
on following the normal route to their winter quarters in
England, there seems no reason at all why so many of them
should have gone so far astray. With the movement on this
occasion (as in other good chaffinch years at Fair Isle) were
many siskins, one of the northern forest species subject to
periodic eruptions. It seems more than likely that this was a
clear case of post-breeding dispersion, not oriented migration,
with the Scandinavian chaffinch population at a high peak
after a good breeding season.

Mass stimulation brought about by strong anticyclonic
developments which move westwards across France in the
autumn may account for the considerable chaffinch invasions

FIB P

which occur from time to time in Ireland. South-east wind penetrating the Irish Sea from Finistère and Brittany in late October sometimes results in big arrivals, and R. F. Ruttledge has shown that at Great Saltee Observatory, off the coast of County Wexford, the dominant form is the central European *Fringilla coelebs hortensis*, not the Scandinavian bird as in England. His observations elsewhere in Ireland confirm that this is the commonest chaffinch throughout the winter. The meteorological background of most of the big influxes suggests that they enter Ireland on south-east winds during post-breeding dispersion rather than as intending winter visitors to that country.

The weather is never the same two years in succession. Even though most autumn seasons have their anticyclonic spells, the weather earlier in the year may have favoured certain species and frowned upon others, so that the pattern of movement as we see and record it is dependent upon two important variables —the success or failure of a species to produce a large population surplus for export, and the play of the anticyclones during the autumn months. Because of these variables movements and migration are entirely unpredictable, and so long as we enjoy a fickle maritime climate bird-watching in the British Isles will have a quality of surprise and excitement probably unparallelled anywhere else in the world.

§

While brewing the early morning cup of tea on late October and November mornings I would switch on the radio and hope to hear the seven o'clock oracle saying, "Before the gales forecast, here is a fine weather warning . . .!" But it never happened, and those late autumn days were mostly wild and windy and dripping wet—but tremendously exhilarating for all that. Usually I set off to do the round of the traps on foot (because it was impossible to keep a bicycle on the road) when it was still too dark to identify birds other than by their voices. As the light squeezed into the world I became aware of flocks of squeaking redwings and chuckling fieldfares as they arrived from over the sea, or rose from a brief rest on the moor and hurried overhead towards the village. With them were song-thrushes and blackbirds, robins and goldcrests, small numbers of bramblings and chaffinches, and often snow buntings flashing by like big pied butterflies. Occasionally a skein of wild geese drove a wedge into the wind, or golden plovers wheeled in a well-drilled platoon over the hill. There was always something of interest, and the possibility of a surprise beyond every turn—a great grey shrike on the wall, or a long-eared owl despising you with wide orange eyes as you disturbed his slumbers in the entrance to the Gully Trap.

You had to be at the Gully in the gloaming if you wanted to catch redwings. In the semi-darkness the steep slopes of this narrow defile were sprinkled with tired, sheltering birds; but after they had rested briefly they became as wild as the wind and joined the shy fieldfares on the open moor. After daybreak the blackbirds, soon followed by the goldcrests, came up from the cliffs in an almost constant procession, so that by going continually between the traps it was possible to get a good catch. When the collecting-bags were full I took them along to the observatory, where Esther weighed and measured and ringed—for at this late season we were usually alone, and we allowed the birds to dictate our day. We breakfasted when trapping became slack, which was seldom before eleven o'clock. By then the few blackbirds left on the cliffs had decided to stay there for the rest of the day, the redwings and fieldfares were happy to keep to the soggy moorland, and the robins and goldcrests and other small fry had followed the stone dykes south to the crofts. The drill then was to go after them and look around the stubbles, search the battered turnip rigs and sheltered cabbage gardens, peer among the rocks and shingly beaches, and tramp the wet grassland below Meoness and Malcolm's Head. By mid-afternoon the light was usually too poor for further observation, but good enough for a final round of the traps on the way home to a belated lunch.

We never ceased to marvel that a creature so tiny as a gold-crest, at five or six grammes hardly heavier than the feathers it wears, can cross 500 miles of the North Sea in wretched weather in a single sustained flight—yet this miracle was revealed to us anew each year. At times they arrived by the hundred and as we walked round the 'banks' our ears caught their thin, high-pitched trills as they sought food on the sparse vegetation of the cliff-face. In the crops goldcrests were everywhere: it was odd to watch a bird so closely associated in one's mind with forest trees leaping actively among cabbages and salt-blackened turnip-tops in search of insect food. They did not stay long at Fair Isle, passing on quickly to the Scottish mainland in quest of better feeding grounds.

Rumour has it that goldcrests occasionally cross the sea as passengers on the backs of bigger birds, and the short-eared owl which comes at the same time is usually credited with solving their transport problem. The belief is (or was) widely held among Norfolk shore-shooters, and wildfowlers have attested to seeing the tiny olive-green mites leap from the plumage of newly-arrived owls they had shot. The observation is not unique, for several Indian tribes believe that the even tinier ruby-throated humming-bird reaches Canada as a stowaway on the backs of wild geese and sandhill cranes. One might argue against the likelihood of the same story arising independently among people half the world apart, and without any cultural contact, unless there were some observational foundation for it. It is a matter of daily observation at Fair Isle and elsewhere that starlings frequently go for short rides on the backs of sheep, using them as handy perching-places and look-out stations for insects disturbed by the animals' hooves—just as, in Africa, the carmine bee-eater uses the backs of storks and bustards for the same purpose. Such behaviour is regular enough to be regarded as a useful adaptation in the species concerned, but the goldcrest's ride (if it exists!) cannot be other than a purely fortuitous affair. Could it really happen? Ought we to keep an open mind? A migrant goldcrest, drifting over an apparently limitless expanse of sea and fast using up its little strength, would be singularly deficient in the basic instinct of self-preservation if it let a golden opportunity like a short-eared owl go by!

§

The gales were often at their worst during the hours of

darkness, and with so much noise of breakers chastising the rocks, shingle grating on the shore, wind howling round the corners and underneath the floor-boards, pebbles pelting against the wooden walls, and windows and doors rattling as though the collapse of the place was imminent, there were nights when we got little sleep. So long as the noises were identifiable we did not care unduly—it was only when we heard unfamiliar bangs and bumps that we grew apprehensive. One day, after just such a night, the wind suddenly died away to a whisper at noon; the rain stopped and the sun shone warmly, and vast clouds of seaweed-flies came out of the South Haven wrack, all of which must have been immersed by that morning's flood. They swarmed on the window-panes, and as I walked across the causeway between the two Havens their hard bodies stung my face with the intensity of hailstones. The short-lived sunny period must have caused a mass emergence. It was a remarkable change, but the calm did not last, and by nightfall another gale was threatening from the south-east.

Whenever the wind was in this airt we looked for birds. The long-awaited fall of woodcocks arrived on the hill, and the dim figures of islanders strode in silhouette against a leaden sky. Blackbirds thronged the isle and kept me busy going between the traps with a daisy-chain of aluminium rings around my neck. Under these hectic conditions there was no time to weigh and measure them in the lab, and because we regarded blackbirds as most profitable for their recoveries abroad—in Norway, Sweden, Denmark and north Germany—the more that took away our rings, the better we were pleased. The blackbird has responded to a half-century of milder winters by vastly increasing its numbers and extending its range, and its expansion northwards to the Lofotens and eastwards into Finland can be followed by plotting the distribution of ringing recoveries in recent years.

And how it could rain! Sometimes it would come as a thin, shimmering, semi-opaque curtain billowing in the wind, almost like a colourless replica of the magic folds of the northern lights. I would crouch in the lee of a dyke and watch the folds furling across the hill, until I was wet to the skin with the rain spraying through the holes and crannies with shower-bath intensity. The glistening misty glow over the sleeping moorland of Homisdale and Swey would produce wonderful effects. When the rain stopped and the sun shone great soap-suds of spume would float through the sky, riding the wind from the south coast over a mile away. Progress was a continual battle against the wind as one leaned on the gusts and lurched forwards in the lulls—and shouted (if you had a companion) to make yourself heard. It was tremendous, soul-satisfying fun.

Soon after dark one night we cycled to Skadan Lighthouse at the southern tip of the isle, and with the Principal Keeper's permission spent the night on the lantern gallery, catching, ringing and watching birds. It was an incredible sight. The hazy ink-blue sky shuddered with movement, hundreds of confused birds being held prisoner in the revolving beams. The thin *see* of redwings, like a creaking hinge, and the loud chuckling notes of fieldfares were neverending; the hundreds of fieldfares looked strangely beautiful as the glare caught the shining white undersides of their wings. It struck me as strange that blackbirds were hardly ever to be seen in the rays, though they were the commonest birds at the lantern; probably their uniformly dark plumage, lacking all contrast, explains their cloak of invisibility.

Redwings were common, song-thrushes less so, and we took a few skylarks, starlings and bramblings at the light. Occasionally a long-billed, cumbersome woodcock flew past, looking huge in the beams, and all night long a lone common gull flew round and round the tower, ghostly at the end of dim tunnels where successive beams pierced the haze a hundred yards away. It must have flown many, many miles without getting anywhere. Once or twice a short-eared owl made a brief appearance and we suspected it was hunting the hapless migrants; there are a number of recorded instances of owls, attracted to lighthouses, turning this enforced delay to good account.

One of the woodcocks collided with the lantern glass, and glanced off apparently unscathed—it was more fortunate than many of the smaller birds. Those we caught and ringed we put into holding-boxes until we had gathered sufficient to warrant a journey down the long spiral stair, when we took the boxes into the yard and distributed the birds singly in dark window embrasures, nooks and crannies in a wood-pile, and indeed any shadowed corner we could find. We trusted they would rest there quietly till the dawn. We left a few of the blackbirds where we found them, on the foot-wide iron grating encircling the base of the lantern, and they kept us amused all night. There were six altogether, hopping round the grating, each turning tail to go bounding off in the opposite direction whenever it came face to face with a neighbour. It was as though each was intent on establishing and holding a fragment of territory even under these unnatural conditions.

A walk beneath the tower when the haze cleared at two o'clock revealed many birds, either dazed or injured, resting on the grass or the rocks above the shore. A low hillock a hundred yards away, which the revolving beams just cleared, was covered with roosting redwings, fieldfares and blackbirds, and all we had to do was pick them up, put on our rings, and re-place them gently in the grass. These were the fortunate ones, still sound in body and limb; but there were many others which only too obviously had collided with the tower and lay huddled with broken wings, blind bloodshot eyes and bleeding mouths. For every one hale enough to hold a ring another had to be destroyed by the firm pressure of a thumb against the heart. After dawn we scoured the whole area and found and killed a dozen more whose migration had come to a sorry end.

There are lighthouses which take a much heavier toll of bird-life than this, for at Skadan such a night is a compara-tively rare event, falling perhaps once or twice in the year. At some, the bodies have been wheeled away by the barrow-load after a particularly disastrous night. This tremendous loss of life is distressing to lightkeepers and bird-watchers alike, and a lot of it could be avoided with very little expense. The Royal Society for the Protection of Birds is doing a great deal to re-duce the wastage by erecting perches round the galleries, and installing floodlights to illuminate the towers. But the installa-tion of such equipment is very costly and there are never likely to be sufficient funds to meet all needs. Much could be accom-plished by mounting a dozen electric bulbs, with suitable re-flectors, round the tower immediately above the lantern to light up the dome—for it is against this dome, in the utter blackness above the blinding beams, that most of the birds are killed. Many times that night we watched birds swerve upwards from the rays as soon as they became aware of imminent collision with the lantern-glass, only to crash with a sickening thud against the dome they could not see. Some which checked their flight and merely brushed the dome stayed there until morning, in the safest place of all; but after the impact the great majority spilled off the sloping roof and fell over a hundred feet to the ground below. Most lighthouses, though they use paraffin for the light, have an electricity supply, and the illumination of this deadly dome should present no practical difficulties. It would certainly save the lives of thousands of migratory birds every year.

CHAPTER XVI

RARE BIRDS

FAIR ISLE has the distinction of having put more birds on the British 'list' than any other locality. If you were a rare bird, you might think of this 'list' as an exclusive club to which you could get elected if you were able to claim at least one well-authenticated appearance somewhere in the British Isles. You would need one or more competent observers as sponsors, whereupon your credentials (and theirs!) would be scrutinised by a select committee which has been dubbed 'the Ten Rare Men'. It is symptomatic of our more enlightened approach to rare birds, and indeed wildlife in general, that whereas your election would necessarily have been posthumous a decade ago (since only specimen records were acceptable!), you have now only to be seen, and properly vouched for, to be believed.

Before the establishment of its bird observatory Fair Isle's potentialities for attracting rare birds had been explored successively by Dr William Eagle Clarke, Mary Duchess of Bedford (whose *Diary* of her days at the isle makes interesting reading), Surgeon Rear-Admiral J. H. Stenhouse, George Waterston, and a few others who had made shorter visits, besides several of the islanders whose interest in birds had been encouraged by these ornithologists. When we went to Fair Isle in 1948 its contribution to the British avifauna stood at ten species plus a number of geographical races or subspecies—that is to say, birds belonging to a distant population which is demonstrably different in size or coloration from the one which breeds in or close to our own area. Most of these newcomers have been seen elsewhere in Britain or Ireland since, but Fair Isle had the first of the few—including red-rumped swallows from south-east Europe in 1906, a thrush-nightingale and a pine bunting in 1911, the Pechora pipit (first detected by an islander, Jerome Wilson) in 1925, and a pallid harrier (shot by another islander, George Stout of Field) in 1931. There were also four asiatic warblers—lanceolated in 1908, Blyth's reed in 1910, paddyfield in 1925, and booted in 1936.

We did not add to this impressive list until 5th October 1953, when our hostel manservant, Willie Eunson, saw a small bird which he took to be one of the local rock pipits feeding in the approach to the Observatory Trap. He promptly caught it, and I must confess that when I peeped into the bag that contained it I thought the world had gone mad! It was not in the least like any bird I had seen before. I can best describe it as a dwarf thrush no bigger than a skylark, with a uniformly olive-brown back and tail, and heavily spotted whitish under parts suffused with buff on the throat. It proved to be a young gray-cheeked thrush, a North American species found only once before in Europe. We thought it must have crossed the Atlantic some days before, since its weight did not seem unduly low, suggesting that it had had time to make good some of the loss it must have sustained during its arduous flight; however, more recent information on the autumn weight of this species indicates that at 22 gm. our bird may have been newly arrived. It came in excellent company, for at this time no fewer than three yellow-billed cuckoos crossed the Atlantic to Scotland, and a black-billed cuckoo was found dead on the island of Foula 45 miles to the north of us a week later. Peter Davis caught a second gray-cheeked thrush at the isle on 29th October 1958, and a third was found dead on Bardsey off the Lleyn Peninsula on 10th October 1961.

The autumn of 1954 brought more new members for the 'club'. This time they were Siberian birds—two young citrine wagtails* and a female Baikal teal. Since the duck is sometimes kept in captivity there was a suspicion that it might have escaped from a collection of ornamental waterfowl; it is a rarity in such collections, however, and is treated as an accidental visitor in the wild state to a number of European countries between Italy and Iceland. Its appearance at Fair Isle coincided not only with the citrine wagtails but also with yellow-

---

* Formerly called yellow-headed wagtail, *Motacilla citreola*.

browed warblers and other rare eastern birds. Moreover, a male Siberian thrush (also new to Britain) was trapped on the Isle of May in the Firth of Forth—and it may well be doubted that any asiatic newcomer to Britain will ever arrive with better credentials than this Baikal teal.

The next on the list was a Hudsonian whimbrel which we found accompanying passage-migrant European whimbrels on the short-cropped grassland below Malcolm's Head at the end of May 1955. This bird replaces our own whimbrel on the barrenlands of the Canadian arctic, and so is regarded as a geographical race; and although one has been seen in Ireland since, this Fair Isle bird had only a single predecessor in Europe, shot by Lord Lilford in Spain in May 1872. We spent a good deal of time stalking it and comparing it with its familiar companions, and this involved a lot of wriggling and squirming over the damp and rocky ground (to say nothing of hide-and-seek behind dykes and plantacrubs), which doubtless amused those Fair Isle folk who unashamedly admit that they enjoy watching the bird-watchers enjoy watching the birds. When it fed alongside the other whimbrels there was little enough to distinguish the new bird at a glance, except that it was slightly smaller and more slenderly built, while the breast exhibited a beautiful pearly mottling quite unlike the brown striations on the other birds. It had the long down-curved bill of the curlew kind and the blackish head-bands which serve to differentiate the whimbrels from their larger relatives the curlews; but in flight the difference was striking, for whereas the European bird has a large expanse of white on the lower back, the Hudsonian's rump is as brown as the rest of its upper parts. We were unable to detect the slightest suggestion of a yankee accent in the whinnying call-note which was common to both birds.

§

That autumn we notched another interesting newcomer, this time from the Far East, and one that had not been recognised in Europe before. We were looking for birds among the root-crops on the morning of 6th October when a big reddish-brown warbler showed itself for a few seconds and was gone. It was flushed again, only to dive into cover, and the next time it deserted the turnip-rig for a bed of hogweed on the banks of a nearby burn. We left it there while we held a council of war. The bird was such an inveterate skulker that there seemed little chance of getting critical views of it, and trapping (since shooting plays no part in modern bird observatory work) seemed to afford the only surety of a satisfactory identification. We draped a net over the hogweed and closed one end of this rough and ready trap with a portable aluminium catching-box which was kept handy at the Haa for such occasions. With this apparatus we had caught the second of the citrine wagtails of the previous year, to say nothing of many other desirable rarities. The bird was urged gently forwards, threading its way dexterously through the reedy grass and other cover along the burn, and a moment or two later it was fluttering in the catching-box.

We made no attempt to examine the bird in the field, lest we should lose it irretrievably, but took it in a carrying-bag to the observatory. There a brief examination convinced us that no such creature figured on the European list. It had a superficial resemblance to a great reed-warbler, a bird nearly as big as a thrush, in its warm olive-brown head and mantle and rusty rump and tail; but there was no eyestripe, and it also differed in its short, arched bill and strongly rounded wings and tail. With the aid of Hartert's and Dresser's works on palearctic birds we identified it as the thick-billed warbler *Acrocephalus aedon*, an inhabitant of southern Siberia and northern China which has its winter quarters in India, Burma and Thailand. It is a bird of marshy places, haunting bushes and low trees close to water, and is said to be extremely shy, hiding in the dense herbage at the least sign of danger—a trait which in the present instance proved its undoing! It is very remarkable that a bird with so distant a range should stray so far to the west as the very edge of maritime Europe—yet it is by no means the first to have done so, and experience tells us it will not be the last.

Another American wader was found at the end of May 1956 —a small one, looking not unlike a sanderling in change to summer dress. It kept company with a flock of turnstones and dunlins on the high tide wrack at South Harbour. We watched this charming bird for a long time before we were given a clue to its identity. There are two American 'peeps' which have partially webbed toes, the semi-palmated and western sandpipers, and when this bird stood for a few seconds on top of a sea-smoothed boulder we saw it must be one or the other. But which one? The books at our disposal were not very helpful regarding these closely similar species, and it was obvious that here was another problem which would remain unsolved unless we could trap the bird for a more complete examination. We put a mist-net over the wrack and rushed upon the little flock of waders when they were feeding near—and the American was the only one to get caught! After looking at it long and earnestly in the lab we named it a semi-palmated—wrongly, as it turned out, for subsequent research on the characters of the two species leaves no doubt that the Fair Isle bird was a somewhat atypical western sandpiper *Calidris mauri*, whose home is in Alaska.

§

Our final autumn at Fair Isle produced what was undoubtedly the handsomest of these newcomers, though in this case (as with the Hudsonian whimbrel) it was a well-defined subspecies of a fairly common European bird. Hervør and I came across it when working through a turnip field in the hope of catching some warblers in one of the almost invisible nylon mist-nets which we had strung between bamboo poles at the far end. The 'drive' was still-born when we were barely half-way down the field, for sitting on one of the poles was a fairly large pale bird—and when we brought our binoculars to bear we could see it was some sort of shrike. It was extraordinarily tame, and superficially like the great grey shrikes which came in October, though several features of its plumage were not quite right. It was too pale a grey, the breast had a lovely vinous-buff suffusion, and there was too much white in the wings. It had a beautiful head, with a broad black patch behind the eye ending squarely on the ear-coverts, contrasting with a narrow white line above and white cheeks below. The bill was interesting—even at twenty or thirty yards it appeared to be pale brown or even flesh-coloured, whereas in the great grey shrike it is black.

This was a tantalising bird—so very desirable, so very close to the net, and yet so astute in avoiding capture. No matter how we tried to outwit the creature during its frequent sallies into the crop after insects it would choose its next perch with meticulous care, always on one or other of the poles or the guy-lines supporting them. Eventually it went on a long and deeply undulating flight to the neighbourhood of the Haa, and as there is a Heligoland trap in the garden our hopes rose. By this time, in response to vigorous and urgent hand-waving, two other bird-watchers had joined us, and as we walked together to the Haa I thought hard about shrikes in general (they are a very confusing assemblage) and felt that this one must belong to the race *Lanius excubitor pallidirostris*, one of the eastern desert forms of the great grey. This thought merely emphasised the need to catch it and make a full examination, but at the first try it flew high over the wire netting roof and alighted on a stone dyke on the blind side. Following up, we all watched it for a few minutes and I scribbled down such field-notes as had already impressed themselves on my mind, or were obvious now that we could study the bird at close range—a very proper procedure, for if we should be denied the bird a detailed description was the next best thing. We then returned to the hunt, and fortune favoured us. The shrike passed in front of the trap at the precise moment that a flock of starlings, rising from the garden, took an instant dislike to it and hustled it under the netting.

A happy cavalcade of cyclists, one bearing a precious white bag (which he handled as though it contained all the riches of the orient), was soon on its way north to the observatory. At the end of a stimulating half-hour with the bird and the books we found that the authorities agreed with our diagnosis of *pallidirostris*, though they seemed unable to make up their minds about its English name, calling it variously Grimm's shrike, Bogdanow's shrike and the steppe shrike (which shows how important it is to settle for a scientific name!). There was one previous record for western Europe, of a bird shot on the

Norwegian isle of Utsira in September 1953. It is an inhabitant of the arid regions that lie beyond the Caspian Sea, and to us a bird every whit as romantic as the fabulous cities of Bokhara and Samarkand whose minarets it may well have seen.

My last experience of a novelty of this kind was in May 1959, when revisiting Fair Isle as a member of the National Trust for Scotland's 'Islands Cruise' with M.S. *Meteor*. An American song-sparrow, found and captured among the war-time wreckage on Ward Hill nine days before, had lived since its release along the low cliff of South Haven behind the Bird Observatory. It had, in a manner of speaking, raised the Stars and Stripes, for it defended this territory each day with jingles of pleasant song, which an enterprising ornithologist staying at the hostel had committed to tape as a permanent and highly satisfactory record of its occurrence. Cruising with us were several visitors from the United States—and here they were at the cliff-edge, with the warden Peter Davis as mentor, brandishing their binoculars and chatting animatedly as they jostled each other to get a better view of a little streaked bird they had all seen *ad nauseum* in their 'yards' at home! Needless to say, they were jostled just as hard by their Scottish and English friends, for it is not every day, even at fabulous Fair Isle, that one has the opportunity of watching and hearing a new European bird.

§

What is it that brings birds from more than half the world away to this small island where the North Sea and the Atlantic Ocean meet—or, for that matter, to any other part of the British Isles? Ornithologists have tried hard to answer this question satisfactorily. The geographical separation of the homelands of the two extremes, the western sandpiper in Alaska and the thick-billed warbler in Manchuria, is of the staggering order of 11,000 miles. Since 1947 over thirty new birds have been added to the British list, bringing the number of species reliably reported in these islands to more than 450. Ten of these newcomers were from European and asiatic countries, while the remaining two-thirds crossed the Atlantic from America. The most startling of these was a sea-bird called the magnificent frigate-bird, found dying at Tiree in the Inner Hebrides on 10th July 1953—and in case you are thinking, "Hurrah, here's one that had nothing to do with Fair Isle!", I hasten to add that it was identified by the local bank-manager, who happens to be a Fair Isle Wilson! The best year was 1954 with no fewer than eight new birds, including five Americans and the three Siberian species mentioned above. In more recent years the additions have been almost exclusively from the New World—summer tanager, rose-breasted grosbeak, northern waterthrush, Baltimore oriole, purple gallinule, song and fox sparrows, slate-coloured junco, eastern yellow warbler. A most impressive array, and one wonders how long it can go on.

Now quite obviously, vagrants like the thick-billed warbler, Siberian thrush and steppe shrike (to say nothing of the Americans) are hopelessly lost. Their homes are thousands of miles away, and it is hardly likely that they ever return. There are other rarities which, though nesting much closer to Britain, have in common with these distant wanderers a migration route which ought to take them south-east across Eurasia in the opposite direction to Fair Isle. The first thing to ask, then, is whether those vagrants that come this way are in fact true migrants.

A little is known about the navigational abilities of birds; carefully controlled experiments with captive migrants have shown that those species which usually migrate by day are able to 'fix' their positions by observation of the sun's movement in the sky, while nocturnal migrants apparently use the stellar pattern for their path-finding. This seems very remarkable, but experiments by Sauer with captive warblers in specially designed cages under the artificial sky of a planetarium leave little doubt that the star-picture is fundamental to avian orientation; for when the apparent position of the bird on the earth's surface was changed by shifting the planetarium dome, the bird directed its movements in such a way as to compensate for its 'displacement'. We must assume that when the sun or stars cannot be seen, owing to fog or frontal rain and drizzle, birds have great difficulty in determining their routes; and

A nonconformist Puffin: they are said to carry their sand-eels
arranged alternately head to tail—but not this one.

An apprehensive Oystercatcher sits on her crazy-paved nest.

Docility: an Arctic Skua chick is ringed and examined.

Truculence: a young Fulmar prepares to spit oil at the photographer.

indeed Sauer failed to get any response from his subjects when he blacked out the planetarium stars.

It seems highly probable from the enormous mass of data collected in recent years by the bird observatories that many birds then fly with the wind. This theory of down-wind drift, first developed at Fair Isle, has been much criticised, but it is difficult to see what other phenomenon could account for the frequent occurrence of North American birds in this country, while it is equally obvious that only a down-wind movement could bring south European species such as the melodious and Bonelli's warblers into the Irish Sea basin when they should, in theory, be going to Africa. For a land-bird blown out to sea an active down-wind flight would be the best guarantee of survival, for by adding wind-speed to its own flight-speed it would cover the greatest distance in the shortest time and would have a better chance of reaching land before its energy-giving resources ran out. This is the essence of cyclonic approach from Greenland and Iceland (chapters XIII and XIV). Such behaviour would save the lives of many American birds: on the other hand, it is difficult to believe that these could remain alive for the much longer period, of days not hours, which would be necessary if they were merely carried passively by the wind (which has been suggested as a more likely alternative), since this would involve a highly complex and circuitous route.

So far as land-birds flying over the land are concerned, it might be thought that they have every opportunity to alight and stay 'off-passage' until conditions improve; they could then correct for displacement, and continue on their way. If they were true migrants they would be best able to do this in col and anticyclonic weather; and as the bulk of the rare vagrants arriving in this country from the east do so in precisely this kind of weather, we must assume that they are not migrating birds at all. In a recent paper I have suggested that young birds are affected to a much greater extent than adults, and that they are aimless wanderers caught up in the anticyclonic airstreams which blow westwards across Eurasia in the late summer, at a time when the season's young are engaged in dispersion. They have a wander-lust, invaluable in that it prevents overcrowding on the breeding grounds when the

FIB Q

population is at its peak and the food-supply already in decline; invaluable too in enabling the species to pioneer new territory on or beyond the periphery of its range, with a view to taking advantage of climatic or land-use changes which may favour its spread.

With many species it is impossible to separate the year's young from their parents on plumage or structural characters, and with others it is difficult because the age-marks are obscure. Only in a few cases is segregation easy, and in this category are two of the most frequent of our extra-limital vagrants. They are the barred warbler and red-breasted flycatcher, both of which have a migration route to the south-east across Europe, directly away from Fair Isle, since their nearest nesting grounds are in Denmark, southern Sweden and Germany. Yet the barred warbler is an annual visitor to the Shetland area in August and September, and I have seen it as far north as the Faeroe Islands and as far west as St Kilda. The many that I have watched and trapped were all young birds, as are all the British-taken specimens I have seen in museum collections, and I know of no satisfactory record of an adult in Britain at this season. There have been occasional records of adult red-breasted flycatchers, and also of melodious warblers which have flown north out of France to the bird observatories fringing the English Channel and Irish Sea, but the great majority of the records refer to young. The annual visitation of scarlet grosbeaks from Fenno-Scandia and yellow-browed warblers from Siberia (to mention only two of the more regular rarities for which Fair Isle is famed) may well comprise birds of the year, but unfortunately there are no plumage distinctions by which this can be shown.

Later, when the pioneers have performed this function of dispersal, they must develop some sort of navigational faculty which will enable them to move to winter quarters. We can make an 'inspired guess' at the nature of this faculty, from the results of experiments carried out by Dr A. C. Perdeck of Vogeltrekstation Texel in Holland. He captured thousands of migrating starlings during their autumn journey from eastern Europe to England, ringed them, and subjected them to an artificial displacement by sending them, by 'plane, to Switzerland. The scatter of recoveries following their release was most interesting: the adults were found either in England or in France *en route* to their normal destination—clearly they have a 'goal orientation' and can correct for displacement during a migratory journey. Not so the young: they were found mostly in south-west France and Spain, indicating a 'one-directional orientation' along a route parallel to the one they had been pursuing when captured in Holland. In recent years there have been a number of recoveries to the south-east of birds ringed at Fair Isle and other British observatories (for example, the robins of 1951 mentioned on pp. 222-3, and the redwings discussed on pp. 205-9), and it looks as though these might represent the later 'one-directional orientation' of young birds of an eastern population wind-drifted to our shores during dispersion flights.

Together with them, especially in 'invasion years' when one or a few species preponderate in the east coast falls, it seems likely there must also be a proportion of adults which, although unready for real migration at that stage, will later find their way to their true winter range successfully. If the wind-aided anticyclonic drift has carried them far beyond their home in a direction away from the wintering-grounds, it seems unlikely that the 'one-directional' young can eventually join them; and indeed, like Perdeck's starlings, these may open up an entirely new winter range for their group. Some of Perdeck's birds returned to the new winter territory in south-west France and Spain in later years when they were adult; so if the displaced pioneers are able to winter successfully, and backtrack without mishap in spring, the stage is set for an expansion of the total range. Winter survival, rather than the suitability of conditions in the new breeding area, may be the key to range expansion; and it may well be in the new winter quarters, or the journey there and back, that wastage sets a barrier to further expansion. Many of the eastern species which have spread into Europe during the present century have their winter home in India—and to the west of that great country, for many thousands of miles, is a vast expanse of desert and semi-desert country which takes heavy toll of migrants, and is inhospitable in the extreme as an off-season home.

The thought occurs that this situation contains material for an interesting, indeed exciting biological experiment. In some years more than a dozen yellow-browed warblers (to mention only one extralimital 'rarity') are reported by the British bird observatories. The few that are trapped are examined, ringed, and then committed to the unknown—with the faintest flicker of hope stirring in the ringer's breast that one day one such bird will provide a meaningful recovery. How much better it would be to impound this pioneer 'wastage' and attempt to over-winter such birds successfully under controlled aviary conditions at some convenient centre, with a view to releasing the survivors for field-study in a suitable habitat late the following spring. It is conceivable that we might soon be the richer for a delightful new breeding species; and even if we were not, the potential gain to knowledge of dispersion and its aftermath would make such an experiment well worth the small effort and expense that its organisation and execution would entail.

§

Let us turn now to the other side of the world. The Atlantic Ocean is more than 3,000 miles wide, and for a long time ornithologists steadfastly refused to believe that small American birds could get across it unaided. They said that such of these Americans as were not escaped cage-birds must have had 'assisted passage'—not on the winds, but in ships. Bigger birds, such as American gulls, ducks and waders, constituted less of a problem, as it was thought that when tired they could rest on the sea for a while before flying on. (Actually, as observations at ocean weather-ships have shown, waders cannot do this: they very quickly become water-logged and drown.) If Continental birds from near Europe and farther Asia, and almost any point between, are borne to us by the winds, then it is equally feasible that the same is true of the New World waifs and strays, though the nature of their journey is somewhat different. This could be true not only of small passerines and cuckoos, but also of bigger birds like the lesser yellow-legs and pectoral sandpiper, which bird-watchers in Britain now find almost every autumn on lake-shores, estuaries, reservoirs and sewage-farms. Well over 150 pectoral sandpipers have been identified in the British Isles, and a few other American waders such as the killdeer plover, white-rumped and buff-breasted sandpipers, have been seen on more than a score of occasions. The Hudsonian whimbrel and western sandpiper are two of five species which have turned up at Fair Isle.

If such a marathon trek were to be made non-stop from one side of the Atlantic to the other the birds would have to move very fast to finish the course before their strength gave out, or they would either perish in the sea (as indeed thousands must every year), or arrive too exhausted to survive. What we have learned at the bird observatories about the rate of weight-loss in migrants makes it seem highly improbable that these Atlantic travellers can, *in the main*, turn 'assisted passage' to their advantage. Even if they found the right kind of food aboard a ship, their food intake would hardly be sufficient to compensate for the rapid depletion of their fat reserves. There are a number of well-attested cases of birds crossing the Atlantic, or part of it, on ships, and flying ashore off the coast of Ireland or in the English Channel; but if the majority use this means, then why is it that nearly all this avian traffic goes one way—and, moreover, has its terminus in Britain and Ireland rather than in France, Portugal and Spain? Just as many liners and tramps sail from Europe to America as in the opposite direction, but European birds are very, very scarce in Canada and the United States. The suggestion that the thrushes, warblers and finches are escaped cage-birds does not hold water either, unless one assumes that cage-doors are carelessly left open only at the migration seasons; besides, the American laws forbid the exportation of wild birds, and very few are offered for sale in Europe.

It is well-known that North Atlantic weather is dominated by a storm-track where the gales which buffet our western sea-board originate. These winds are strong and sometimes span the greater part of the ocean for days on end, and if a bird were to be blown offshore when disoriented by bad weather on the American side, or merely when wandering on post-juvenile dispersion, then it could travel the west wind belt at an average speed of sixty or seventy knots and reach Britain or Ireland in something like fifty or sixty hours. Relatively few reach France, and still fewer the Iberian Peninsula, since these countries are further from the storm-track and usually lie outside a down-wind course. It is entirely feasible that such journeys could be undertaken by birds as small as the American wood-warblers (of which no fewer than nine species are known to have reached Europe), small thrushes like the gray-cheeked and olive-backed, and the yellow-billed cuckoo which has now occurred about a score of times—and the more fortunate ones would still have a sufficient energy-store remaining to stay alive. Several 'Americans' have been weighed on being trapped at British bird observatories, showing losses of up to 40 per cent from the normal body-weight, and one or two have been re-captured later showing good 'off-passage' gains.

During the last half-century an interesting climatic change has been taking place in the north-east Atlantic, the winter temperature in places like Spitsbergen, Iceland and south-west Greenland rising markedly. This can only mean that the depressions of the Atlantic storm-track are bigger and more boisterous than they were, since the higher mean temperatures are the result of their transporting large bodies of tropical air in their warm sectors to these northern regions. The greater activity of the depressions explains in part why more American birds are getting across the ocean waste than before, and why two-thirds of the newcomers to our British avifauna since the war have come from this source. We must also be careful to bear in mind, of course, that there are many more bird-watchers than there were, and that the standard of field identification of rare birds is higher than it has ever been; but if the greater incidence of American waders and other birds were due to this alone, then we might expect there to be an equal increase in the recording of rare eastern birds. And this does not seem to have changed, at Fair Isle at any rate, since Eagle Clarke's time.

Bird-watching in Britain is at an exciting phase: nobody can say how long this climatic amelioration will continue; if it is reversed, then we may already have had the best of the American rarities, but if it continues then we can look forward confidently to an unfailing supply of New World birds at our bird observatories, reservoirs, estuaries and sewage-farms for several years to come. Either way, it will give migration studies added spice.

Part III

A LIST OF THE BIRDS OF FAIR ISLE

A LIST OF THE BIRDS OF FAIR ISLE

Peter Davis

The first comprehensive list of the birds of Fair Isle was published by William Eagle Clarke, as Chapter 21 of his celebrated book *Studies in Bird Migration*, in 1912. To mark the fiftieth anniversary of this publication, I started in 1962 to compile a new list of the island's birds, and this was printed in four instalments in the Fair Isle Bird Observatory Bulletin during 1963 and 1964. The work has now been fully revised, and includes all available records up to the end of 1964.

The history of ornithological observations on the island begins with Eagle Clarke's first visit in the autumn of 1905. Having discovered the 'British Heligoland', as he called it, he became a frequent visitor until the outbreak of the first world war, and returned for a last stay in 1921. He encouraged and equipped the first of the remarkably skilled native observers and collectors, George Wilson Stout of Busta, who left the island in 1909. From this year the official watcher was Jerome Wilson of Springfield, who continued to report regularly on the birds of the island until the early 1930's, and intermittently until his death in 1948. He was the chief contributor of Fair Isle records to the long series of annual 'Reports on Scottish Ornithology' compiled by the Misses Baxter and Rintoul from 1909 onwards. The activities of those who followed Clarke and Wilson in maintaining observations on the island are mentioned in Kenneth Williamson's introduction to this book.

Apart from the Fair Isle chapters in *Studies in Bird Migration* and in the Duchess of Bedford's *A Bird-Watcher's Diary* (edited by A. B. Duncan and printed in 1938), nearly all the Fair Isle bird-records published before 1948 appeared in the *Annals of Scottish Natural History* and its successor *The Scottish Naturalist*. Kenneth Williamson abstracted these records, adding a number from MS. sources, and compiled a 'status-book' for the years up to 1948. A few other old records have since come to light, but the 'status-book' is probably a fairly complete compilation of the written records before the observatory's time. Inevitably it contains a number of reports of rarities and sub-rarities which are unverifiable because no description of the birds was ever made. At the risk of treading on one or two surviving toes, I have omitted or 'square-bracketed' many of these, including some which were given general acceptance at the time.

The even greater mass of anecdotal records, never written down, or only recounted in the vaguest terms some time after the event, must also be largely ignored. It has frequently happened, that in discussing a 'first for Fair Isle' or some other very unusual record with the islanders, we have been told that there have been several such occurrences many years ago. We can only regret that no one had the time or inclination to take note of them; though in fairness it may be added that this failure was often due to the 'What's missed is mystery' attitude inculcated by many visiting ornithologists until quite recent times.

The seventeen seasons of regular observation since 1948 have given a reasonably clear picture of the status of most regular and near-regular species, and the general statements in the list are based chiefly on these observatory records. It should be noted, however, that the series of regular observations between November and April is still too limited; regular watching in these months has only been done since 1957, and until now there has usually been a break in recording from at least mid-December to late January. The status of many species in winter is therefore known only from scattered observations over a long period of time.

SYSTEMATIC LIST

BLACK-THROATED DIVER *Gavia arctica*. One seen on 15th and 20th November 1963. There is also an earlier undated record for about 1930, but no details are known.

GREAT NORTHERN DIVER *Gavia immer*. Scarce but regular on autumn passage, in very small numbers (no record of more than five on one day). Mainly October-November, but occasionally as early as August (3rd, 1953; 18th, 1960). Once December, once January, once March. Recorded in most years between 1949 and 1956 in May or June, and once early July (3rd, 1950), but no spring records since 1956 and only one before 1949 (15th May 1924).

WHITE-BILLED DIVER *Gavia adamsii*. An adult in full summer dress on 14th May 1961.

RED-THROATED DIVER *Gavia stellata*. Regular passage-migrant in very small numbers. A slight predominance of records in May and June, but almost as many in July, August, and September; very few April and October-November. Extreme dates recorded are 19th March (1963) and 25th November (1962). Once February (25th, 1952).

GREAT CRESTED GREBE *Podiceps cristatus*. 'Two or three' are said to have been seen in May 1940. One was observed in North Haven on 13th-16th February 1958, and found dead on the beach on 23rd.

RED-NECKED GREBE *Podiceps griseigena*. Seven records, all of single birds: 9th February 1915 (obtained), 8th-11th February 1922, 26th October to 1st November 1926, 13th February 1929, 10th February 1937 (found dead), 16th September 1956, and 16th September 1963.

SLAVONIAN GREBE *Podiceps auritus*. Seen most years on autumn passage (15th August to 7th December, mostly October), and occasionally in spring (13th February to 10th May, mostly March and April). Usually single birds, and no record of more than three on one day.

LITTLE GREBE *Podiceps ruficollis*. Clarke (1912) gives several October records between 12th and 27th; one 9th December; also one spring occurrence, 9th May 1908. The only dated records since then are for 8th October 1925, 23rd March 1954, 16th-24th September 1960, and 26th August 1964, though the species is said to have been seen on a number of occasions 'in the winter'.

[BLACK-BROWED ALBATROSS *Diomedea melanophrys*. An albatross believed to be of this species was present for much of the day on 14th May 1949.]

LEACH'S PETREL *Oceanodroma leucorrhoa*. One or two occasionally seen on the crossing in September, usually nearer to Sumburgh than to Fair Isle but rarely on the Fair Isle side. No records on or from the island, until one was heard at night on 17th July 1964.

STORM PETREL *Hydrobates pelagicus*. Small numbers often seen on the crossing, May to October. Bred regularly on Ward Hill, at Dutfield, in the Kirn of Skroo, and elsewhere up to 1943. No certain breeding-records 1944-61 but probably continued to nest in inaccessible places. A nest found at Buness, and a broken egg at North Haven, in 1962. Birds have been seen on or near the island between 8th May and 10th November, but many of these were probably non-breeding visitors. Birds ringed on the island have been recovered within a few days at Mousa and Foula (Shetland), and two from Foula have been caught in later years at Fair Isle. Breeding-season data are very few, but suggest egg-laying from about 20th June to end July or early August, considerably later than in Wales.

MANX SHEARWATER *Procellaria puffinus*. Occasionally seen from the island and on the crossing, in very small numbers; extreme dates, 8th April and 26th October. Never proved to breed, though at least two records of single birds calling over the isle at night, in recent years. Local name (obsolete) 'Lingy-bird'.

GREAT SHEARWATER *Procellaria gravis*. Single birds seen off-shore by L. S. V. Venables on 14th and 21st September and 8th October 1936.

SOOTY SHEARWATER *Procellaria grisea*. Single birds, and rarely up to four, seen from the island and on the crossing in most autumns. Extreme dates, 9th August and 13th November; mostly late August and first three weeks September.

[BULWER'S PETREL *Bulweria bulwerii*. A large all-black petrel seen by James A. Stout on the crossing, 18th January 1952, was probably of this species.]

FULMAR *Fulmarus glacialis*. In the nineteenth century, only seen at off-shore fishing-grounds. Present around cliffs in 1902, and breeding first recorded 1903 (about a dozen pairs in N.W. cliffs, and probably some Sheep Craig), 'increased tremendously' by 1912 (Clarke). The increase has apparently continued to the present time. Counts and estimates gave c. 3,000 occupied sites in 1949 and c. 5,000 in 1959. In the early years of breeding the birds deserted the cliffs by mid-September and did not return until December or January, but by the early fifties they were absent only a month or six weeks in September-October; now they are seldom absent for more than ten days in late September, and in some years the cliffs are never completely deserted except in severe gales. Eggs are laid from about 10th May, and last chicks leave cliffs about mid-September (late date, 27th, 1958). Blue-phase birds are common offshore in winter, and are seen occasionally in summer; have bred on several occasions. Birds ringed on the island have been recovered as far away as the Murmansk coast, Faeroes, Newfoundland, and North Spain. Local name, 'Maalie' or 'Maalimuck'.

GANNET *Sula bassana*. Seen offshore in all months, generally common April to June, abundant July to October, and in only small numbers November to March. Flightless juveniles, presumably from the Shetland colonies, sometimes come ashore in rough weather in August-September. Local name, 'Solan'.

CORMORANT *Phalacrocorax carbo*. Regular on spring and autumn passage in very variable numbers, but on peak days rarely more than twenty in spring or forty in autumn. Mainly April-May and late August to mid-October, but recorded in all months. Visits the island fairly frequently in most winters, and often stays for some days or even weeks, but doubtful if any individuals spend the whole winter around the island. Comparatively few June records, and rare in July. A 1962 chick from Gairsay, Orkney, was found at Fair Isle in April 1963.

SHAG *Phalacrocorax aristotelis*. An abundant breeding-bird. Clarke described it as a 'very abundant resident' in 1912; a census in 1959 gave c. 1,200 nests. Less numerous in winter (October to March). Passage seen offshore in most months, but especially September. Recoveries of birds ringed as young on the island show dispersal mainly to Shetland, Orkney, and northern Scotland, but some have reached Norway, Germany, Holland, S.E. and S.W. England, and N. France. Local name, 'Skarf'.

HERON *Ardea cinerea*. Regular on spring passage, mainly March to early May, occasionally late May or early June. More frequent during post-breeding dispersal, late June or July to October, the largest arrivals (up to c. 30 at peak) being normally in late August or September. One or two birds have over-wintered successfully in recent years, and a few also visit the island casually in all winter months. Local name (obsolete), 'Hegri'.

LITTLE BITTERN *Ixobrychus minutus*. A female obtained by L. Anderson on 10th April 1940, and two or three others reported seen in the early summer of the same year.

WHITE STORK *Ciconia ciconia*. One seen 4th-6th April 1930.

MALLARD *Anas platyrhynchos*. Regular passage-migrant in small numbers, mainly March-May and August-November, rarely exceeding 20 at peak but up to fifty recorded. Frequent visitor during the winter months, and some have over-wintered, but this is usually prevented by shooting. Occasional visitor in June and July.

TEAL *Anas crecca*. Regular passage-migrant in spring and autumn. Spring records from 'first week March' to 16th June; mainly late April and May; the numbers have rarely attained double figures. Autumn records 26th July to early December, mostly late August to early October; often more than ten but rarely more than twenty on peak-days. A few records in late December and January, but none February; and none at midsummer. One ringed September 1962 was recovered in Jutland, Denmark in September 1964.

GARGANEY *Anas querquedula*. Two shot in the spring of 1935, a male and a female seen 24th May 1964.

BAIKAL TEAL *Anas formosa*. A female present from 29th September to 7th October 1954. The B.O.U. List Sub-Committee considered that it might have been an escape, despite the fact that it coincided with several other Siberian vagrants.

GADWALL *Anas strepera*. Six spring records in 1912, 1927, 1937, 1950, 1961, and 1962; five of these were between 19th April and 14th May, the other on 18th June. Two birds were present on three of these occasions. Three autumn records, 11th October 1911, 6th-7th and 19th September 1961.

WIGEON *Anas penelope*. Regular passage migrant. Very small numbers in spring (late March to late May, occasionally early June), more frequent and numerous in autumn (mid-August to early December, mainly mid-September to mid-November), when often up to twenty and sometimes forty or more on peak-days. Occasional visitor in winter, though few records in February. No records between mid-June and mid-August until recent years, but one 1st-2nd July 1958, four different birds July 1960, and one 24th June 1962.

PINTAIL *Anas acuta*. Scarce and irregular in spring (30th March to 6th June, mainly late April and May). Two July records (3rd, 1950 and 22nd, 1959). One or two occur most years in autumn, 9th August to 24th November; once as many as seven. No winter records.

SHOVELER *Spatula clypeata*. Only one record before 1948, on 18th August 1923. Since 1948, one or two recorded six times in spring (6th April to 8th June), and on eleven occasions in autumn (29th July to 27th September). One 18th January 1952 (J. A. Stout).

SCAUP *Aythya marila*. A few spring records (22nd February to 31st May), but only three in the past sixteen years. Recorded almost every year on autumn passage, though rarely more than one or two; extreme dates 28th July to 3rd December, but great majority October and early November.

TUFTED DUCK *Aythya fuligula*. Very small numbers in most years on spring and autumn passage; up to four seen on peak-days in spring, up to five in autumn. Spring dates: 24th March to 12th June (mostly May). Autumn records: 23rd July to 28th November, mostly late September and early October. One midsummer record, two birds on 1st-2nd July 1953, and one in winter, 7th February 1963.

POCHARD *Aythya ferina.* Two spring records, 25th March 1914 (two), and 10th-11th April 1944. Two at midsummer, 8th-9th July 1912, and 6th July 1955. Ten in autumn, between 10th August and 23rd November, mostly October; four of these are in the past fifteen years. One winter record, 20th December 1911.

GOLDENEYE *Bucephala clangula.* One or two seen most recent years in early spring, and will probably prove fairly regular; seen mostly late March to mid-April (late date, 25th May). Regular passage-migrant in autumn, recorded from 26th August onwards, the great majority in October and November. Few winter records before 1962, but one or two present all winter in 1962-63 and 1963-64. Numbers rarely exceed five, but up to seventeen on record.

LONG-TAILED DUCK *Clangula hyemalis.* Regular spring and autumn passage-migrant, and occasional visitor during the winter; in very variable numbers. In spring rarely more than one or two present; most records in April-May but seen to 11th June. Recorded in autumn from 12th September, but mostly October-November; seldom more than ten to fifteen on peak-days, but up to thirty-eight observed. Four midsummer records, 28th June 1911, 4th July onwards, 1924, 9th July 1943, and 4th to 18th July 1956. Local name, 'Calloo'.

VELVET SCOTER *Melanitta fusca.* About eleven spring records (seven or eight since 1949), between 21st March and 15th June. Annual in autumn, usually one or two individuals, but up to five recorded. Extreme dates are 12th July and 8th December, but most are in September-October. One winter record, 28th-29th January 1952.

[SURF SCOTER *Melanitta perspicillata.* Three sight-records, and one 'washed ashore': in 'winter' 1934, February and November 1936, and December 1940; but no details were recorded.]

COMMON SCOTER *Melanitta nigra.* Irregular in spring and autumn; seen in ten years since 1948. About twice as many records in spring as in autumn. The extreme dates are 13th March to 4th July (mostly late May and early June), and 4th September to 25th November. Most records are of single birds, but occasionally up to three, and once six present.

EIDER *Somateria mollissima.* A common breeding-bird on the coast and the hill-ground. A census on 3rd May 1963 gave 407 birds, and this was thought to be an unusually good year, previous estimates being around 300. There is however no evidence of any great change in this century. Remains numerous during the winter, though some may leave in the late autumn. No certain evidence of passage-movements. Local name, 'Dunter'.

KING EIDER *Somateria spectabilis.* An adult male seen by W. E. Clarke on 13th May 1910; a male obtained 11th November 1935; and one reported seen offshore on 31st March 1936.

RED-BREASTED MERGANSER *Mergus serrator.* A regular visitor, recorded in all months, though very few August records. Rather more frequent in April and May than in the other spring months, and autumn movements most pronounced from late September to early November. Rarely more than five seen at one time. A pair nested in 1934, probably on the Stack of North Haven, the female and young later seen off Buness.

GOOSANDER *Mergus merganser.* Four late-winter and spring records: one 18th February to 4th March 1929, one 11th-12th April 1950, one 5th-10th

June 1950, and one 3rd-4th June 1957. Six autumn records: one 20th-22nd September 1962 and the rest between 20th November and 10th December. Four of these late-autumn records are since 1959, and the species will probably prove to be more frequent than the available data suggest.

SMEW *Mergus albellus*. Four records: one obtained 21st January 1913, two seen about 20th January 1937, 'two or three' seen December 1941, and one 26th September 1961.

SHELDUCK *Tadorna tadorna*. A few seen most years (annually since 1952). Slightly more autumn than spring records. In spring recorded between 14th March and 16th June (mostly May); and in autumn between 15th July and 27th November (mostly August-September); also mid-winter records on 21st January and 2nd February 1937, and 15th February 1964. Most records are of single birds but occasionally up to four and once eight seen.

GREY-LAG GOOSE *Anser anser*. Usually the commonest goose at Fair Isle in recent years, though remarkably few records before 1948. Regular on autumn passage (30th August to early December, mainly late October and early November) in very variable numbers, often up to twenty on best days, but rarely up to 150 recorded. Occasional visitor between December and March, and occurs most years on spring migration (mainly late April and early May) in very small numbers. A few June records and one July (four 1st to 4th, 1951). One apparently of the Eastern form *A. a. rubrirostris* was present 19th-28th March 1963.

WHITE-FRONTED GOOSE *Anser albifrons*. Occurs in most autumns (15th September to 27th November, mostly October), usually in very small numbers, but up to fifty recorded. Three dated records in late December and January, and said to have occurred on several other occasions in winter. The only spring occurrences on record were in 1937 (four 6th-7th and two 10th May) and in 1961 (three 18th April, one 19th (shot), and three 24th). The Greenland form *A. a. flavirostris* apparently predominates, there being six determinations of this form (including one party of twelve) against only two of the typical form, in recent years.

BEAN GOOSE *Anser arvensis*. Three records: one obtained 10th January 1913, 'several' shot October-November 1936, and one present from 'early spring' 1950 until it was shot about 20th June.

PINK-FOOTED GOOSE *Anser brachyrhynchus*. Recorded almost every year on autumn passage (21st September to 11th December, mostly October), usually in small numbers but up to thirty-three noted. A few winter records, late December to early March. No dated spring records until 1955, but a few seen in all but two springs since then, 25th March to 11th June. One ringed near Annan, Dumfries, on 26th October 1954 was shot on the island on 17th May 1956.

BRENT GOOSE *Branta bernicla*. Apparently a frequent visitor in the first three decades of this century, with at least twenty-two dated records up to 1928. Half of these were in autumn (3rd September to 21st November), four were in winter (10th January to 12th February), and seven in spring (21st April to 15th May). The numbers recorded were usually less than five, but up to twenty-five (19th October 1914) and once forty (6th October 1922) noted. It is however by no means unlikely that some of these birds were actually Barnacle Geese, since there are very few records of that species before 1948, and some of the islanders still make no distinction between the two kinds of black geese. Since 1928 there have been only five records; three birds 30th September to 1st October 1949, one 27th May 1950, two 8th to 13th September 1955, one 3rd October 1960, and three 12th October 1963. The only ones racially assigned were the 1949, 1955, and 1963 birds, which were of the Pale-breasted form *B. b. hrota*.

BARNACLE GOOSE *Branta leucopsis*. Fairly regular on autumn passage (seen every autumn 1957-62), usually in very small numbers but up to eighteen recorded. One August record (18th, 1927), one in November (12th, 1962), and one December (7th, 1962), otherwise all between 17th September and 28th October. Three winter records: one on several dates between 8th January and 1st March 1909, one 9th February 1915, and one 12th March 1952. Three spring records: up to twenty-five present 25th April to 7th May 1953, one 19th April 1961 (shot), and two 24th April to 1st May 1961. Has apparently become much more frequent in recent years, as only the two old winter records and the August one date from before 1952 (but see remarks under Brent Goose). One shot on 12th November 1962 had been ringed in Vest-Spitsbergen as a flightless adult on 24th July 1962.

CANADA GOOSE *Branta canadensis*. Four on 6th June 1962, one of which was present until the 24th. These were heavy-looking and remarkably tame birds, which had probably wandered north from Britain. Another present 3rd-10th June 1964.

[MUTE SWAN *Cygnus olor*. George Stout believes he saw one about thirty years ago.]

WHOOPER SWAN *Cygnus cygnus*. Regular on spring and autumn passage, in very variable numbers; but in some years frequent in parties of up to ten and occasionally up to forty birds. Occasional visitor during the winter, particularly in hard weather; and a few have spent several weeks on the island at this season. The spring records are mainly end March to third week April, but several in late May and once June (10th, 1955). In autumn, one August record (3rd-6th, 1958), a good many in late September (from 12th), but mostly October and early November.

BEWICK'S SWAN *Cygnus columbianus bewicki*. Four old records: 18th November 1910 and 30th November 1911 (both shot); seven seen 12th January 1922; one shot 17th April 1925.

GOLDEN EAGLE *Aquila chrysaëtos*. An immature bird 7th-8th April 1961.

BUZZARD *Buteo buteo*. Not recorded before 1949, but at least one in most years since then. Recorded once in April (15th-17th, 1961), five times in late May (from 19th), seven times in June, twice in July, three times in August (one of which stayed until October), six times in September, twice in October, and once November (7th, 1959).

ROUGH-LEGGED BUZZARD *Buteo lagopus*. Three spring records, 18th April 1956, 26th-27th May 1952, and 29th May 1963. Occasional autumn records, the only dated ones being in 1925, 1926 (three or four birds), 1936, 1953, 1959 (two), 1960 (two) and 1963. Apart from one on 29th August (1936) and one 12th-14th September (1925), all are between 13th October and 16th November. There were mid-winter records 20th-22nd January and 4th-6th February 1937.

SPARROWHAWK *Accipiter nisus*. Apparently rare in the early years of this century, and not recorded at all until 1913, and subsequently only in 1921 and 1927. In the Bird Observatory's time it has proved to be regular on both passages, though in very small numbers (no more than three recorded on one day). The spring records fall between 3rd April and

27th May, mostly late April and early May; the autumn birds between 2nd August and 3rd December, mainly mid-September to mid-October. There were winter records on 18th January and 8th to 17th February 1952, 8th December 1952 to 13th January 1953, 7th March 1963, and 6th March 1964. Birds ringed on autumn passage have been recovered in the same autumn and winter in N.E. Scotland (three, December-January), in Holland (November), and in western France (two, October and December); in the next April on Heligoland, and in the next August in Lincolnshire. One ringed on the Isle of May, September 1957, was caught at Fair Isle in the following May.

GOSHAWK *Accipiter gentilis*. A bird very probably of this species was seen by James Wilson and James A. Stout on 16th November 1953 and in early January 1954. One was present 16th to 24th November 1962.

WHITE-TAILED EAGLE *Haliaëtus albicilla*. Bred on the island until sometime between 1825 and 1840; the eyrie being on the Sheep Craig, with perhaps an alternative site in the high N.W. cliffs (a prominent knoll south of Ward Hill is called 'Erne's Brae'). Only two dated records are recorded for this century, adults on 18th September 1935 and 19th June 1949, but birds are said to have been seen on a number of other occasions. Unidentified 'eagles' were reported on 8th-9th April 1927, 7th April 1944, and first week August 1944.

HONEY BUZZARD *Pernis apivorus*. One seen 20th September 1961. (Originally recorded as a 'probable', but the description was later examined and approved by the Rarity Records Committee.) One seen 1st-2nd June 1964.

[MARSH HARRIER *Circus aeruginosus*. An undocumented sight-record for 'spring', 1932.]

HEN HARRIER *Circus cyaneus*. No definite records before 1950, though 'ring-tails' probably of this species (which breeds, now commonly, in Orkney) occurred in November 1931, autumn 1932, and in May 1936. Since 1950 the species has been identified on fourteen occasions in eleven different years, and there have been 'ring-tails' on ten other occasions since 1948. Five of the definite records were in spring, between 6th April and 5th June; the six spring 'ring-tails' were all in May. Of nine identified in autumn, one was on 24th-25th August 1956, the rest between 20th September and 21st December; the autumn 'ring-tails' occurred between 20th September and 31st October.

PALLID HARRIER *Circus macrourus*. An immature male obtained by G. Stout on 8th May 1931, after being present for some days (first British record). An adult male said to have been seen for a week from 6th May 1942. A female either of this species or Montagu's seen 20th October 1949.

[MONTAGU'S HARRIER *Circus pygargus*. A male reported to have been seen in May 1937.]

OSPREY *Pandion haliaetus*. One reported seen 4th November 1935, an exceptionally late date. Single birds present 16th-17th September 1957, 25th April 1962, and 6th June 1963.

HOBBY *Falco subbuteo*. Single males obtained on 7th May 1913 and 9th June 1914. One reported seen on 21st November 1914, 27th October 1919 (both extremely late dates), and 24th April 1933. One present 1st to 4th September 1957 and one 1st May 1964.

PEREGRINE *Falco peregrinus*. One pair normally breeds, but there were two in 1957. They are mentioned in the literature as far back as 1633, and there are said to have been two or three pairs in some years in the

nineteenth century. The adult birds are apparently often resident throughout the year, though in some recent years there were no records in February
and March. The young fledge in the last days of June, so the eggs must be
laid in mid-April. The juveniles depart between August and October.
There is no direct evidence of passage (all records of more than two birds
are in the summer), but obviously a few migrants will occur.

GYR FALCON *Falco rusticolus*. One 13th April 1921, either Iceland *F. r.
islandus* or Greenland *F. r. candicans*; two reported seen for about a fortnight
at the end of April 1943, thought to be Iceland birds; one of the Greenland
form seen 9th February 1952, and an immature bird (race unknown) on
18th October 1956.

MERLIN *Falco columbarius*. Regular passage-migrant in variable numbers,
and occasionally recorded outside the migration seasons. Adult birds are
very seldom recorded, especially in the autumn. Spring passage from
early March to 3rd June, mainly late April and May, rarely more than
one or two present. Four midsummer records between 18th June and 7th
July. Autumn passage recorded 28th July to early December, mainly end
August to mid-October; up to eight recorded on best days, but seldom
more than four or five. Odd birds sometimes stay through December and
January, but few February records. A majority of the trapped birds have
been referred to the Iceland form *F. c. subaesalon* and a small minority to
the Continental form *F. c. aesalon*; however it seems certain that some must
be from Shetland, where the species is widespread and part of the population
emigrates. C. J. Booth reports that he has twice seen ringed birds at nests
in Unst and Mainland while engaged in photography, and these are more
likely to have been ringed at Fair Isle than anywhere else. A nestling
ringed in Shetland was caught at Fair Isle in September 1963. Birds ringed
on autumn passage have been recovered during the same autumn and
winter in N. and E. Scotland (five, two October, two January, one March),
in N.W. Germany (October), in Belgium (two, October), and in S.W.
France (October); one was in Cumberland next April; and one was found
in S.W. France in November over seven years later.

RED-FOOTED FALCON *Falco vespertinus*. A first-summer male 4th-11th
June 1955, trapped on the 8th.

KESTREL *Falco tinnunculus*. Regular on both passages, mid-March to
mid-June (mostly May) and late July to late November (mostly late
September and early October). Occasional visitor late June and July, and
December to early March, odd birds have overwintered. Seldom more
than two or three present, but twice as many as fifteen in autumn (17th-18th
September 1953, and 18th September 1960). Three recoveries within four
months of ringing in autumn, one in N.W. Germany in November, one
Holland in December, and one W. France in December.

QUAIL *Coturnix coturnix*. Irregular visitor, recorded in eleven of the
seventeen years 1948-64. Known to have bred in 1905 (one nest), 1936
(one), 1943 (estimated eight or nine pairs, at least three nests found); 1958
(one) and 1964 (at least one), and may have done so in 1926. Bird or birds
present for some weeks in spring and summer of 1948, 1949, 1952, 1961, and
1964; in other recent years only one or two isolated records between May and
early July, but few species are more difficult to detect unless calling. The
extreme dates recorded are 30th April and 12th October.

CRANE *Grus grus*. Two 29th May, and one 19th July to 28th August 1962.

WATER RAIL *Rallus aquaticus*. Recorded most years on spring passage, and regular in autumn; a few winter or attempt to winter in most years. Wintering birds normally leave by mid-March. Spring passage mostly end March and early April but stragglers recorded to 11th May; most records are of single birds, rarely two or three present. Autumn migrants occasionally August (from 8th), more usually early September onwards, main passage mid-October to late November; more numerous than in spring but seldom more than five or six seen on best day. Two autumn migrants were recovered in Orkney and in Northern Ireland in the following January.

SPOTTED CRAKE *Porzana porzana*. One caught on 9th August 1949. (Another was released on the island after capture in Shetland, 13th August 1952.)

BAILLON'S CRAKE *Porzana pusilla*. A female obtained on 11th May 1929.

CORNCRAKE *Crex crex*. Breeds; but rather irregularly in recent years; also passage-migrant in very small numbers, mostly May and September. Formerly a common breeder in the crofts, up to ten-twelve pairs recorded, even as late as 1948. Not more than four or five pairs 1949 to 1953, no direct evidence of breeding 1954 or 1955, no birds present 1956, only one calling 1957, none 1958, but one to three nests found each year 1959-62. Calling birds present in 1963 and 1964, but probably did not breed. A limited amount of breeding-season data shows earliest egg laid about 12th June, most laid last week of June or early July, some late eggs late July or even August (one record of bird incubating 31st August, but perhaps infertile clutch). Birds normally arrive first half of May, but sometimes late April (from 21st); depart by mid-September but in a few years not until end September or early October; and three records in late October, to 30th. Two ringed in spring were recovered in Orkney next July and in Aberdeenshire next August.

MOORHEN *Gallinula chloropus*. Regular on spring passage, and occurs most years in autumn, in very small numbers. One pair bred 1933 and 1943, and said to have nested on several other occasions. Occasional visitor December to February; odd birds have probably overwintered successfully. Spring passage end March to late April, stragglers or off-passage birds to late May (1st June 1952); no more than four recorded on one day. One recent midsummer record, 27th June 1957. Autumn records rarely late August (from 28th), occasionally September, more usually October-November; no record of more than two birds.

COOT *Fulica atra*. Up to three irregularly on spring or autumn passage; about twice as many recorded in spring as in autumn. Noted once in late December, twice in January (one staying some days), and once February. Spring records are from 14th March, mostly end of March and early April. Seldom seen in May, but one stayed until 20th June 1963, and one or two are said to have stayed 'all summer' in 1933. Autumn records are between 9th October and 13th December. One ringed as young on the island of Rantum-Becken (Frisian Is.), Germany, in 1963, was found at Fair Isle on 5th November 1963.

OYSTERCATCHER *Haematopus ostralegus*. About forty-fifty pairs breed; said to have increased and spread inland onto the hill ground in this century. Breeders are summer visitors, first arriving early or mid-February, main body normally late February or early March; departure August and early September, stragglers to November. Some passage seen August and September, but difficult to detect in spring. One or two occasionally overwinter. First eggs are laid first week May, most in second and third weeks. Birds ringed as young on Fair Isle have been recovered in the first autumn and winter in Lincolnshire (September), Morecambe Bay (August, November and February), Cheshire (February), Anglesey (January), and western France (August, two September); in the following spring in Dumfries (May) and Glamorgan (April); the next summer in Fife (July); in their second autumn and winter in Dumfries (October), Fife (January) and Donegal (January); and when almost two years old in Meath (May). One was found in Flintshire when over seven years old (November). One ringed as adult was wintering in Orkney in January. Two birds ringed as young have been recovered on the island six and ten years later.

LAPWING *Vanellus vanellus*. Breeds; regular and often numerous on passage. The breeders are summer visitors, arriving from early February, mostly end February or early March, and departing late July and early August. Other birds visit the isle in all months of the year, though rather scarce December to February except with hard weather. The largest numbers are normally in March-April (up to 1,000 recorded), with lesser peaks late September to November (up to 150). First eggs are laid from mid-April (early date, 11th). The species bred 'in fair numbers' during the nineteenth century, though only one pair by 1898; no further records until the 1930s ('a few pairs now breeding regularly' in 1936); one pair recorded 1943 and 1944; none 1948-49, two pairs 1950-55, three 1956, three or four 1957, eight or nine 1958, ten or eleven 1959 and 1960, about sixteen 1961, and about twelve 1962; but only three pairs 1963 (following a severe winter), and only two in 1964. A 1963 chick was recovered in Oviedo province, Spain, in December 1963.

RINGED PLOVER *Charadrius hiaticula*. A few breed; regular on spring and autumn passage. 'One or two pairs' bred in the early years of this century, but the islanders speak of larger numbers both in the late nineteenth century and in the second and third decades of this century. There was apparently no breeding for 'many years' before 1952, but one or two pairs each year since then. The breeders arrive early February to early March, depart in August. Eggs are laid end April or early May; one pair has been double-brooded (rearing young from both layings) in recent years. Passage-migrants occur in very small numbers (rarely reaching double figures) from February to late May, with no marked peak; and second half July (occasionally early July) to early October, peaking late August and early September, often thirty-forty and rarely sixty-seventy on best days. One or two occur infrequently October to January. Birds of the High-Arctic form *Ch. h. tundrae* have been identified on several occasions in September and probably occur in May also. A migrant ringed late August 1954 was recovered in N. Spain in late May 1956, and another, ringed late August 1961, near Rabat, Morocco, on 13th December 1964.

KENTISH PLOVER *Charadrius alexandrinus*. One seen on 14th May 1949.

GREY PLOVER *Charadrius squatarola*. Two spring records, 2nd April 1958 and 3rd June 1954. Irregular visitor in autumn (though each year 1959-64), usually single birds but up to four recorded; extreme dates 26th August and 6th November, mostly late September and early October.

GOLDEN PLOVER *Charadrius apricarius*. Regular passage-migrant in spring and autumn; occasional visitor in winter, sometimes fairly large parties with hard weather, and may stay for some weeks. Two pairs probably bred in 1924, one pair did so in 1925-26. Spring passage mostly end March to early May, stragglers to early June; autumn movements from late June or early July to November, mostly late August to late October. Daily totals rarely reach fifty in spring, and seldom exceed that figure in autumn, but up to sixty-eighty recorded. Birds in summer dress nearly all show the characteristics of the Northern form *Ch. a. altifrons*.

LESSER GOLDEN PLOVER *Charadrius dominicus*. One seen 14th-15th September 1956.

DOTTEREL *Charadrius morinellus*. Ten or eleven records, all since 1949. Three were in spring, 10th and 24th May, 10th-11th and 23rd June: and the rest in autumn, 3rd to 29th September and one 14th November. No more than three birds at one time.

TURNSTONE *Arenaria interpres*. Regular passage-migrant and winter visitor. Spring passage mainly April-early May, often difficult to detect but sometimes marked increases of twenty-thirty birds; usually departs by end May, but stragglers in early June. No records between 16th June and 10th July. Autumn passage in very small numbers mid or late July on, larger numbers late August or early September to mid-November (usually sixty-eighty on best days, maximum 135). Winter population usually less than thirty, but liable to fluctuations in cold weather, and as many as ninety seen January.

SNIPE *Capella gallinago*. A few breed; regular on spring and autumn passage; small numbers winter, and may be considerably reinforced with hard weather between November and April. Nesting was first suspected in 1923, and a few nested annually 1924-26; no further breeding-records until 1948 when one pair summered and may have bred. After a series of inconclusive records in 1949 to 1953, breeding by one pair proved in 1954, and one or two pairs have bred annually since then, with temporary increase to probably eight pairs in 1961. Apart from weather-movements, passage usually involves increases of no more than twenty on daily-census samples, and occurs March to May (mostly April) and late July to late November (mainly late September to mid-November). Arrivals involving 'hundreds' or 'innumerable' numbers were recorded in the earlier years of this century but there has been nothing comparable since 1948. The breeding birds resemble the Faeroe race *C. g. faeroeensis*, and birds of this type have been collected or trapped on both passages and in winter, but the typical form and many indeterminable birds are also recorded on passage. One ringed in October was found in Cornwall exactly two years later; another, ringed August, was in Cork in January two and a half years later. A 1959 chick was recovered in Co. Kilkenny in December 1964.

GREAT SNIPE *Capella media*. Occurred fairly frequently in the first three decades of this century; two spring records (5th and 15th May) and eight or nine in autumn (5th September to 4th October) up to 1927, and said to have been seen in winter but no dated records. There are two or three observatory records, 7th November 1951 and 4th and 19th October 1960; and also recent unconfirmed reports in February, May, and September.

JACK SNIPE *Lymnocryptes minimus*. Regular on autumn passage, in small numbers; occasional visitor during winter, especially with hard weather, and individuals may overwinter at times; irregular, and rarely more than odd birds, on spring passage. The species was described as 'abundant' by Clarke (1912), and such terms as 'great numbers' and 'many' are used to describe autumn movements during the first quarter of this century; spring birds were also more regular and numerous. The bird has been much less common in recent years; there is no record of more than twenty (5th October 1961) since 1948, and numbers rarely exceeded five. Spring passage occurs late March to May (late date, 20th), mainly April; and autumn passage early September (early date, 29th August) to early December, mainly late September and October.

WOODCOCK *Scolopax rusticola*. Regular and often numerous on passage; falls of several hundreds occasionally in spring and most years in autumn. A few usually winter, and falls of some size may occur in hard weather, especially in January. Spring passage mainly last week March and first week April, stragglers into May, and one or two recorded June to August in some years. Autumn passage: odd birds occasionally in September, usually from early October onwards, peaking in second half October and first half November, smaller arrivals into December. One ringed in April was found in the following January in Harris; another, ringed in May, was in Cork the next December, while a late October migrant was in Aberdeenshire two weeks later. A November capture of 1960 was recovered at Bohusla, Sweden, in May 1963.

CURLEW *Numenius arquata*. Regular on passage; odd birds often winter or visit the isle at that season, sometimes more with cold weather. Numbers seldom exceed fifty at any time, but over 100 occasionally. Spring passage late February or March to early June, mostly April and early May but seldom any marked peak. Midsummer and autumn movements from late June or early July (sometimes large arrivals at this time) continuing until November or December, with main passage normally mid-August to early October.

WHIMBREL *Numenius phaeopus*. Regular on passage, usually rather more numerous in spring than in autumn. Rarely exceeds fifteen on peak days, and highest numbers recorded are only thirty in spring and twenty-three in autumn. Spring arrivals normally end April (early date, 15th) or early May to early June; frequently one or two at mid-summer. Southward passage begins early or late July, in some years completed by early September but in others continues to late September with stragglers in October. In 1907 several present through November, one to 12th December, and in 1911 one stayed to 23rd December; otherwise no records later than 18th October. A bird of the American form *N. p. hudsonicus* (Hudsonian Curlew) was seen 27th-31st May 1955.

BLACK-TAILED GODWIT *Limosa limosa*. Four spring records, 4th May 1958 (two), 18th-25th May 1943 (up to four), 18th to 23rd May 1964, and 26th May 1914 (two); three in autumn, 9th August 1950, 26th-30th August 1962, and 31st August 1960, all single birds; and one in winter, a male obtained 8th January 1908. Most will presumably be of the Iceland form, *L. l. islandica*.

BAR-TAILED GODWIT *Limosa lapponica*. A few annually in autumn since 1948, though only one record before then; three in spring, 27th-29th March 1962, 18th April 1964 and 20th May 1913. Autumn records 3rd July to 30th October, mostly late August and September; usually single birds and no more than four on one day, except for twenty-five on 27th August 1964. One ringed in September 1956 was shot near Noril'sk in N. Siberia in June 1960.

GREEN SANDPIPER *Tringa ochropus*. Recorded most years in spring (annually 1958-63) and regular in autumn. Spring dates 16th April to 13th June, mostly May, no more than two present. Two midsummer records, 24th June and 27th June to 5th July. Autumn dates 16th July to 3rd October, and once 28th October, mostly in August; no more than four recorded on one day except in 1912, when over twenty on some days in early August.

WOOD SANDPIPER *Tringa glareola*. Up to three irregularly in spring (seen in seven of past seventeen years) between 8th May and 13th June. Almost annual in autumn (recorded all but three years since 1948), between 8th July and 30th September, mostly August; no more than three on one day.

COMMON SANDPIPER *Tringa hypoleucos*. Regular in spring and autumn in small numbers. Spring movements 23rd April to 24th June, mostly May; autumn records 7th July to 2nd November, mostly August and seldom after mid-September. Numbers recorded are rarely more than five or six on best days, but up to ten-fifteen noted in three recent autumns.

REDSHANK *Tringa totanus*. Regular on passage and in winter; a few often present at midsummer. Winter population normally about twenty-thirty in recent years, may increase in hard weather; in the early years of the century apparently did not winter regularly, and odd winter birds were noteworthy, but it seems there was a wintering population by 1927. Spring passage mostly April and early May, usually rather small numbers; stragglers to late May and often through June. Return passage starts last days of June or early July and continues to November, mostly end July to late October with no regular peak-period; often fifty-eighty and occasionally over 100 on best days. Some of those handled are referable to the Icelandic form *T. t. robusta*, others to the typical form. One ringed in April 1958 was retrapped in September 1962, which suggests the same individuals may winter regularly. Another, ringed August 1962, was recovered at Busum (Schleswig-Holstein), Germany, in April 1963.

SPOTTED REDSHANK *Tringa erythropus*. One spring record, 7th May 1952. Autumn records in 1930, 1936, and in nine of past seventeen years, between 8th August and 20th October, mostly late August and early September. No more than three at one time.

LESSER YELLOWLEGS *Tringa flavipes*. One obtained 24th September 1910; one seen 31st May 1953.

GREENSHANK *Tringa nebularia*. Irregular in spring and regular in autumn, in very small numbers. Spring records in 1911 and in ten of past sixteen years, between 15th April and 20th June, mostly May; usually single birds. Autumn passage 14th July to 10th October, mostly August, and one 20th November 1960; seldom more than two or three present, and never more than six recorded.

KNOT *Calidris canutus*. Irregular in spring; annual in autumn though in very variable numbers. Spring records in 1913, 1953, and in six years since 1955, all between 7th and 27th May except one 9th-10th June 1962; usually single birds but once six. Autumn records 7th July to 9th October, mostly August and first week September; in some years fails to reach double figures (as in six of past seventeen), and until 1958 never exceeded thirty at peak, but has since peaked at thirty-five-sixty each autumn except 1961, and over 200 on 4th August 1962.

PURPLE SANDPIPER *Calidris maritima*. Regular winter visitor and passage migrant. Winter population usually about ten-thirty birds in recent years, may fluctuate with hard weather. Winter birds usually decrease in March or early April; spring passage late March to early May, seldom more than twenty seen but rarely up to forty; stragglers to late May and occasionally early June (late date, 14th). Autumn movements sometimes from late July (early date, 20th), more usually small numbers from mid or late August, though sometimes very scarce until late October; main arrivals normally late October to early December, frequently up to thirty but rarely over fifty seen on one day.

LITTLE STINT *Calidris minuta.* Two acceptable spring records, 20th-23rd May 1964 and 2nd June 1913. Irregular in autumn, though 'single birds annually' in 1905-11. In the observatory period, recorded in 1953 and each year 1956-64 except 1959. Records are all between 14th August and 12th October (mostly September), apart from one collected 9th November 1908. No record of more than four birds except in 1960, when there was a strong and protracted passage peaking at seventeen on 17th September.

TEMMINCK'S STINT *Calidris temminckii.* Five records between 1908 and 1913, all single birds and at least three of them collected: 14th August 1908, 8th and 14th-15th June 1912, 8th August 1912, and 13th-16th May 1913. Several parties of up to four birds said to have been seen in September 1936. Only one record in recent years, 21st-23rd May 1964.

WESTERN SANDPIPER *Calidris mauri.* One 27th May to 3rd June 1956, trapped on 28th. Originally identified as Semipalmated Sandpiper *C. pusilla.* First record for Britain.

AMERICAN PECTORAL SANDPIPER *Calidris melanotos.* One 16th-29th September 1961; one 27th August, two 29th August to 3rd September, one to 9th September 1962.

DUNLIN *Calidris alpina.* Regular spring and autumn migrant; odd birds or small parties occasionally with hard weather in winter. Spring passage mid-March to early June, mostly May; in some years stragglers to late June; numbers very variable but in most years up to ten, and occasionally up to thirty at peak. Autumn movements sometimes from early or mid-July, more usually end July or early August to early October, with occasional birds into November. In most years the peak period is mid-August to mid-September, but rarely (as in 1961) large arrivals in early October; peak numbers often up to twenty-five and as many as sixty recorded. Both Northern *C. a. alpina* and Southern Dunlins *C. a. schinzii* occur, but the majority of those trapped cannot be determined with any confidence. A bird ringed in August was in S.W. France a month later and two ringed in May were recovered in the same area of N.W. Spain in May the following year.

CURLEW SANDPIPER *Calidris testacea.* One spring record, 24th-26th May 1956; and seven in autumn, 21st August 1912 (two), 4th September 1925, 6th September 1948 (three), 15th August 1949, 17th September 1960, 5th-8th September and 3rd-9th November 1963.

SANDERLING *Crocethia alba.* Almost annual in spring (seen in twelve of past sixteen years); all records of one to four birds, between 6th May and 21st June, except in 1952 when nine reported 17th-18th March and one 5th April. Regular in autumn, between 11th July and 10th October (mostly mid-August to first week September), with stragglers recorded on 11th November 1958, 14th November 1911, and 2nd December 1951, and 'a few' 28th December 1922. Peak numbers are usually less than ten but occasionally up to twenty.

BUFF-BREASTED SANDPIPER *Tryngites subruficollis.* One on 18th September 1958.

RUFF *Philomachus pugnax.* Two spring records, 5th-6th June 1913 and 20th May 1950. Annual in autumn in very variable numbers; in some years only odd birds, in others small parties, and up to thirty-two recorded (apart from a rather doubtful record of possibly 100 on 16th September 1937). Extreme dates are 13th July and 16th November; normally only odd birds in July, and October records are confined to the three years 1960-62. The peaks tend to be in late August or early September, but the largest fall on record was on 4th August 1962. A juvenile ringed in September 1958 was shot in the Marismas del R. Guadalquivir, S. Spain, in November 1959.

AVOCET *Recurvirostra avosetta.* One obtained 8th May 1947.

GREY PHALAROPE *Phalaropus fulicarius.* Six records: one obtained 2nd and one seen 29th January 1909, one October 1909, one 15th November 1925, one 13th November 1958, and at least one 26th October 1961. A phalarope probably this species 14th September 1963.

RED-NECKED PHALAROPE *Phalaropus lobatus.* Five good records: one obtained 4th June 1910, one 6th June 1930, and one seen 18th June 1959; an adult trapped 3rd and a juvenile (trapped) 16th-24th August 1961.

STONE CURLEW *Burhinus oedicnemus.* An adult female obtained 7th June 1913; single birds present 23rd-25th May 1963 and 18th-19th May 1964. One reported seen in autumn 1930.

PRATINCOLE *Glareola pratincola.* A female of the black-winged phase ('*nordmanni*') seen 18th May 1927 and obtained next day. Single birds of the Collared or brown-winged phase were reported seen in May 1934 and May 1935.

BONXIE *Catharacta skua.* Said to have bred in the early years of the nineteenth century, but absent for many years until one pair nested in 1921. Probably bred intermittently during the 'twenties, but up to three pairs regularly in the 'thirties. Only one pair reported 1943, but four 1944. Again four pairs 1948 and 1949; since then has tended to increase, despite occasional setbacks, and at least thirty pairs in 1963; but only about twenty in 1964. Many were shot by the islanders in 1963, owing to their interference with the sheep, and numbers are likely to be controlled in the future. Arrival-dates were normally from mid-April until the recent increase, but now usually from first week April (early date, 31st March 1959). Most birds depart by mid-September, but some stragglers or passage-migrants on or near the isle most years to mid-October (late date, 2nd November 1957). Said to have occurred offshore very occasionally in the winter, but the only dated records of birds on the crossing are for 2nd March 1927 and 4th March 1958. Eggs are sometimes laid second week May, but mostly from mid-May. Recoveries of birds ringed on the island as young are from N. Spain in January three and a half years later, and from S.W. Greenland in July two years later. Local-born birds have been found as first-time breeders on the island at four years (two birds) and six years old.

ARCTIC SKUA *Stercorarius parasiticus.* Nested in small numbers during the nineteenth century, but reduced to one pair by 1905, then none until the early 'twenties. Four pairs in 1926, twelve by 1935, then numbers apparently fairly static at eight to twelve pairs until 1947; about fifteen pairs 1948 and since then has increased every year (except 1953) to reach seventy pairs 1962, perhaps small decrease in 1963. First birds normally arrive in third or fourth week of April (early date, 6th), most in early May; many depart mid-August but some remain to early September, stragglers or migrants seen occasionally to early October (late date, 25th October 1961). Eggs are laid from middle of May onwards. Birds ringed as young have been reported during their first autumn in E. Scotland (August), S.W. Norway (September), Denmark (August and November), N.W. Germany (August), Belgium (September and November), N.W. Spain (August), Portugal (October) and Algeria (August); also in later years in Norfolk (August), Denmark (August), N.W. Germany (September), of Portugal (November), and off Angola (October and November). Five birds have been found in or near other skua colonies in Orkney and Shetland in summer. Some fifty local young were recaptured on the island as first-time breeders at between three and six years old. There were no recoveries oversea of the large number of adults ringed at Fair Isle, until one (ringed in 1960) was found near Aberdeen in September 1964. Local name (obsolete): 'Kju'.

POMARINE SKUA *Stercorarius pomarinus*. Ten dated records: 2nd June 1949, 4th June 1955, 29th May 1956, 10th June 1964; 'October' 1934 (two), 21st to 30th October 1963, 29th October 1910 (obtained), 16th November 1951, 27th November 1906 (obtained); and said to have been seen on other occasions in autumn.

LONG-TAILED SKUA *Stercorarius longicaudus*. One record: an immature bird, thought to be of the Greenland form *S. l. pallescens*, seen on 23rd June 1956.

IVORY GULL *Pagophila eburnea*. One seen 28th December 1933; an adult found dying on 9th February 1952.

GREATER BLACK-BACKED GULL *Larus marinus*. Breeds; present throughout the year; considerable numbers (occasionally over 500) settle on the island with rough weather at most times of year, but especially in October-December. Described as a numerous breeding species in the early twentieth century, but estimated only twelve to twenty pairs in early 'thirties; about forty pairs in 1959. Eggs are laid last week April and early May. Birds ringed as young at Fair Isle have been found in Sutherland next December, Aberdeen next January, and in August four years later, in Banff next March, Shetland next July, and in Holland in September of the second autumn. Visiting birds caught at roost in November and December have been reported from central Norway in April, from N.W. and S.W. Norway in June (all adults), from Shetland in July (adult); from Caithness in June of the next year, in Aberdeen just over two years later, and in Pembrokeshire in July eighteen months later (all immatures). One ringed as young in the Barents Sea, N. Russia, was found dead at Fair Isle the next February. Local name (obsolete): 'Swaabie'.

LESSER BLACK-BACKED GULL *Larus fuscus*. Summer visitor and passage-migrant. The British form *L. f. graellsii* breeds; formerly 'common' but only about twelve to twenty pairs in 1949-62, about thirty 1963. Eggs are laid mid-May. The breeders return occasionally late March, usually April (early date, 12th March); depart late August and early September, stragglers occasionally in early October. There are sometimes large falls of adults in late summer (over 200 15th July 1958, sixty 5th August 1955 and 5th September 1961) otherwise passage-movements are difficult to detect. Local young have been recovered in the first autumn in N. Ireland (September) and S. W. Spain (December), and in May nearly two years later on the Mediterranean coast of France (Hérault); while one ringed in Shetland was at Fair Isle eight weeks later (late August). Birds of the

Scandinavian (typical) form occur most years in autumn and rarely in winter and spring; seldom more than six present but up to twenty noted. The autumn records fall between 1st September and 22nd October, with one 12th December; mostly in mid-September. The winter and spring birds were between 11th February and 17th May.

HERRING GULL *Larus argentatus*. Breeds; present throughout the year; passage-migrant. Numbers often come to land during rough weather; up to 3,000 seen ashore in October-December. Breeding-population was much greater during period when Fair Isle was a fishing-station (up to about 1920) than at present; estimated only about 140 nests in 1959; but marked increase over preceding years in 1963. Eggs are laid end April and early May. Local young have been recovered in Aberdeen in August of the next year, in E. Lothian about two years after ringing, in Northumberland in May of the first year, in Lincolnshire in October of the same year, and in Holland in June three years later. An adult caught December 1959 was found long dead in Shetland in July 1964. A chick from Noss, Shetland reached Fair Isle in its first September. Birds caught at roost in December 1961 were found subsequently in Northern Norway (two, June 1962 and April 1963) and Denmark (April 1962); while one ringed as young on the Murmansk coast, N. Russia, in 1960 was taken in the same roost. This bird was from the breeding-area of *L. a. omissus*; a yellow-legged bird collected 28th September 1921 may also have been referable to this form. Local names: adult, 'Maa'; immature, 'Scorie'; sometimes also applied to other gulls.

COMMON GULL *Larus canus*. Common passage-migrant, and frequent visitor at all seasons. Spring passage mostly late March to early June, largest numbers generally mid-April, though rarely over 200 recorded at peak. Autumn movements of small parties from late June or early July, often large numbers from end July or early August; up to 1,500 seen together in August and up to 700 in September, October, and early November; but varies greatly from year to year. August birds are nearly all adults, but immatures well-represented earlier and later. Usually only very small numbers intermittently from late November to early March, but over 100 seen with cold weather in January. Local name: 'Landpicker'.

GLAUCOUS GULL *Larus hyperboreus*. Formerly a regular winter visitor, late October to February, but markedly scarcer since about 1935, perhaps earlier, apart from big falls in the winters of 1951-52 and 1952-53. Now fairly regular in autumn in very small numbers, but irregular in winter and spring; a few recent summer records. Autumn birds are from 20th September, mostly second half October and early November since 1952, though earlier the biggest arrivals came in December. Numbers have rarely exceeded five birds recently, whereas over 100 were present in December 1951 and over fifty in December 1952. Since then the highest totals were thirty-five 17th October 1955 and ten 17th November 1959, with no more than four irregularly December to February, occasionally March. There are a few old records in early April, and three in the observatory period, the latest being 29th, 1961. Summer records of immature birds on 19th May 1928, 11th June 1959, 11th-18th July 1959 (at least two), 19th July 1955, 2nd August 1958, and 8th August 1949. One ringed December 1951 was recovered in Faeroes next February. Local names: this and the following species were both known as 'Iceland Maa', the immatures formerly called 'Valkie'.

ICELAND GULL *Larus glaucoides.* Occurred regularly in the early years of this century between late October and early April (extreme dates, 19th October and 4th April) though in smaller numbers than the Glaucous Gull. Since 1948 there have seldom been more than two or three birds in any year, except in the winter of 1951-52, and in some years no records. In 1951-52 there were 'several' from 3rd November, 'many' in late December, and up to twelve between 8th and 12th February. Most other recent records were between 24th October and early December; none late February or March but two birds from 6th April 1949 (one until 15th May), two from 23rd April 1950 (one until 31st May), and one 13th April 1964.

LITTLE GULL *Larus minutus.* Reported by the islanders to have been seen on a good many occasions, but there are no observatory records. The only dated occurrences known are for June 1934, 25th September 1935, and 10th February 1954, the last staying for two weeks.

BLACK-HEADED GULL *Larus ridibundus.* Regular on spring and autumn passage; occasional visitor during the winter. Spring passage March to early June, with two peak-periods, one less regularly in late March (apparently drifted birds) and the other more consistently in late April and early May (probably Shetland breeders); peak numbers seldom exceed thirty at either period, but as many as 100 on 30th March 1958. Protracted autumn movements commence late June or early July and continue into November; peak numbers rarely exceed twenty-five and may occur at any time from mid-July to mid-October; over 100 on 6th October 1951. Winter records mostly December-January, rarely more than one or two birds. A young bird ringed in Norway (Rogaland) in 1949 was found on Fair Isle on 16th August of the same year, and another ringed in Jutland, Denmark, in 1961 was caught at Fair Isle on 19th March 1963.

MEDITERRANEAN GULL *Larus melanocephalus.* A second-winter bird 31st August to 2nd September 1957; a first-winter 14th October 1957.

KITTIWAKE *Rissa tridactyla.* Breeds; a few offshore through the winter. Recorded as 'nesting in great numbers' before 1912; a count in 1959 gave about 2,750 nests. Birds return to land between mid-February and late March, though not ashore regularly until mid-April; eggs are laid in mid-May. Departure from mid-August, numbers offshore until mid-October but seldom more than odd individuals or small parties near the island later in the winter. In some years, large gatherings of first-summer birds around the isle between June and August. A chick ringed by J. Wilson in 1939 was recovered at Notre Dame Bay, Newfoundland, in September 1941, and a 1964 chick at White Bay, Newfoundland in October of the same year. Local name (obsolete): 'Rippack'.

COMMON TERN *Sterna hirundo.* Common and/or Arctic Terns are recorded rather irregularly from May to early July, more frequently mid-July to mid-September, some stragglers to early October. Extreme dates are 5th May and 26th October, with one extraordinary record on the crossing, 16th January 1952 (J. A. Stout). Numbers rarely exceed ten but there have been over fifty on a few occasions in late July and September. Common Terns have been identified between 24th May and 27th September; they appear to be barely half as numerous as Arctics, except for an extraordinary arrival in a hurricane, 120 on 26th September 1963.

ARCTIC TERN *Sterna macrura.* For status see preceding species. This bird has been identified between 23rd May and 6th October. The 'pictarrs' which Eagle Clarke was told formerly bred, in the early part of the nineteenth century, were most probably of this species.

SANDWICH TERN *Sterna sandvicensis*. A rare visitor, reported to have been seen 'on occasions' before 1936, and recorded in six years since 1953, all between 26th May and 24th July; usually one or two individuals but up to seven present in July 1958.

[GREAT AUK *Alca impennis*. Eagle Clarke refers to a statement in Baikie and Hedle's *Historia Naturalis Orcadensis* (1848), that one was seen off Fair Isle in June 1798. The species is said to have bred at Papa Westray, about forty miles away, at that time.]

LITTLE AUK *Plautus alle*. Considerable numbers winter regularly near Sumburgh Head and are seen on the crossing to Fair Isle; hundreds and even thousands may be observed in November to February, and smaller numbers October and March. Much less often seen from the island but over 100 occasionally observed during the peak-period, and odd birds not infrequently; in some winters live or dead birds are found on the land. One was seen on 29th August 1957, otherwise the extreme dates are 15th September and 20th March. Local name: 'Rotchie'.

RAZORBILL *Alca torda*. A common breeding bird; a few occasionally seen offshore outside the breeding-season. Returns to the cliffs sometimes in late January, more often late February onwards. Eggs are laid mid-May. Departure completed by the end of August. No census has been made, but the population is of the order of 750-1,000 breeding pairs. No evidence of any marked change in numbers in this century. Fourteen recoveries of local young were reported in autumn and winter in S.W. Norway (all south of 62° N., mostly south of 60° N.); and two in Denmark. One was in N. Spain in its first November, and one in Northumberland in March of its second winter. The distribution of recoveries is undoubtedly greatly biased by the incidence of autumn auk-shooting in Scandinavia. Local name: 'Wilekie'.

GUILLEMOT *Uria aalge*. Status very similar to that of Razorbill, but probably about twice as numerous (estimated 1,500-2,000 pairs in 1959), and tends to arrive rather earlier. First ashore in first week January in 1963, but more usually early February onwards. Counts of 'bridled' birds have ranged between ten per cent and nearly twenty per cent of the samples in different years. Ten ringed young were killed in autumn and winter in S.W. Norway, though one north of 63°, another nearly 64° N., and one at 68° 40' N., were further north than any Razorbills so far reported. Another was found in Co. Durham in its first February. Local name: 'Longvie'.

BLACK GUILLEMOT *Cepphus grylle*. Breeds; population of the order of 200 pairs in recent years; smaller numbers winter inshore. Eggs are laid late May and early June. Two ringed as young were recovered in Essex in late November of the first autumn, and in N. Ronaldshay, Orkney, in July a year later. Another was found freshly-dead at Fair Isle when a year old, and one breeding in its natal colony at four years old. Local name: 'Tystie'.

PUFFIN *Fratercula arctica*. The commonest breeding bird at Fair Isle; estimated over 20,000 pairs, has probably increased in this century. First gathers offshore in late March, and comes to land towards end of first week or in second week April. Eggs laid end April and early May. Most depart by mid-August; seldom seen ashore after 20th, but sometimes to end of month (late date, 2nd September). Very rarely seen near the land in the winter half of the year. Two birds ringed as young have been reported from Co. Durham next December and January; one in Essex next January, and one off S.W. Greenland next November. Local name: 'Norie'.

PALLAS'S SANDGROUSE *Syrrhaptes paradoxus*. Eagle Clarke was informed by the Rev. H. A. MacPherson that a flock of forty arrived at the beginning of June 1888, but only five survived to the end of the month.

STOCK DOVE *Columba oenas*. Irregular on spring and autumn passage; recorded in eight springs and nine autumns in the past seventeen years. Spring records fall between 17th March and 3rd June, well-spread but slightly more in April than at other times; autumn records are from 9th August to 12th November, mostly late September and early October. The only note of more than two birds refers to five on 7th April 1952.

ROCK DOVE *Columba livia*. Breeds; noted as a passage-migrant in early spring and late autumn; a few winter in most years. Bred commonly in the nineteenth century, when many were caught for food; but became extinct as a breeding bird about 1895. Apparently known only as a passage-migrant or winter visitor until at least 1927. Three or four pairs were nesting in 1948 and a few, probably under ten pairs, have bred until the present. Most breeders apparently return in April, young appear late May onwards. In most recent years flocks of up to forty birds have arrived on, or passed over, the isle between late September and December, mainly November; as many as 100 noted 20th December 1943. Occasional small parties or single birds pass north between February and April.

WOOD PIGEON *Columba palumbus*. Regular on spring and autumn passage, usually in very small numbers; recorded in all months. Spring movements mid-March to late May, mainly early April to mid-May, with odd birds through June in some years. Occasional records in July and early August. Autumn passage sometimes from late August, more usually from late September or early October, through November; odd birds irregularly in all winter months. Seldom more than five present on best days at either migration, rarely more than singles at other times of the year. The species appears to have become more common in the past five years, and all the highest scores are in this period: c. fifteen 10th April 1960 and 1st April 1963; and an exceptionally strong arrival in November 1959 peaking at thirty on 18th, at least one of these remaining until late February 1960. An adult ringed July 1963 was found on the island of Sylt, W. Germany, in May 1964.

TURTLE DOVE *Streptopelia turtur*. Regular in spring and autumn, in very small numbers; rather more birds in spring than autumn, but recorded maxima are only four in spring and three in autumn. Spring occurrences 5th May onwards, and has been seen on most dates to 21st July, though mostly late May and early June. Autumn records 9th August to 10th October, mostly first half September. A Turtle Dove bearing a Belgian carrier-pigeon ring was found on the island on 8th September 1927; the domestic bird carrying this ring had been lost near Ghent in May 1927, but no details of the transfer were discovered.

COLLARED DOVE *Streptopelia decaocto*. Single birds seen 18th April and 18th June 1960, 12th and 14th May 1961, 13th May and 15th-16th June 1962; probably at least five different birds between 30th April and 20th June 1963; one on six dates between 9th May and 16th June 1964.

CUCKOO *Cuculus canorus*. Regular on spring passage; usually no more than one or two present, but 'exceptional numbers' in mid-May 1910 and up to seven in mid-May 1951. The extreme dates for spring migrants are 26th April and 9th July, mostly mid-May to mid-June. One or two birds, nearly all juveniles, appear irregularly in summer, mostly late July (from 13th) and early August, and rarely September (to 8th, once 24th). Two or three birds are said to have stayed all summer in 1936; it is possible that some of the recently-fledged juveniles seen in July were reared on the island, but no satisfactory proof of breeding. One ringed on 6th May 1955 was found near Bergen, Norway, only two days later.

BARN OWL *Tyto alba*. Five records. Single birds of the White-breasted (typical) form present January-February 1926 (obtained), seen October-November 1940, 11th April 1944, and 12th November 1958; and one reported to be of the Dark-breasted form *T. a. guttata* present October-November 1943.

SNOWY OWL *Nyctea scandiaca*. Said to have occurred on a number of occasions, but only three dated records known: 26th October 1907, 17th April 1956, and 23rd December to 14th January 1961-62.

LONG-EARED OWL *Asio otus*. Occurs almost every year in spring and regularly in autumn, in very small numbers. Spring records are between 18th February and 26th June, mostly late March to early May, no record of more than two birds. Autumn records in the past fifteen years have all been between 7th October and 8th December, mostly late October and early November; usually single birds but up to eight noted at peak. The species is said to have occurred several times in August (from 2nd) and September in earlier years. One ringed in November 1950 was found near Stavanger, Norway, in early December 1954, and another, ringed November 1964, was recovered in Noord Holland, Netherlands a week later.

SHORT-EARED OWL *Asio flammeus*. Regular in spring and autumn, in very small numbers. Spring records 29th February to 10th June, mostly late April and May, no more than two recorded on one day. A few July records between 7th and 24th. Autumn birds from 3rd August to 26th November, mostly October; usually less than three seen on best day, but in 1950 up to six (27th October), in 1960 up to at least eight (26th-29th October), and in 1963 up to twenty (8th November). Three January records; 2nd, 1929, one (dead some days) in mid-January 1963, and one 5th January 1964.

NIGHTJAR *Caprimulgus europaeus*. Ten records in spring (eight since 1949); all between 7th May and 30th June except for one exceptionally early bird reported 12th April 1949. A record of 'remains found' in mid-July 1949 and one 'quite recently dead' 21st August 1908. Two or three autumn occurrences; 14th and 21st September 1956 and 24th September 1961.

ALPINE SWIFT *Apus melba*. One seen 20th June 1962.

SWIFT *Apus apus*. Regular visitor in summer, in very variable numbers. The extreme dates are 30th April and 7th October, but birds seldom appear before mid-May or after mid-September. The peak numbers, rarely more than twenty, are most frequently observed in late May or early June, but sometimes late June-early July, or late August, and rarely at other times. An exceptionally big movement in late August 1958 produced about 150 birds on 21st and over 120 on 24th; the only occasions on which recorded totals have exceeded fifty. One ringed on 30th April 1962 was recovered in Jamtland, N. Sweden, in June 1962.

NEEDLE-TAILED SWIFT *Chaetura caudacuta*. One seen and described by G. Stout, 6th August 1931.

HOOPOE *Upupa epops*. Eleven dated records; four between 9th and 21st May, one in 'mid-June', one 22nd August, and five between 3rd and 21st October. Only three of these are since 1948. The high proportion of October records suggests a late 'reversed migration' like that made by the Red-breasted Flycatcher.

GREATER SPOTTED WOODPECKER *Dendrocopos major*. Irregular in autumn; singly or in very small numbers except in irruption years; three spring records of single birds. Small irruptions, composed almost entirely of birds of the year, reached Fair Isle in 1909, 1928 (?), 1935, 1949, and 1962; and there are records of odd birds in 1927, 1929, 1951, 1953, 1956, 1958, 1960 and 1963. The extreme dates are from 1st August to 4th January, mainly late September and early October, and probably no fresh arrivals after mid-November; the highest totals on record are ten 6th October 1949 and twelve 11th October 1962. The spring dates are 7th-11th May 1936, 10th-30th May 1950, and 12th-25th May 1954. All closely examined were referable to the Northern (typical) form except for a small-billed bird caught on 18th September 1953.

WRYNECK *Jynx torquilla*. Recorded almost every year in spring and autumn (all but two springs and one autumn since 1948). Only one record of more than three in spring (six to eight 7th-12th May 1950) and none of more than six in autumn since 1948; but formerly occurred in larger numbers: 'remains of a number' found September 1905, 'considerable passage' May 1910, 'a good few' May 1936, 'scores' September 1943. Spring dates are from 22nd April to 7th June, mostly mid-May; autumn passage 19th August to 8th October, mostly end August and early September.

SHORT-TOED LARK *Calandrella cinerea*. Irregular visitor in autumn; seven spring records. The spring birds, six between 20th April and 20th May, and one 18th June, were all of the southern form *C. c. brachydactila*. Two midsummer records, both southern birds, 19th July to 8th August 1957, and 9th-11th July 1964. Over twenty autumn records (including about thirteen in seven years since 1952); often several individuals in the years the species has occurred, though never more than two at once. Extreme dates are 22nd September and 4th December, mostly October; the majority of birds resemble the Eastern form *C. c. longipennis* though southern-type birds have occurred between 25th September and 14th November (?28th November 1910).

[CALANDRA LARK *Melanocorypha calandra*. One reported to have been obtained in spring about 1925, but no details known.]

CRESTED LARK *Galerida cristata*. One seen 2nd November 1952.

WOODLARK *Lullula arborea*. Irregular visitor in spring and autumn. Formerly more numerous and frequent, wintered on the island in some years up to at least 1928; usually 'small numbers' but as many as twenty recorded (December 1926). Since 1948 only some eleven records in spring, between 18th March and 15th May, mostly end-March and early April; and a similar number in autumn, 20th September to 30th November, mostly late October and November. No more than two birds present except in 1949, fifteen on 11th October. Once recorded as late as 2nd June 1927.

SKYLARK *Alauda arvensis*. A common breeding bird (probably 100-120 pairs in 1963); regular and often quite numerous on passage in spring and autumn, late February to early April and September to November. The breeders are summer visitors, and only small numbers (usually well under fifty) winter, though these may increase with weather-movements. The species was apparently more abundant on passage in the early decades of this century: 'often in vast numbers' before 1912, 'enormous numbers' November 1927; whereas recently there have hardly been more than 500 birds in the largest arrivals in spring or autumn. The winter population also seems to have decreased with the decline of arable farming on the isle. The eggs are laid from late April, mostly May; some birds are probably double-brooded. A bird ascribed to the eastern form *A. a. intermedia* was collected 3rd November 1935 but the various eastern forms of the species have been revised since then, and the specimen has not been re-examined. One ringed in March 1950 was recovered at Bell Rock, E. Scotland, in the following October, and another, ringed October 1956, near Boston, Lincs., in January 1963.

SHORELARK *Eremophila alpestris*. Rare visitor in spring and irregular in autumn; formerly more frequent in autumn ('annual' to 1912) but no record of more than two at once. Once March (6th), and four between 16th April and 12th May. Autumn records between 10th September and 16th December, mostly October-early November.

SWALLOW *Hirundo rustica*. Regular in spring and autumn; has bred at least once. In most years the spring totals, probably composed largely of birds overshooting Scotland, are much larger than those in autumn. The earliest record is for 14th April, but seldom seen before last week of month; main spring movements May (especially second half) and early June; often over twenty but rarely over fifty birds on best day. Small numbers irregularly late June and early July, rarely early August; most autumn records late August to late September, often less than ten at peak, but occasionally as many as fifty-sixty (17th-18th September 1949, 18th September 1961) with southerly gales. Occasional records October, latest date 26th. A publication of 1936 stated that the Swallow 'has bred'; a pair bred successfully in 1962, laying eggs in mid-July. One ringed on 6th July 1953 was caught at nest in Caithness in July 1954 and 1955.

RED-RUMPED SWALLOW *Hirundo daurica*. One obtained, out of three reported seen, 2nd June 1905 (first British record). One reported seen 19th June 1931.

HOUSE MARTIN *Delichon urbica*. Regular in spring, rather irregular in autumn, though records to at least early August in all of past seventeen years; numbers usually smaller than those of Swallow, but once over 100 in spring (1st June 1950). Earliest date is 28th April, more usual from first week May, main spring movements late May and early June; stragglers to end June and irregularly through July. Occasional records in August, most autumn birds in September but no more than twenty-five recorded (6th September 1963) apart from 'many' on 10th September 1927. Stragglers in October some years, once seen as late as 14th November. Two pairs nested in 1922, one in 1935 and 1946.

SAND MARTIN *Riparia riparia*. Regular spring migrant, irregular in autumn, in very small numbers; no record of more than five at either season, apart from 'many' 19th May 1910, and ten on 5th September 1963. Spring records extend from 5th April to 1st July, mostly May; autumn birds (seen in all but four years since 1948) 18th July to 18th October, mostly September.

GOLDEN ORIOLE *Oriolus oriolus*. Seven records; five between 1908 and

1913. Four spring birds were all between 11th and 26th May; three in autumn between 1st and 25th September.

RAVEN *Corvus corax*. Resident and breeds; occasionally recorded on passage. Said to have been as many as six pairs about 1897, then cut down, and only one or two pairs in the early years of this century. Usually three, occasionally four, pairs in recent years, despite control measures. Eggs are laid late March or early April. Young leave the island July to September. Definite records of passage are sparse though a few strangers must often reach the isle. Isolated records suggest movement especially in late March and early April (twenty-four present 6th April 1956, twenty moving N. 9th April 1959) and during September-October (twenty-four to twenty-seven 12th-18th September 1956, seventeen on 13th September 1959); and numbers apparently fluctuate during the winter. Local name: 'Corbie'.

HOODED/CARRION CROW *Corvus corone*. Hooded Crows *C. c. cornix* are resident and breed; also regularly noted on passage in the early part of the century, but migrants seldom detected in recent years. Breeding population said to be about six pairs before 1912; probably about ten-twelve pairs recently. Eggs are laid late April and early May. Arrivals used to occur mostly in March-early April and in October-November, occasionally 'great numbers' (from 3rd October 1911) or 'considerable immigration' (10th-18th November 1926); and small arrivals have been suspected at the same periods in recent times. Fluctuations have also been noted in mid-winter. Local name: 'Craa'. Carrion Crows *C. c. corone* (or black hybrids) were formerly rare visitors, unless confused with Rooks, but have been annual for at least the past fifteen years, and odd birds have summered several times, mated with Hooded Crows, and produced hybrid young in 1959 and perhaps other years. Records cover the period 8th January to 27th November, with most consistent arrivals in May (up to eight and once fifteen on best days) and a less regular peak in September; though daily totals rarely exceed two or three birds.

ROOK *Corvus frugilegus*. A few regularly on spring passage, and most years in autumn. One or two sometimes winter on the island, and considerable increase may occur with hard weather. Single birds visit the island during June to August in some years, occasionally staying for some weeks. The species was much more abundant earlier in the century. Spring movements occur from late February to early June, mainly late March and early April, but peak numbers in the observatory period have never exceeded forty and usually less than ten, whereas up to 600 were seen in several springs before 1915. Autumn passage seldom begins before mid-September, with most records in late October and early November; but no score of more than eighteen at this time since 1948, compared with a former status of 'common' (up to 1912) and records of 100 on 10th November 1923 and 'hundreds' 5th November 1926. The only recent large arrival in winter totalled thirty-eight birds on 21st-25th January 1952. Local name: 'Scotch Craa'.

JACKDAW *Corvus monedula*. Almost annual in spring, less regular in autumn; has wintered in at least two years (1935-36, 1953-54) and odd birds or small parties occasionally arrive with hard weather in December-February. Spring passage mainly late March and early April, usually less than five birds at peak, but as many as fifty-six seen (5th April 1960); small numbers late April and May in some years, rarely early June (to 13th). Two 6th July 1952. Autumn movements 8th September onwards, mostly late October and early November, usually only one or two birds but up to sixteen (23rd October 1950) on record. Birds with pale blue-grey napes, presumably of the Scandinavian (typical) form, and ones with dark napes, presumably of British or Central European form *C. m. spermologus*, occur at both seasons, often in company; but the majority cannot be determined with any confidence.

[JAY *Garrulus glandarius*. One reported seen mid-May 1940, but no details available.]

GREAT TIT *Parus major*. Birds of the Continental (typical) form recorded in five autumns since 1910: one 17th November 1910; up to a dozen from 27th October 1914, two present until at least 23rd January 1915; one 22nd September 1936; one 13th October 1959 to 29th March 1960; one 21st-22nd October and 31st October 1961 to 15th February 1962.

BLUE TIT *Parus caeruleus*. Five records: 24th April 1962 and 20th October 1926, 3rd November 1935 (three birds), 3rd October 1961, and 6th November 1962. The 1926 and both the 1962 birds were examined in the hand and were of the Continental (typical) form.

COAL TIT *Parus ater*. One seen by L. S. V. Venables on 21st September 1936.

WILLOW TIT *Parus montanus*. One seen (with Blue Tits) on 3rd November 1935.

[LONG-TAILED TIT *Aegithalos caudatus*. A party of three or four said to have been seen about 1930, but no date or details known.]

[NUTHATCH *Sitta europea*. Single birds reported seen 29th-30th May 1936 and 1st May 1939, but no description available.]

TREE CREEPER *Certhia familiaris*. Single birds of the Northern (typical) form on 14th April 1913; 27th December 1906, and 17th-18th October 1959; all obtained or handled.

WREN *Troglodytes troglodytes*. Resident and breeds; small numbers detected on autumn passage in some years. The breeding population (probably about forty-fifty pairs in most years), was separated as *T. t. fridariensis* by K. Williamson (Ibis 93: 599); the upper parts being intermediate in colour between the typical and St Kilda forms, paler and less russet than the typical, Hebridean, or (especially) the Shetland birds; whereas the underparts are not whitish like the typical and St Kilda Wrens, but suffused buff, intermediate between the bright buff of Hebridean birds and the pale buff of the Shetland ones. The size is between that of the typical and the larger Shetland Wrens. Eggs are laid in late May and June. Rarely nests away from the sea-cliffs. Typical Wrens, presumably from Scandinavia, are recorded irregularly (in six of past seventeen years) in very small numbers between 25th September and 11th November, mostly October.

DIPPER *Cinclus cinclus*. Nine or ten spring records and three or four in autumn. Spring birds were between 19th March and 10th May, mostly end March and early April; autumn birds between 13th October and 24th December (one late November arrival stayed about five weeks). All were of the Black-bellied (typical) form from Scandinavia, except for those on 10th May 1946 (obtained) and 30th April to 7th May 1963 (trapped) which were brown-bellied birds of the British *C. c. gularis* or Middle-European form *C. c. aquaticus*.

MISTLE THRUSH *Turdus viscivorus*. Probably annual in spring (every year since 1958) and most years in autumn (all but two since 1957); a scarcity of records in 1948-56 being due to lack of coverage in early spring and late autumn. Always in very small numbers, but more in spring than autumn. Spring records are between 6th March and 13th May, mostly late March and early April, no record of more than six birds. One 27th July 1962. Autumn records 17th September to 20th December, mainly late October and early November, no record of more than two birds.

FIELDFARE *Turdus pilaris*. Regular on spring and autumn passage; a few winter, and numbers may increase with hard weather. Spring passage from late February or March, mainly mid-April, with sizeable falls in early May in some years; stragglers to late May and occasionally early June, rarely late June (late date, 30th); seldom more than 100 at peak, but up to 300 recorded. Autumn migrants rarely August (recorded from 5th), more regularly from mid-September onwards, though occasionally no records until early October. Main falls seldom occur before mid-October (500 30th September 1952 and 6th October 1955 were abnormally early) and main passage normally late October and early November, maxima varying between 100 (1961) and over 2,000. Fairly large arrivals continue to early December in some years, and a late wave of movement, apparently unrelated to hard weather and sometimes involving several hundred birds, reaches the island occasionally in the last two weeks of December, or early January.

SONG THRUSH *Turdus philomelos*. Regular on passage in spring and autumn, in extremely variable numbers; a few winter in some years, and also occur most years at midsummer (especially July). One pair bred in 1905 and 1911, two pairs in 1926. Spring movements late February or March to late May or June, mainly end March and early April; seldom more than twenty birds at peak, but occasional large falls, as on 30th March 1958 (500) and 5th-6th April 1961 (800). Autumn immigrants rarely August, more regularly from early September, with main passage last week September and early October, with small arrivals into November and sometimes a few appearing December; peak numbers usually up to fifty and occasionally up to 250. Most migrants are of the Continental (typical) form; but a few thought to have been of British origin have been examined in spring; and the midsummer birds, often in heavy moult, are usually darker and warmer brown than the majority. Five recoveries of birds ringed in March-April came from Denmark in the following May, from W. France in January, Cheshire in February, and Perthshire in June of the following year, and from Inverness two years later. Seven reports of birds ringed in late September or October were from S.W. France in November of the same year, from N. Spain in November of the following year, in late February over two years later, and in early December over three years later; from Dorset in January fifteen months later, from Denmark in October three years later, and from Portugal in March six and a half years later. One ringed late December was in Denmark the following April.

DUSKY THRUSH *Turdus eunomus*. A bird probably of this species was seen by G. Stout on 7th October 1937. A first-winter female was present 18th-21st October 1961 (trapped on 19th).

REDWING *Turdus iliacus*. Regular in spring in very variable numbers; invariably one of the most abundant migrants in autumn; a few winter in most years, and small numbers arrive in weather-movements. A pair, believed to be of the Icelandic form *T. i. coburni*, bred at Setter in 1935.

Spring movements late February or early March to mid-May and occasionally later (late date, 18th June); peak period late March and early April, maximum often less than fifty birds but sometimes up to 1,000. Except in 1935, no July records and only one in August (5th, 1961). Autumn migrants rarely early September (from 6th), more usually from third week September, until December; largest falls normally in October (especially first half) but occasional large falls early November; usually over 500 on best days, and up to 10,000 recorded. The great majority are normally of the Continental (typical) form. The Icelandic birds tend to migrate a little later in both spring and autumn, mainly mid-April and last three weeks October (early date, 30th September); always very small numbers in spring and in some years in autumn also; autumn peaks in best years are seldom over 200-300 but up to 1,000 recorded (18th October 1956). Both forms occur in winter. One Continental bird ringed on spring passage was in Portugal next January; fourteen ringed in autumn were reported as follows: six in the same autumn and winter in Banffshire (November), Holland (December), Norfolk (December), Athlone (January), and S.W. France (two, February); one next spring (end March) in Holland; four in the second autumn and winter in N.E. France (November), S. Spain (December), S.W. France (January and early March); one in S. Sweden in mid-April eighteen months later, one in Portugal in February over two years later, and one in Estonia in mid-April five and a half years later. A bird ringed as a juvenile in W. Norway in 1956 reached Fair Isle in October 1957. Eight Icelandic birds, all ringed in autumn, have been recovered: three the same autumn and winter in S.W. Norway (November), Belgium (November) and N. Ireland (January); one next spring in Aberdeen (April), one next autumn in S.W. Ireland (November), one in Lewis in April of the second year, one in S.W. France two years after ringing (November), and one in N.W. Ireland three years later (December). An adult ringed near Reykjavik in April 1963 was caught on Fair Isle the next October.

RING OUZEL *Turdus torquatus*. Annual on spring passage; almost annual (all but one of past seventeen years) in autumn. Odd birds have summered on the island (probably 1932, 1962). Earliest spring date is 18th March; first arrivals usually last days March or first week April, main arrivals (up to thirty birds recorded, but often less than ten) may occur at any time between early April and mid-May. Stragglers most years to late May and sometimes June (late date, 1st July). Autumn migrants seen from 30th August, more often from middle or end September, mostly early October (recorded maxima only six birds), with stragglers most years to early November. Several late November records (to 27th); one 18th December 1909. One ringed 22nd May 1960 was recovered in S.W. France 20th October 1960.

BLACKBIRD *Turdus merula*. Regular and often numerous in spring and autumn; a few winter, and may increase slightly with hard-weather movements in December-January. Apparently did not winter in the early years of this century, but recorded by 1927-28. Irregular breeder; up to three pairs recorded nesting in most years 1948-59, but not before or since; one or two have summered in other years. Spring migrants late February or early March to late May or early June, mainly late March and early April; maximum under fifty in some years but up to 2,000 recorded. Autumn passage occasionally late September, normally from early October, main

movements late October and early November, usually over 250 and sometimes over 2,000 at peak. Sizeable falls some years in late November,
smaller movements to late December. Nearly 150 recoveries show that
most migrants originate in Norway and winter in N. and W. Scotland and
Ireland; a smaller proportion are from Finland (one), Sweden, or Denmark, and the more southerly wintering areas of this stock in England and
Wales; one was in Belgium in autumn, and one in N. France and another
in S.W. France in winter. One ringed in March was in W. Germany next
July. Two autumn migrants had returned to Norway, one only two days
and the other twelve days after ringing. A bird ringed at Heligoland in
November was caught at Fair Isle twelve days later; one ringed at Spurn in
November was at Fair Isle exactly a year later; a nestling from S.W.
Finland reached the isle in its first November.

WHITE'S THRUSH *Turdus dauma*. Four records: single males obtained
19th October 1929 and 18th October 1944, one seen mid-November 1948,
and one seen 6th November 1958.

BLACK-THROATED THRUSH *Turdus ruficollis atrogularis*. A male (trapped)
8th December 1957 to about 22nd January 1958.

GRAY-CHEEKED THRUSH *Hylocichla minima*. First-winter birds on 5th-6th
October 1953 (first British record) and 29th October 1958, both caught.

ROCK THRUSH *Monticola saxatilis*. One reported seen 8th November
1931; a male seen by L. S. V. Venables on 16th October 1936.

WHEATEAR *Oenanthe oenanthe*. The most numerous breeding passerine;
normally abundant as a passage migrant in spring and autumn. First
birds arrive end March or beginning April (early date, 13th March),
main arrivals of local birds second half April, sometimes into early May;
Greenland/Iceland birds *Oe. oe. leucorrhoa* and 'schioleri' normally first
appear third week April, main passage early May, stragglers to mid-June
in some years. Drifted birds of European stock probably arrive in small
numbers in May also. Autumn movements sometimes begin early August,
most local and Shetland birds leave by late August; Iceland birds pass
mainly late August and early September; Greenland birds mainly through
September, peaking mid-month. Occasional large falls of drifted European
birds occur in September. Smaller movements involving both large and
small Wheatears arrive to mid-October, stragglers to end October or early
November in most years (late date, 19th November). Most eggs are laid
late May. Nineteen recoveries of local-born young show autumn passage
through England (Staffordshire and Sussex) in September, S.W. France
(four birds) late August and September, and the western half of Iberia
(two September, nine October-November) with one Morocco in November,
one S. Spain in February; while another was in Aberdeenshire next May.
Fourteen recoveries are of birds of uncertain origin: one ringed 19th May
was caught at sea about 300 m. N.W. of Fair Isle two days later; another
May bird was in Majorca next April; of the remainder, all ringed in autumn,
nine were found in the same or subsequent autumns in Scotland (one),
Holland (one, three days after ringing), N.W. France (one), S.W. France
(three), S.W. Spain (two), and Morocco (one), between August and October; one (probably a Greater Wheatear) was in Belgium in April, and two
in Shetland (April and July). Of seven recoveries of definite Greater
Wheatears, one was in N. France in November, three September returns
were in S.W. France, N.E. Spain, and S.W. Spain; whilst there are spring
recoveries near Marseilles in April, in the Dordogne (inland S.W. France)

and off Shetland in May. The spring birds in Majorca and Marseilles are well east of any reported in autumn. One bird (origin unknown) ringed at Foula in August was caught at Fair Isle next April. Local name: 'Chack'.

DESERT WHEATEAR *Oenanthe deserti*. Three records of male birds, all obtained. One 6th October 1928 was assigned to the typical form (western Sahara); one 26th October 1928 to the eastern race *Oe. d. homochroa*; and one 18th November 1940 was of uncertain race.

BLACK-EARED WHEATEAR *Oenanthe hispanica*. Two records of males of the Black-throated phase of the western (typical) form; one obtained 25th September 1907, one seen 8th-13th November 1951. A female was trapped on 19th May 1964, and a first-winter bird on 27th September 1964.

BLACK WHEATEAR *Oenanthe leucura*. Single birds seen 28th-30th September 1912 (male), and 19th October 1953 (probably female).

WHINCHAT *Saxicola rubetra*. Regular on spring and autumn passage, in very variable but normally rather small numbers. Spring records 21st April to 27th June, mostly mid-May; often less than ten at peak, but up to fifty recorded. Autumn migrants: once 22nd July, otherwise 8th August to 3rd November, mostly late August and first three weeks September with few records after first week October; usually ten to thirty on best days, occasionally up to fifty, and once 500 (4th September 1956). One ringed 6th September 1956 was found in Hampshire 10th October 1956.

STONECHAT *Saxicola torquata*. Annual in spring, except perhaps in periods of extreme scarcity following exceptionally severe winters (e.g. 1940, 1947; only two birds 1963 and only three in 1964); irregular in autumn. Spring dates are 17th February to 3rd June, mostly March and early April, few records of more than three, and none of more than seven birds on best day. Autumn records 24th August to 10th November, mostly late September and early October; nearly all single birds but rarely (as in October 1961) up to four present. One is said to have occurred in 'July and August' 1935. All the birds critically examined resembled the British stock *S. t. hibernans*, except for a female attributable to one of the eastern forms (probably *S. t. maura*) 13th-21st October 1961, trapped on 17th, and a similar female seen 1st November 1964.

REDSTART *Phoenicurus phoenicurus*. Regular in spring and autumn, in very variable numbers. In spring, said to have been seen as early as 22nd March (1909), also 24th March (1928); both dates would be more appropriate to the next species. No recent record before 9th April, and rarely arrives before third week April. Most spring birds occur in May, few records after mid-June, but seen to 28th; peak numbers seldom exceed twenty, but up to 300 recorded. One 22nd July 1950, otherwise autumn records 7th August to 11th November, mostly late August to early October; maxima often under twenty but over 1,000 present on two occasions, 4th September 1956 and 20th September 1957. A male showing the characters of Ehrenburg's Redstart *Ph. ph. samamisicus* was observed 6th September 1948.

BLACK REDSTART *Phoenicurus ochruros*. Annual in spring, and occurs almost every year in autumn. Spring records 19th March to 13th June, well-spread but slightly more in April than at other times; no record of more than three birds at once. Autumn passage rarely August (from 11th) and September, mainly late October and early November, late date 2nd December; mostly single birds and no more than two on one day.

NIGHTINGALE *Luscinia megarhynchos*. One trapped 22nd May 1949.

THRUSH NIGHTINGALE *Luscinia luscinia.* One obtained 15th May 1911 (first British); single birds, both trapped, 10th May 1957 and 15th-17th May 1958. An unidentified Nightingale was present 7th-8th May 1958.

BLUETHROAT *Cyanosylvia svecica.* The Red-spotted (typical) form is regular in spring and autumn, in very small numbers. Extreme dates for the species in spring are 22nd March and 13th June, but most if not all records before late April refer to the White-spotted form *C. s. cyanecula,* males of which have been noted on seven or eight occasions between 22nd March and 21st May. The typical form occurs mainly in May (not before 5th in recent years), sometimes only odd birds and rarely more than five at peak, but up to sixty recorded (7th-8th May 1936). Autumn records are between 1st September and 11th November, mostly September; often five to ten on best days but no more than twenty recorded; few records after mid-October. Only the typical form has been identified in autumn. A female ringed 24th May 1959 was found dying at Ostende, Belgium, four days later.

ROBIN *Erithacus rubecula.* Regular and sometimes numerous on spring and autumn passage; a few winter in most years. Spring movements late February to early June, mainly end March to mid-May, sometimes under twenty at peak but more often fifty to 100, and records of up to 500 (30th-31st March 1958). Stragglers some years late June, a few isolated records July and August. Autumn passage occasionally from late August, more regularly from mid-September, main movements normally October (especially first half) with smaller arrivals through November. In some years very few, but falls of up to 500 (5th-9th October 1961) are on record. Six birds ringed in spring have been recovered: one caught 18th May 1960, and retrapped to 25th, was on Trischen Island, Heligoland Bight, on the 30th; and one ringed 25th April 1963 was at Ottenby, Sweden, on 4th May; another was in W. France next October, others in Norfolk in March a year later, in N.E. Yorkshire in November of the following year, and in N.W. Germany in March two years after ringing. Three October birds were recovered within eight months; in N.E. France in November, Portugal in January, and near Oslo in May; while one ringed late November appeared in Bressay, Shetland, the next February. Birds ringed near Amsterdam and in Suffolk in October reached Fair Isle the following April.

SAVI'S WARBLER *Locustella luscinioides.* One obtained, of two seen, 14th May 1908.

RIVER WARBLER *Locustella fluviatilis.* One trapped 24th September 1961, seen again 25th. First British record.

GRASSHOPPER WARBLER *Locustella naevia.* Scarce and irregular on spring and autumn passage; about twice as many spring as autumn records. Spring occurrences 16th April to 29th May, mostly second and third weeks May; seen in ten of past sixteen springs. Autumn records 30th August to 15th October, mostly late September; seen in six of past seventeen autumns. No record of more than two at once in spring, and only single birds in autumn.

LANCEOLATED WARBLER *Locustella lanceolata.* Ten records. Once in spring, 4th May 1953; the rest in autumn, between 9th September and 1st November, mostly late September. One 9th September 1908 was the first British record.

PALLAS'S GRASSHOPPER WARBLER *Locustella certhiola.* One seen 6th-9th October 1949; one trapped 2nd October 1956.

GREAT REED WARBLER *Acrocephalus arundinaceus.* One 8th-11th June 1964 (caught on 8th).

REED WARBLER *Acrocephalus scirpaceus.* Rare in spring; probably annual in autumn (every year since 1955) in very small numbers. In spring, single birds obtained or trapped on five occasions, 11th May 1936, 10th June 1915, 29th June to 2nd July 1962, 23rd June 1963, and 18th June 1964; a few other sight-records have been claimed. Autumn birds recorded between 3rd August and 24th October, mostly late September, no record of more than three on one day. One ringed 4th September 1964 was recovered seventy-five miles north, in Northmavine, Shetland, three days later.

MARSH WARBLER *Acrocephalus palustris.* About seventeen identified in spring (all but three since 1950); and about eight in autumn, but only one of the autumn birds was an adult (2nd September 1962) and in the light of recent discoveries about the identification of young Reed and Marsh Warblers, the remainder should perhaps be regarded as uncertain records. Spring dates are between 29th May and 30th June; autumn ones between 16th August and 6th October. The species has apparently become more frequent in recent years; about twelve of the spring records are since 1959.

BLYTH'S REED WARBLER *Acrocephalus dumetorum.* Six or seven occurrences; one (obtained) 29th-30th September 1910 (first British); four or five present (four obtained) on 24th, 26th, 29th and 30th September and 1st October 1912; one obtained 24th September 1928.

PADDYFIELD WARBLER *Acrocephalus agricola.* One seen 26th September 1925, obtained on 1st October; one trapped 16th September 1953.

SEDGE WARBLER *Acrocephalus schoenobaenus.* Regular in small numbers in spring; rare and irregular (though each year since 1958) in autumn. Spring dates 1st May to 27th June, mainly last three weeks of May; seldom more than ten present, but up to twenty-five recorded. All autumn records are of single birds, between 28th July and 5th October, mostly mid-August to mid-September.

AQUATIC WARBLER *Acrocephalus paludicola.* Seven acceptable records: 23rd October 1914, 4th October 1935, 20th August 1950, 11th August 1956, 6th to 10th and 15th September 1958, 14th-18th September 1960, and 23rd August 1962. All except the 1950 bird were obtained or trapped.

THICK-BILLED WARBLER *Acrocephalus aedon.* One trapped 6th October 1955. First British record.

MELODIOUS WARBLER *Hippolais polyglotta.* One trapped 16th September 1955, and one 12th June 1964. A *Hippolais* almost certainly this species was seen 1st September 1962.

ICTERINE WARBLER *Hippolais icterina.* Scarce and irregular in spring and autumn; about twice as frequent in autumn as in spring. Spring records are all between 22nd May and 11th June, and all single birds except for three early June 1911; seen in eight of past sixteen springs. Autumn birds seen between 5th August and 19th September, usually singly but up to three on one day; seen in nine of past seventeen autumns, though every year 1957-63.

BOOTED WARBLER *Hippolais caligata.* One obtained 3rd September 1936 (first British); one trapped 29th August 1959, seen to 31st.

BLACKCAP *Sylvia atricapilla.* Regular in spring and autumn, in very variable numbers; has a marked tendency to 'trickle' through, rather than arrive *en masse*, even in years of abundance. Spring records 7th April to

1st July, mainly late May and early June, seldom more than three at once and never more than six. Autumn movements 24th August to 5th December, mainly late September and first three weeks October, a few regularly in early November, and often late November, in recent years; often up to ten and occasionally up to 30 at peak. One ringed 25th October 1950 was recovered in South Ronaldsay, Orkney, on 6th November; one ringed 19th October 1959 was at Elche (Alicante), Spain on 26th April 1960; and one ringed in Fife in July 1963 was caught at Fair Isle on 10th September 1963.

BARRED WARBLER *Sylvia nisoria.* No spring records; annual in small numbers in autumn. The extreme dates are 3rd August and 10th October, most records second half August and first half September; often up to three and rarely up to eight seen on best days. All records are of young birds.

GARDEN WARBLER *Sylvia borin.* Regular on spring and autumn passage; usually in rather small numbers. Spring records range from 24th April to 29th June, but seldom appears before third week of May, and most birds are seen last ten days of May and first ten days of June; daily totals rarely exceed five birds, and no record of more than twelve. One on 9th July 1959. Autumn migrants 31st July to 7th November, once 25th (1963), mostly late August and September and rarely after mid-October; often up to twenty and rarely up to fifty present at peak.

WHITETHROAT *Sylvia communis.* Regular in spring, sometimes in considerable numbers; annual but invariably in very small numbers in autumn. Spring dates 11th April to 7th July, mainly last three weeks of May; often up to fifteen and rarely up to sixty recorded on best days. Autumn records 21st July to 15th October, mostly end August and first three weeks September; sometimes only single birds, rarely more than five, and no record of more than ten at peak.

LESSER WHITETHROAT *Sylvia curruca.* Regular on spring and autumn passage; usually in small numbers. Spring birds usually much outnumber autumn ones. Spring records 23rd April to 25th June, but rarely seen before second week of May; most occur mid-May to first week of June; daily maxima seldom reached ten birds in recent years, once fifteen (11th May 1950) and once fifty (20th May 1951). Was probably much commoner before 1912, for Clarke described it as the commonest of warblers after the Willow; but no record of large numbers after 1912 except for a report of 'hundreds' 7th-16th May 1936. Autumn records 8th August to 25th October, mainly September; sometimes only one or two seen, but often a succession of small arrivals; seldom more than four and never more than six at peak. Birds showing the wing-formula of the Siberian race *S. c. blythi* (first recorded for Britain at Fair Isle in October 1921) have been obtained or trapped on many occasions in September and October, mainly late September.

SUBALPINE WARBLER *Sylvia cantillans.* Six records: male obtained 6th May 1908; single males (all trapped) 20th-27th May 1951, 9th June 1951, 12th June 1958, and 23rd April 1964; a female trapped 13th and seen 14th June 1958.

WILLOW WARBLER *Phylloscopus trochilus.* Regular in spring and autumn, in variable numbers but usually the commonest warbler; more numerous in autumn than in spring in most years. Owing to confusion with the Chiffchaff, the earliest and latest dates are rather uncertain. In spring, reported seen as early as 23rd March, but earliest acceptable record is for 8th April; the main movements occur in May, with light passage early

June, and stragglers recorded to 1st July. Peak numbers in some springs less than ten, often twenty to fifty, once 300 (15th May 1960); also a report of 'vast numbers' 12th-15th May 1911. Acceptable autumn records are from 29th July to 28th October, with old sight-records for 4th and 22nd-23rd November; main passage second half August and first week September, fewer to early October; often thirty-fifty birds at peak, and up to 500 recorded (5th September 1956). Many of the migrants at both seasons are referable to the Northern form *Ph. t. acredula*.

CHIFFCHAFF *Phylloscopus collybita*. Regular passage-migrant in spring and autumn, in small numbers; usually more numerous in autumn. Earliest spring date unknown, but said to have occurred many times in late March; three 'Willow Warblers' seen 23rd March 1954 were more probably this species. Observatory spring records range from 31st March to 1st July: mostly second half April, with odd birds through May in most years, and irregularly in June; no record of more than seven on one day. Autumn records from 21st July but rarely before early September, main movements usually first three weeks October, fewer into early November in most years, and stragglers recorded until 27th, also 'early December' 1944; sometimes only odd birds in autumn, but often five-ten at peak, no record of more than sixteen. Spring birds are mainly of the typical form and the Scandinavian form *Ph. c. abietinus* or intergrades, though Siberian Chiffchaffs *Ph. c. tristis*, are said to have been identified in May. Autumn birds include a few resembling the typical form (chiefly early in the passage), the main October movements being composed largely of 'Northern' Chiffchaffs with good examples of *tristis* occurring sparsely in October-November and much outnumbered by specimens closer to *abietinus*.

BONELLI'S WARBLER *Phylloscopus bonelli*. A first-winter bird trapped on 22nd September 1961.

GREENISH WARBLER *Phylloscopus trochiloides*. Six records. One trapped 2nd and seen 3rd June 1949; single birds (all trapped) on 19th September 1950, 15th-23rd July 1955, 7th-9th September 1960, 19th August 1961; and one seen 4th September 1961.

DUSKY WARBLER *Phylloscopus fuscatus*. One trapped 14th October 1961.

WOOD WARBLER *Phylloscopus sibilatrix*. Scarce and irregular in spring; almost annual, in very small numbers, in autumn. Recorded in only five springs, but in thirteen autumns, between 1948 and 1964; but in the early years of the century it was apparently more frequent in spring than in autumn. Spring records are between 26th April and 18th June, mostly May; usually single birds but once four present (6th May 1952), and 'many' 12th-18th May 1910. A report for 29th March 1954 seems very improbable. Autumn records 30th July to 22nd September, mainly August, seldom more than two present and no record of more than four (22nd August 1963).

ARCTIC WARBLER *Phylloscopus borealis*. Twenty dated records (thirteen, involving fifteen birds, since 1950, including each year 1959-62 and 1964), and others are said to have been seen. All were in autumn, and all between 14th August and 28th September, except for single records on 30th July and 18th October. All single birds apart from two present on 30th August 1950, and 12th September 1964. Two different individuals occurred in September 1954, three in September 1959, and four in August-September 1964.

YELLOW-BROWED WARBLER *Phylloscopus inornatus*. Regular in small numbers on autumn passage; seen every year 1948-64 except 1952. Acceptable records are between 29th August and 29th October, with one reported 24th November 1925; mainly late September and early October; sometimes only single birds, more often several records of one or two individuals each autumn, but up to six recorded on one day. The *Handbook* refers to a spring occurrence on 31st March 1936, but no details of this record are known.

GOLDCREST *Regulus regulus*. Regular on spring and autumn passage; usually far more in autumn than in spring. Spring occurrences between 17th March and 1st June, mainly mid-April; no record of more than six on one day. Autumn records 23rd August to 22nd November, main passage end September and especially early October; occasionally only odd birds but often up to twenty at peak, and up to 300 (5th October 1959) on record.

SPOTTED FLYCATCHER *Muscicapa striata*. Regular in spring and autumn, generally more numerous in spring. Spring records 20th April to 4th July, but seldom seen before second and often not until third week of May, main movements late May and first week June, stragglers later. Peak numbers reached double figures in only five springs since 1949, maximum forty on 3rd June 1963; but Clarke refers to big 'rushes' in the early part of the century, as on 12th-15th and 20th May 1910, and large numbers were reported 7th-16th May 1936. Has always been rather scarce in autumn; recorded on 2nd August (1952) and between 20th August and 22nd October, with peak numbers at any time between late August and early October; seldom more than five and never more than twenty on best days. One ringed 27th August 1960 was recovered at Valdagno (Vicenza), Italy on 27th October 1960.

PIED FLYCATCHER *Muscicapa hypoleuca*. Regular in spring and autumn. Spring records 1st May to 24th June, mainly mid-May, seldom more than three to five birds present at peak, but up to forty recorded (13th May 1960), and said to have occurred in 'enormous numbers' 7th-12th May 1936. Autumn occurrences from 22nd July to 29th October (but rarely before mid-August or after mid-October), main movements end August and early September, often ten-twenty at peak and up to 200 (5th September 1956) on record. Was apparently less numerous in autumn in the early decades of this century than in recent years. One ringed 21st September 1960 was recovered at Zarauz (Guipuzcoa) Spain about 23rd October 1960, and one ringed 31st May 1961 was at Agadir, Morocco, on 9th May 1963.

RED-BREASTED FLYCATCHER *Muscicapa parva*. A few most years (every year 1957-64) in autumn; four or five spring records. Spring dates are between 20th May and 21st June (the last being perhaps a bird seen earlier on 4th-5th June). Autumn records 25th August to 7th November, mostly late September and early October, though the record total of five birds was on 5th September 1958. Most records are of single birds.

HEDGE SPARROW *Prunella modularis*. Regular on spring passage, almost annual in autumn. Spring records are between 11th March and 21st June, mainly end March and April, only stragglers in late May and in some years in early June. Birds often trickle through over a period of weeks with no pronounced peaks; few records of more than ten present, none of more than thirty except for an arrival of 150 18th-20th April 1962. Autumn occurrences 5th September to 13th December, mainly late September and early October (but peak said to have been 'last week October' before 1912); often only odd birds but occasionally up to fifteen (23rd September, 3rd and 6th October 1961) recorded. The great majority at both seasons are of the pale-bellied Continental (typical) form, but birds resembling the darker British *P. m. occidentalis* or 'Hebridean' *P. m. hebridium* forms occurred 4th-6th April 1961 (two or three), 17th-18th March 1963 (at least four) and perhaps 14th May 1949. One ringed 29th April 1961 was caught at Heligoland on 17th May 1961; another ringed 27th April 1962 at March, Cambridgeshire, on 3rd May 1962; and one ringed 30th March 1963 at Isle of May on 11th April 1963; all suggesting that spring birds reach the island by overshooting, and quickly return south.

ALPINE ACCENTOR *Prunella collaris*. Single birds seen 6th October 1908 and 27th-28th June 1959; said also to have occurred on 14th September 1930 and 24th September 1933, but no details available.

MEADOW PIPIT *Anthus pratensis*. A common breeding bird; numerous on passage in spring and autumn; few winter records. Usually first seen in early or mid-March but not in numbers until mid-April; departs mainly in late August and early September, with stragglers into October. Eggs are laid from early May (perhaps occasionally late April), mainly mid-May onwards; some may be double-brooded but most late nests are probably replacements. According to Clarke (1912) the species was then 'not a native bird', but the same writer had described it as a 'common summer visitor' in 1906. Passage-migration occurs chiefly from mid-April to mid-May and from mid-August to late September, with moderate falls in early October and small arrivals to mid-November in some years. Last dates are from first week November onwards, and occasional birds attempt to winter but rarely survive until January. One stayed to 14th January 1952, and records on 19th January 1915, 27th January and 14th February (both before 1912) may refer to such wintering individuals. In 1964 there were several records from 26th January onwards, and three birds on 26th February. Ten local young birds have been recovered in the first autumn and winter: in S.W. France (three, October to January), Portugal (four, September to January), and S.W. Spain (three, October to January), while another was in S.W. Spain in February of its third year. Of twenty others ringed in late August to early October, thirteen were recovered within six months: in Fife (November), Holland (February), S.W. France (three October, one February), N. Spain (October), Portugal (November and January), S.W. Spain (October, November and December), and Morocco (November and January); while six were recovered in later years (up to four and a half years later) in Belgium (December), S.W. France (October), Portugal (January), S.W. Spain (November and January) and N. Italy (November).

TREE PIPIT *Anthus trivialis*. Regular in spring and autumn, in very variable numbers. Spring records 14th April to 24th June, mainly May, and seldom seen before last week April or after first week June; often up to fifteen-twenty on best days, once 100 (13th May 1960) and once 500 (6th May 1952). Autumn movements 11th August to 25th October and once 9th November; mainly September; peaks rarely exceed ten-twenty birds but up to 100 (20th September 1957) and once 500 (4th-5th September 1956) on record.

PETCHORA PIPIT *Anthus gustavi*. About fourteen acceptable records, since the first British record on 23rd-24th September 1925, and said to have been seen but not recorded on many other occasions. All dated records are between 18th September and 19th November, mostly late September and early October, but one is reported to have occurred in 'late August' 1931. All were single birds except for two or three (one obtained) on 27th October 1930.

RED-THROATED PIPIT *Anthus cervinus*. About five spring and nine autumn records; said to have been seen on other occasions but not recorded. The spring records were in 1936, 1952, 1954, 1958, and 1959, all between 8th and 31st May, and all single birds except for 'six' 8th May 1936. The autumn occurrences were between 16th September and 1st November, in 1908 (two records), 1931, 1937 (two), 1957, and 1960 (three); all were single birds.

RICHARD'S PIPIT *Anthus novaeseelandiae*. Irregular in autumn (though each year 1957-64), mainly single birds but several records of up to three and once five (14th November 1951). Recorded once in August (two between 17th and 24th, 1953) otherwise all between 21st September and 14th November, mostly end September and early October. Said to have occurred in April 1935, and one seen 21st May 1964.

TAWNY PIPIT *Anthus campestris*. Four documented records: one obtained 'spring' 1933, one observed 6th June 1963, one 15th-17th September 1951 (trapped 17th) and one obtained 8th October 1935. One is also said to have been seen in early May 1943.

ROCK PIPIT *Anthus spinoletta*. A common breeding bird, present in numbers at all seasons, though some (probably all birds of the year) emigrate in autumn. The local birds belong to the form *A. s. kleinschmidti*. Passage is difficult to detect, but increases are noted in most years in late August or September, occasionally early October; and rarely in early May. Birds resembling the Scandinavian race *A. s. littoralis* have been obtained or seen on several occasions in mid-May; an American Water Pipit *A. s. rubescens* was observed on 17th September 1953. The breeding birds are mainly on the coast, but some inland on the hill ground; eggs are laid from early or mid-May, mainly second half of May. Local young have been recovered up to two and a half years later in Orkney (December), Caithness (December and January), Banffshire (January), and Aberdeenshire (April), while one ringed in July 1956 was found long dead at Den Helder, N. Holland, in March 1958. Local name (probably applied sometimes to Meadow Pipit also): 'Stinkle'.

WHITE/PIED WAGTAIL *Motacilla alba*. The White Wagtail (typical form) is regular in spring and autumn passage; a pair bred in 1909, 1910, 1911, about 1933, about 1944, and 1963. Earliest spring date is 8th March, first usually arrive second half March, but in some years not until early April. Main spring movements late April and early May; often fails to reach double figures on best day, occasionally ten to twenty, no recent record of more than twenty-five; but 'abundant', 'very considerable movement' are terms used early in the century. Stragglers occur in some years to June, more rarely in July; single birds have remained for some days or weeks at midsummer. Autumn passage starts end July or early August, main passage late August and early September; usually twenty to forty birds at peak, and up to 200 recorded. In some years all depart by late September or early October; stragglers fairly often in late October and rarely early November, last date 17th. One ringed 22nd April 1963 was found dead in N.E. Yorkshire two weeks later; one ringed late August 1957 was in

Mauretania in October of the following year; and one ringed 4th September 1954 was caught on a fishing-boat in the Moray Firth two days later. A chick ringed at Skipalon, N. Iceland, on 18th July 1962 reached Fair Isle on 26th August of the same year. The Pied Wagtail *M. a. yarrellii* is regular in spring in very small numbers. Records extend from 1st March to 30th June, but mostly second half March and first half April, few later; often up to three present but no record of more than five. This race is said to have bred once, between the wars, but no details are known. A few autumn records were made in the early decades of the century, between 22nd July and 1st October, 'mostly August', but none were definitely identified in recent years until several occurred in September 1964.

GREY WAGTAIL *Motacilla cinerea*. Almost annual in spring, scarce and irregular in autumn. A pair bred successfully in 1950. Spring records are between 16th March and 8th June (except 1950), with no marked peak-period (though with more observations in early April this may prove to be the best time). Autumn occurrences 27th September to 31st October, mainly early October, and once 'November'. Mostly single birds and no record of more than two at either season, apart from the 1950 family. One ringed 1st June 1954 was recovered in Orkney seven weeks later.

YELLOW-HEADED WAGTAIL *Motacilla citreola*. Six records. Single birds, trapped, on 20th-24th September 1954 (first British), 1st-5th October 1954, and 22nd-25th September 1962, others seen on 17th-22nd October 1960, 4th-13th September 1961, and 19th September 1964.

YELLOW WAGTAIL *Motacilla flava*. The species occurs regularly in spring and most years in autumn (all except three autumns 1948-63) in very small numbers; seldom more than two or three present, and no record of more than six present in spring or eight in autumn. The extreme dates appear under the races listed below. The Blue-headed (typical) form has been the most frequent race, identified in spring between 19th April and 13th June (mostly first three weeks of May); up to five seen at one time. Autumn records between 24th August and 20th November (mostly September and first week October), up to seven on best day. The Grey-headed form *M. f. thunbergi* occurs most years in spring, recorded between 25th April and 9th June but mostly last three weeks of May, with up to five on best days; and has been identified on rare occasions in autumn, between 4th September and 6th November, no more than two at once. A male bird showing the characters of Sykes's Wagtail *M. f. beema* was obtained on 18th May 1910, and specimens resembling the Eastern Blue-headed *M. f. simillima* were collected on 25th September 1912, 9th October 1909, and 4th November 1908. The British Yellow Wagtail *M. f. flavissima* appears most years in spring, having been reported 25th March to 1st April 1954 and otherwise records of up to four birds between 21st April and 11th June, mostly late April and early May. There are no autumn records of this form.

WAXWING *Bombycilla garrulus*. Three spring records, 20th February 1937, 3rd-4th April 1944 (two), and 22nd April 1960 (recently dead). Odd birds appear most years in autumn (each year 1957-63), with larger numbers in irruption years such as 1943 ('several hundreds' in mid-October), 1949 (twenty 10th-12th November), 1957 (ten 13th November), and 1963 (fifty 2nd November). The extreme dates are 14th October and 21st December, the majority of records being in November. One occurred 12th-13th January 1964.

GREAT GREY SHRIKE *Lanius excubitor*. Irregular in spring, almost annual in autumn, in very small numbers. Spring records are between 2nd April and 7th May, mostly mid-April, all single birds. Autumn occurrences are between 3rd September and 15th November, mainly October; with one 21st December 1962; mostly singles but up to five (4th November 1963) on record. A bird showing the characters of the Steppe Shrike *L. e. pallidirostris* was trapped 22nd September 1956; another present 17th-18th October 1964 (trapped 18th).

LESSER GREY SHRIKE *Lanius minor*. Seven spring records, including two old sight-records of which no details are known; all single birds, between 25th May and 5th June. In autumn, two undocumented records for 'third week October' 1944 and 1st November 1940; and three birds in 1955, on 16th and 19th September (two) and 8th October; two of these were trapped.

WOODCHAT SHRIKE *Lanius senator*. Six spring records and one in autumn. The spring birds were on 4th June 1913 (female, obtained), 31st May 1945, 22nd-23rd May 1953, and single males 23rd-25th May 1957 (trapped), 12th-15th May 1960, and 2nd-22nd June 1963 (trapped). A juvenile was seen 29th August 1960 and trapped 1st September.

RED-BACKED SHRIKE *Lanius cristatus*. Birds of the western form *L. c. collurio* are regular in spring and autumn (since 1948, absent only in spring 1952), but in very small numbers. Considerably more spring than autumn birds. Spring dates 8th May to 2nd July, mainly late May and first week June; often up to three present but no record of more than seven, except perhaps in 1910 when 'very common' 12th-23rd May. Autumn dates 9th August to 6th October, mainly end August and early September, usually only single birds and no record of more than four present. Nearly all autumn birds are juveniles. A male Red-tailed Shrike *L. c. phoenicuroides* or *isabellinus* was present 12th-13th May 1960 (trapped).

STARLING *Sturnus vulgaris*. A common breeding bird; many of the breeders are resident, though some, mainly juveniles, emigrate in autumn. Abundant on passage in spring and autumn, mainly late March-early April and October-early November; with weather-movements occasionally during the winter. The local birds, which mostly resemble the poorly-defined Shetland form *S. v. zetlandicus*, lay eggs late April to mid-May; some (probably under half the breeding population) are double-brooded. Most of the migrants are Continental (typical) birds; many large movements are nocturnal, seen at the lighthouses, with little or no corresponding increase on the island next day; diurnal movements rarely occur and are usually of small proportions. Nineteen local juveniles ringed in summer and early autumn have been recovered up to five years later as follows: three in Shetland (February, October, November), nine Orkney (four January, two May, July, November and December), Caithness (January), Ross (December), Aberdeenshire (June), Angus (March and September), in the North Sea near Dogger Bank in October, and on a vessel twenty miles south of Iceland in late February. The summer recoveries in Orkney and Aberdeenshire suggest that some local-born emigrants remain to breed further south. Four other birds of doubtful origin, recovered in Shetland (October and February), Orkney (January) and Aberdeenshire (March) were most likely also of local stock. Eleven passage-migrants were recovered later; four in Norway (at Tromso in March, at Trondhjem in April, in Aust Agder in April, and in Sor Trondelag in June) one in Finland (May), one in W. Germany (April), one in W. Russia (May), one Denmark (July), one N. Ireland (January); while the remaining two made southward movements within a short time of being ringed in spring, one to Norfolk only eleven days after ringing, the other found on board a ship in the North Sea within a month of ringing.

ROSE-COLOURED STARLING *Sturnus roseus*. Irregular visitor. About eighteen dated records (eleven in eight years between 1948 and 1963) and the species is said to have been seen on many other occasions. Three records, all old ones, were in spring: single males in 'spring' 1907 and 1908, one for several days in June 1937. One present 2nd July 1951. The remaining birds were between 29th July and 15th November, mostly August and early September, and mainly adults in August and juveniles later in the season; usually only single birds but two present on one occasion (12th September 1958).

HAWFINCH *Coccothraustes coccothraustes*. Eleven records (seven since 1951), all of single birds; ten between 23rd March and 19th June, and one 22nd July.

GREENFINCH *Chloris chloris*. Formerly a regular and sometimes fairly numerous autumn migrant, and annual but scarcer in spring; numbers wintered, or remained well into the winter, in some years. In the observatory period it has been decidedly scarcer and less regular, though a few are seen most years either in spring or autumn or both. Spring records mainly late March to mid-April, odd birds occasionally into May (late date, 20th May, and once 21st June); no more than three birds at once in recent years. Autumn records are from 3rd October, mainly mid-October to early November, and none later than 9th December recently; often only odd birds and no record of more than twelve on best day since 1948 (19th October 1959).

GOLDFINCH *Carduelis carduelis*. One seen 9th September 1929, one 11th and 13th May 1954, and one 21st-25th November 1964.

SISKIN *Carduelis spinus*. Occurs most years on autumn passage (since 1948, every year except 1948, 1951, and 1954) in very variable numbers. Probably irregular in spring (though each year since complete coverage started in 1958), always in very small numbers. Spring records extend from 13th March to 6th July, mainly mid-April to early June, seldom more than one or two present and no record of more than four. Autumn records 8th September to 24th December, mainly end September and early October, with later movements in the larger irruptions. In some years very few; in recent irruption years (1953, 1959 to 1962 inclusive) between thirty and 120 present at peak; described as 'exceptionally abundant' 28th September to 4th October 1909, also 'a good many' 29th September 1913.

LINNET *Carduelis cannabina*. Small numbers annually in spring, and irregularly in autumn; occasional midsummer records; a good many old winter records, but none in recent years. Spring passage early March to early June, mainly end March to early May, rarely more than five present and no record of more than twelve (14th-15th April 1961). A few occurrences late June, July, and August, mostly odd birds but up to five in July. Autumn records well-spread from early September to mid-November with a slight predominance in late September and early October, no record of more than three birds. Up to three birds seen in all months late November to late February in ten years between 1911 and 1937, but none since then.

TWITE *Carduelis flavirostris*. A fairly common breeding bird, though formerly much more numerous. The species is now a summer visitor to the island, arriving from late February or early March, mainly late April and first days of May; departing mostly in early October, with a few into November. Early in the century, the autumn population was 'to be reckoned in thousands', and 'numbers' remained for the winter. In the past decade the population has declined steadily, probably accelerated by the impact of toxic chemicals from 1961; and there is no record of birds wintering since a few did so in 1951-52, though some appear occasionally in all winter months. Eggs are laid from end May or early June, mainly mid-June onwards; with replacements (probably not second broods) in July. Some light passage (probably of Shetland birds) is detected between late August and early October in most years. One ringed 2nd October 1949 was found in Westray, Orkney, on 31st January 1950, and another ringed 26th July 1953 was recovered on board a ship between Germany and Denmark (presumably in the North Sea) in October 1953. Local name (obsolete): 'Lintie'.

REDPOLL *Carduelis flammea*. The species occurs most years in spring, in very small numbers; rarely at midsummer, and annually in autumn, in very variable numbers; a few occasionally remain for all or part of the winter. The Mealy Redpoll (typical form) appears in most years and is the only form noted in winter or from June to mid-August. Winter and spring records cover all periods up to 16th June, with most occurrences between late March and late May; no recent record of more than six, but 'most numerous' 8th May 1911. The July records are all since 1960: 24th July 1960, 11th-22nd July 1962 (up to four), and 9th July 1963. Other autumn records extend from 6th August to the end of the year, but seldom seen before mid-September, and most of the larger arrivals have occurred late October and early November. There were massive irruptions in late October 1910 and 1923 (over 100 on 22nd October 1923), but nothing on the same scale more recently, when arrivals have only once reached double figures (up to thirteen in early November 1962). Most records of wintering, or of visitors during the winter, follow autumns when the race occurs in above-average numbers. Winter scores rarely more than three or four birds. The Greenland Redpoll *C. f. rostrata* is subject to wider fluctuations in numbers than the Mealy, at any rate since 1948. It appears most years in autumn, but much less frequently in spring. Spring records (in 1936 and six years since 1949) are between 1st April and 23rd May, mostly end April to mid-May, no more than four recorded on one day. Autumn records fall between 26th August and 5th December, mostly September and early October, so that arrivals tend to be earlier than in Mealy Redpoll. The main recorded irruptions were in 1905 ('extremely abundant' late September), 1925 (thirty-forty from 28th August), 1955 (from 26th August, up to thirteen mid-September, up to thirty reported mid-November), and 1959 (up to twenty in September); in other years seldom more than five and no more than ten at peak. The Lesser Redpoll *C. f. cabaret* or *disruptis* has eleven records (eight in five years since 1957); all of single birds except for three on 16th May 1936. Six records were in spring, between 24th April and 16th June, and five in autumn between 12th September and 31st October.

ARCTIC REDPOLL *Carduelis hornemanni*. The Hornemann's Redpoll (typical form) has seven dated records, only one in the observatory period (1950). All were in autumn, between 18th September and 12th November, in 1905 (three records, one of three birds), 1925, 1932, 1935, and 1950.

Coues's Redpoll *C. h. exilipes* was obtained three times in 1910 (26th October, 3rd and 5th November) and on 22nd October 1923, all with irrupting Mealy Repolls; an adult female and three immatures were present on 19th October 1961 (two trapped). Other 'Arctic' Redpolls are said to have occurred on a good many occasions 'in winter', but the name is sometimes applied to birds of the Greenland race of *C. flammea*.

SERIN *Serinus canarius*. A female obtained 22nd May 1914, a male seen 25th May 1957, and one 29th May 1964.

BULLFINCH *Pyrrhula pyrrhula*. Seen most years in autumn; less frequent in spring; an occasional visitor during the winter. All specimens examined have been referable to the Northern (typical) form. Autumn records, apart from one reported 4th September 1936, are all from 16th October onwards, mostly end October and early November; up to a dozen were noted in November 1906, and a 'more remarkable visitation' in late October to December 1910, while 'flocks' were reported in October 1934; otherwise no record of more than five, and rarely more than two present. In a few years, birds have remained until the end of the year, otherwise occasional records of one or two December to late February. Spring migrants have appeared between 27th March and 8th May, no more than two at once.

SCARLET GROSBEAK *Carpodacus erythrinus*. Annual in autumn, in very small numbers; many records of up to three, but none of more than four at once. The extreme dates are 24th August to 21st November, mostly September and rarely after mid-October. Winter records were made on 11th January 1930 (three) and 9th February 1945 (adult male), and spring birds were seen on 2nd April 1926 and 7th April 1944. All the autumn birds have been immatures or females.

PARROT CROSSBILL *Loxia pityopsittacus*. Recorded only in autumn 1962 and spring 1963. The autumn birds arrived 27th September (twenty increasing to thirty-three on 4th October), and after a decrease a second wave of twenty-five 11th-12th October (thirty-four trapped and two others examined). Two present (male trapped) 20th March 1963.

CROSSBILL *Loxia curvirostra*. Irregular in summer and autumn, between 24th May and 5th November; no records outside this period, except for one on 27th January 1964 (G. Barnes). Large irruptions were recorded in 1909, 1927, 1929, perhaps 1930, 1935, 1953, 1956, 1959, 1962, and 1963, peak numbers ranging from fifty to 300. Odd birds or small parties were seen in 1910, 1911, 1919, 1957, 1958 and 1964. All large arrivals have been between late June and mid-August, with few records after September. One ringed on 6th July 1953 was recovered at Bergamo, N. Italy, on 25th August 1953.

TWO-BARRED CROSSBILL *Loxia leucoptera*. Seven or eight acceptable records, and said to have been seen on other occasions. The dated records are one in June (13th, 1908), three in July (4th, 1953; 10th, 1909; and 29th-31st, 1962) all the rest in September, on 2nd and 5th, 1927; 12th (three birds) and 18th, 1930; and 29th (three), 1939.

CHAFFINCH *Fringilla coelebs*. Regular in spring and autumn, in very variable numbers; odd birds have wintered, or visited the island in winter, in some recent years, and there are a few records of summering on the island. The species apparently wintered regularly in some numbers early in the century, when a much larger acreage was under grain crops. Spring passage is from March to May or early June, mainly late March and early

April; often less than twenty birds at peak, but up to 1,000 (1st April 1958) recorded. Autumn movements September to November, mainly end September and October, usually fifty to 200 at peak and up to 500 noted (an exceptionally early arrival on 21st September 1961). Most of the migrants resemble the Scandinavian (typical) form; birds with the characters of *F. c. hortensis* (middle Europe) have been caught in spring.

BRAMBLING *Fringilla montifringilla*. Regular in spring and autumn; formerly wintered on the isle, but not recently, though odd birds still appear at rare intervals December to February. Spring passage March to May or early June (late date, 15th), mainly April; seldom more than ten at peak but up to eighty (22nd April 1962) on record. Much commoner in autumn, seen from 10th September but rarely appears before the end of that month, main movements in October with smaller arrivals into November; usually fifty to 200 at peak, and up to 500 (21st October 1955) recorded. One ringed 11th October 1962 was recovered in Liège, Belgium, on 18th October 1964.

CORN BUNTING *Emberiza calandra*. A few bred in 1905 (and perhaps earlier), and at least one pair in 1911. Except in these years, has been an irregular visitor in autumn and winter, and probably annual (all but one year since 1949) in spring. Apart from one 6th August 1952, the extreme dates are 11th September to 8th June, mostly late October-November and late March to May; but a good many records for all midwinter months. Seldom more than two present, but up to six recorded in winter (January-February) and up to thirteen (22nd-23rd October 1959) in autumn.

YELLOWHAMMER *Emberiza citrinella*. Annual in spring, and occurs most years in autumn; formerly more frequent as an occasional visitor in winter, a few over-wintered in 1913-14, but very few recent records December to February. Spring records late February or March to June (late date, 23rd), mostly end March and early April but often seen until late May; usually fewer than five at peak but up to eleven on record (27th February 1926), and 'considerable passage' 26th April to 3rd May 1926. Autumn records begin 'second week September', but rarely before early October, main period late October and early November; no more than five at once except for twelve on 26th October 1961 and fifteen on 20th October 1959; and 'unusually numerous' 17th October 1910.

PINE BUNTING *Emberiza leucocephala*. A male obtained 30th October 1911; first British. (Some authorities treat this species as a race of *E. citrinella*.)

BLACK-HEADED BUNTING *Emberiza melanocephala*. Four records; a female 21st September 1907 and 13th September 1951; a male 27th May 1929 and 5th-13th June 1962. The last was believed to be an 'escape'.

RED-HEADED BUNTING *Emberiza bruniceps*. Ten records, all of males and all since 1950. Probably all or most were 'escapes', one undoubtedly was from the condition of the flight-feathers. Three occurred in spring, between 20th April and 7th June, in 1957 and 1961 (two). Seven in autumn, between 18th July and 22nd September, in 1950, 1951, 1953, 1958, 1960 and 1964. (Now often treated as a race of *E. melanocephala*.)

YELLOW-BREASTED BUNTING *Emberiza aureola*. Eight records. Single birds in 'September' 1907 and 1909 (collected) were not correctly identified until several years later; an adult male obtained 13th July 1951, and five records of immature birds (one possibly adult female), all between 3rd and 16th September, in 1946, 1958, 1962, and 1963 (two).

ORTOLAN *Emberiza hortulana*. Almost annual in spring and autumn; seen in all but four springs and four autumns 1948-64. Spring dates 26th April to 23rd June, mostly May, rarely more than two present but up to sixteen (9th May 1952) recorded, and 'a few on every croft' 8th May 1914. Autumn occurrences 18th August to 11th November, mostly end August and early September and rarely after September, usually only one or two present and no record of more than five at once.

RUSTIC BUNTING *Emberiza rustica*. Six spring records, and twelve or thirteen in autumn. Appears to have had three periods of relative abundance, as four of these records were between 1908 and 1913, three in 1925-27, and nine or ten in 1957-64 (the remaining two were in 1938 and 1946). The spring dates are between 11th May and 30th June (three in each month), and the autumn ones between 19th September and 26th October (all but three arrived in late September). All single birds except for two 14th May 1962 and 27th September 1927. One ringed 12th June 1963 was recovered on the island of Kios (Aegean Sea) in mid-October 1963.

LITTLE BUNTING *Emberiza pusilla*. Rare in spring (ten records, six in five years since 1950); almost annual in autumn (every year since 1957). Spring dates are 4th April to 19th May, mostly May; nearly all single birds but two on two occasions. Autumn dates 26th August to 17th November, mostly mid-September to mid-October, usually single birds (but often several in a season), occasionally two and up to six recorded at once.

REED BUNTING *Emberiza schoeniclus*. Regular in spring and autumn, usually in very small numbers. Spring birds from 13th February; one or two rather irregularly in February and March, regularly April-May with peak period in May; a few June records, to 19th. Peak numbers exceeded ten on only three occasions in 1949-64, maximum thirty 6th May 1952; but 'hundreds' recorded 12th May 1910 and 7th-16th May 1936. Autumn dates 4th September to 28th November, mostly October; seldom more than five present and no record of more than seventeen (5th-7th October 1959). One ringed 6th October 1959 was found at Ste. Eulalie-en-Born (Landes), France on 16th January 1960.

SONG SPARROW *Melospiza melodia*. A male trapped 27th April 1959 remained until 10th May. First British record.

LAPLAND BUNTING *Calcarius lapponicus*. A few almost annually in spring; regular in very variable numbers in autumn. Spring records 20th March to 1st June, but rarely before mid-April or after mid-May; often up to three but no record of more than six (24th April 1961). Autumn dates 23rd August to 3rd December, mainly September and seldom after late October. Maxima of under ten birds in nine years 1948-64; highest recorded numbers forty 10th September 1949 and 19th September 1962, seventy 9th September and eighty 12th September 1953, and ninety 13th September 1960. In earlier years no record of more than twenty, and over ten only in 1912 and 1925.

SNOW BUNTING *Plectrophenax nivalis*. Regular on passage in spring and autumn; a few overwinter and larger numbers occur with weather-movements in winter; occasional summer records. Spring movements mainly late February to early April, often up to 200 and occasionally up to 600 at peak (28th February 1958); smaller numbers to early May and in most years late May; a few June records and single birds (perhaps present since spring) between 6th and 30th July in three recent years. A pair is said to have summered, and was suspected of breeding on Ward Hill, 'one year' about half a century ago. Other autumn dates are from 20th August onwards, though seldom before early September; occasional large movements in second half September and early October (2,000 16th September 1949 but usually under 200 at this time); main passage normally mid-October to mid-November (300-800 on best days), with occasional large falls to mid-December. Winter population often under fifty, but passage of up to several hundreds occasionally late December to March, often moving south out of Shetland with the onset of hard weather or returning north after the end of a cold period. One ringed 31st October 1955 was caught at Spurn, Yorkshire, 28th January 1956; another ringed 7th April 1959 was at Fogo Island, Newfoundland, 1st May 1960. Local name (obsolete): 'Snaafool'.

HOUSE SPARROW *Passer domesticus*. A numerous resident; no evidence of migration. Abundant in the early years of the century (autumn numbers said to have reached 800), but a marked decrease, thought to have been due to 'some disease of an epidemic nature' in 1926, and reduced to about ten pairs in 1927, only four pairs 1928. This was followed by a gradual recovery ('two or three score' in 1935). In recent years the breeding population has been of the order of 50-100 pairs, but probably only thirty-forty pairs in 1963. The birds are normally confined to the crofting area in the south, but occasionally wander as far afield as the North Lighthouse (chiefly in late summer and autumn) and a pair bred at North Haven in 1960 after an unsuccessful attempt in 1959.

TREE SPARROW *Passer montanus*. Resident up to about 1924, perhaps bred 1930 and 1933, at least one pair 1936, and one to three pairs annually 1961-64; irregular spring and autumn visitor, mainly in the recent period of expansion. The size of the pre-1924 population is not known accurately, but there is a record of forty seen in February 1911. The colony's disappearance was followed by isolated records in April 1926, May and August 1927 (perhaps survivors of the breeding stock); from 1927 no exact dates are recorded until 31st August 1936, when three adults and one or two juveniles were seen by L. S. V. Venables, who was informed that 'two or three pairs' had bred. One was recorded 5th-6th June 1937, but no further records known until two birds 4th May 1955; followed by up to three in late May 1957 and one 5th September 1957. In 1958 there was one 4th April and up to fifteen in mid-May, two of which summered; they were joined by up to eleven others in late August, but all had gone by 12th November. In 1959 there were only odd records in October-November, but in 1960 two appeared 27th March and up to seven in May and early June. In autumn 1960 odd birds arrived from 23rd August, increasing to twenty-seven on 8th October; eleven of these wintered on the island. They were joined by others in mid-April 1961 and the flock increased to twenty in late May; some passed on, but at least three pairs bred, not laying until July, and others summered as non-breeders. Seven birds survived the winter of 1961-62, but in March and April only three remained and although fresh immigrants brought the total up to ten in late May, only one pair bred; eggs were laid in early June. Over twenty birds were seen in September 1962, but only six wintered successfully. One or two immigrants arrived in late March 1963, and a big arrival on 21st May brought the numbers up to over thirty for a short time, but only three pairs were proved to nest. Only three survived the winter of 1963-64, but up to twenty-nine appeared in late May, diminishing later; at least two pairs bred.

SELECTED REFERENCES

ALEXANDER, W. B. and R. S. R. FITTER (1955). American land-birds in western Europe. *Brit. Birds*, 48: 1-14.

ASHMOLE, M. J. (1962). The migration of European thrushes: a comparative study based on ringing recoveries. *Ibis*, 104: 314-46, 522-99.

BAXTER, E. V. and L. J. RINTOUL (1918). The birds of the Isle of May: a migration study. *Ibis* (1918): 247-87.

BEDFORD, MARY Duchess of (1937). *A Bird-watcher's Diary*. London (privately printed).

BLAKE, C. H. (1956). Weight changes in birds. *Bird Banding*, 27: 16-22.

BROWNLOW, H. G. (1952). The design, construction and operation of Heligoland traps. *Brit. Birds*, 45: 387-99. *Bird Study*, 2: 86-7.

BRUNT, D. (1944). *Physical and Dynamical Meteorology*. Cambridge.

BUTTERFIELD, A. (1954). *Falco columbarius subaesalon* Brehm: a valid race. *Brit. Birds*, 47: 342-7. Also items on bird weights in *Fair Is. Bird Obs. Bull.*

CHISLETT, R. and G. H. AINSWORTH (1958). *Birds on the Spurn Peninsula*. Hull.

CLARKE, W. E. (1912). *Studies in Bird Migration*. 2 vols. Edinburgh.

CORBETT, G. B. (1956). The phoresy of mallophaga on a population of *Ornithomyia fringillina* Curtis (Dipt., Hippoboscidae). *Entomol. Mo. Mag.*, 92: 207-11. The life-history and host relationship of a Hippoboscid fly *Ornithomyia fringillina* Curtis. *J. Anim. Ecol.*, 25: 403-20. Also contributions to *Fair Is. Bird Obs. Bull.*

CORNWALLIS, R. K. (1954-56). The pattern of migration in—at the east coast bird observatories. *Brit. Birds*, 47: 423-31; 48: 429-46; 50: 105-18. Autumn migration on the east coast of Britain in relation to weather. *Ardea*, 44: 224-31.

——— (1961). Four invasions of Waxwings during 1956-60. *Brit. Birds*, 51: 1-30.

COULSON, J. C. and E. WHITE (1958). The effect of age on the breeding biology of the Kittiwake *Rissa tridactyla*. *Ibis*, 100: 40-51.

CURWEN, E. C. (1944). The problem of early water mills. *Antiquity*, 18: 130-46.

DAVIS, P. (1962). *Fair Isle, Shetland. Map of Place-names*. Edinburgh.

——— (1963). Recent developments at Fair Isle. *Scot. Birds*, 2: 400-10. Also contributions, including 'The birds of Fair Isle', to *Fair Is. Bird Obs. Bull.*, 1958-64.

DAVIS, P. E. and R. H. DENNIS (1959). Song-sparrow at Fair Isle: a bird new to Europe. *Brit. Birds*, 52: 419-21.

DEBES, H. M. (1949). *Føroysk Bindingarmynstur*. Torshavn.

DEGERBØL, M. (1940). Mammalia: part lxv of *Zoology of the Faeroes*. Copenhagen.

DELANY, M. J. and P. E. DAVIS (1961). Observations on the ecology and life-history of the Fair Isle Field-mouse *Apodemus sylvaticus fridariensis* (Kinnear). *Proc. Zool. Soc. Lond.*, 136: 439-52.

DUFFEY, E. (1951). Field studies on the Fulmar. *Ibis*, 93: 237-45.

EGGELING, W. J. (1960). *The Isle of May—a Scottish Nature Reserve*. Edinburgh.

ENNION, E. (1960). *The House on the Shore*. London.

EUNSON, J. (1961). The Fair Isle fishing-marks. *Scottish Studies*, 5: 181-98. Also list of wrecks in SVENSSON (1954).

FISHER, J. (1952). *The Fulmar*. London.

GOUDIE, G. (1886). On the horizontal water-mills of Shetland. *Proc. Soc. Antiquaries Scot.*, 20: 257-97.

JENKINS, D. (1953). Migration in late September and early October 1951. *Brit. Birds*, 46: 77-98, 121-31.

KIKKAWA, J. (1959). Habitats of the field mouse on Fair Isle in spring 1956. *Glasgow Nat.*, 18: 65-77.

KRAMER, G. (1952). Experiments in bird orientation. *Ibis*, 94: 265-85.

LACK, D. (1954). *The Natural Regulation of Animal Numbers*. Oxford.
    (1960). A comparison of 'drift migration' at Fair Isle, the Isle of May, and Spurn Point. *Scot. Birds*, 1: 295-327.

McLEAN, I. and K. WILLIAMSON (1957). Migrants at north Atlantic weather-ships in 1956. *Marine Observer*, 27: 152-6.

MATTHEWS, G. V. T. (1955). *Bird Navigation*. Cambridge.

NISBET, I. C. T. (1959). Wader migration in North America and its relation to transatlantic crossings. *Brit. Birds*, 52: 205-15.
    (1962). South-eastern rarities at Fair Isle. *Brit. Birds*, 55: 74-86.

NISBET, I. C. T., W. H. DRURY Jr. and J. BAIRD (1963). Weight-loss during migration. *Bird Banding*, 34: 107-59.

O'DONALD, P. (1962). The genetics of the colour-phases of the Arctic Skua. *Heredity*, 13: 481-6. Also, *Ecology and Evolution in the Arctic Skua* (unpublished, deposited in library of Fair Is. Bird Obs.).

PERDECK, A. C. (1958). Two types of orientation in migratory Starlings, *Sturnus vulgaris* L., and Chaffinches, *Fringilla coelebs* L., as revealed by displacement experiments. *Ardea*, 46: 1-37.

PETTERSSEN, E. (1941). *Introduction to Meteorology*. New York.

PRITCHARD, N. M. (1957). Notes on the flora of Fair Isle. *Proc. Botan. Soc. Brit. Isles*, 2: 218-25. (Also lists by other workers kept in Fair Isle Bird Obs. library.)

RAINEY, R. C. (1951). Weather and the movements of locust swarms: a new hypothesis. *Nature*, 168: 1057.
    (1963). *Meteorology and the migration of Desert Locusts*. W.M.O. Technical Note No. 54. London.

REINIKAINEN, A. (1937). The irregular migration of the Crossbills and their relation to the cone-crop of the conifers. *Ornis Fennica*, 14: 55-64.

RICHDALE, L. E. (1954). The starvation theory in albatrosses. Auk, 71: 239-52.

RICHMOND, W. K. and K. WILLIAMSON (1954). Correspondence on 'American birds in Britain—drift or assisted passage'. Scot. Nat., 66: 197-204.

RITCHIE, J. (1940). An analysis of the influence of weather on a migratory movement of birds. Proc. Roy. Soc. Edinb., 40: 299-321.

ROTHSCHILD, Hon. M. (1955). The distribution of Ceratophyllus borealis Rothschild 1906, and C. garei Rothschild 1902, with records of specimens intermediate between the two. Trans. Roy. Entomol. Soc. Lond., 107: 295-317.

(1958). The bird-fleas of Fair Isle. Parasitology, 48: 382-412.

ROTHSCHILD, M. and T. CLAY (1952). Fleas, flukes and Cuckoos. London.

SALOMONSEN, F. (1935). Aves: part lxiv of Zoology of the Faeroes. Copenhagen.

(1955). The evolutionary significance of bird migration. Dan. Biol. Medd., 22: 1-62.

SAUER, F. and E. SAUER (1955). Zur Frage der nachtlichen Zugorienterung von Grasmücken. Rev. Suisse Zool., 62: 250-9.

SCORER, R. Weather. London.

SOUTHERN, H. N. (1943). The two phases of Stercorarius parasiticus (Linnaeus). Ibis (1943), 443-85.

SPENCER, R. (1954-). Annual Reports of the Bird-Ringing Scheme, published as Supplements to Brit. Birds.

SUTTON, O. G. (1960). Understanding Weather. Harmondsworth.

SVARDSON, G. (1957). The 'invasion' type of bird migration. Brit. Birds, 50: 314-43.

SVENSSON, R. (1954). Lonely Isles. Stockholm.

THOMSON, A. L. (1951). Reproduction, migration and moult: factors controlling the annual cycle in birds. Proc. Xth Internat. Orn. Cong., 241-4.

VENABLES, L. S. V. and U. M. VENABLES (1955). Birds and Mammals of Shetland. Edinburgh.

WATERSTON, G. (1946). Fair Isle. Scot. Geogr. Mag., 62: 111-6. (Also appeal booklet, 'Fair Isle Bird Observatory'.)

WILLIAMSON, K. (1946). Horizontal water-mills of the Faeroe Islands. Antiquity, 20: 83-91.

(1948). The Atlantic Islands: the Faeroe Life and Scene. London.

(1950). The distraction behaviour of the Faeroe Snipe. Ibis, 92: 66-74; 93: 106.

(1951). The Wrens of Fair Isle. Ibis, 93: 599-601.

(1952). Regional variation in the distraction displays of the Oystercatcher. Ibis, 94: 85-96. The incubation rhythm of the Fulmar. Scot. Nat., 64: 138-47. Migrational drift in Britain in autumn 1951. Scot. Nat., 64: 1-18.

(1953). Migration into Britain from the north-west, autumn 1952. Scot. Nat., 65: 65-94.

(1954). 'Northern Chiffchaffs' and their area of origin. *Brit. Birds*, 47: 49-57. A synoptic study of the 1953 Crossbill irruption. *Scot. Nat.*, 66: 155-69. The fledging of a group of young Fulmars. *Scot. Nat.*, 66: 1-12. American birds in Scotland in autumn and winter 1953-54. *Scot. Nat.*, 66: 13-29. Gray-cheeked Thrush at Fair Isle: a new British bird. *Brit. Birds*, 47: 266-7. The migration of the Icelandic Merlin *Brit. Birds*, 47: 434-41. The Fair Isle apparatus for collecting bird ectoparasites. *Brit. Birds*, 47: 234-5, plate 44.

(1955). Two Yellow-headed Wagtails on Fair Isle: a new British bird. *Brit. Birds*, 48: 26-9. Migrational drift. *Acta XI Cong. Internat. Orn.*, 179-86.

(1956). The autumn immigration of the Greenland Redpoll (*Carduelis flammea rostrata* (Coues)) into Scotland. *Dansk Orn. Foren. Tidsskr.*, 50: 125-33.

(1957). The annual post-nuptial moult in the Wheatear (*Oenanthe oenanthe*). *Bird Banding*, 28: 129-35. Mist-nets versus Heligoland traps. *Bird Banding*, 28: 213-22. A desert race of the Great Grey Shrike, new to the British Isles. *Brit. Birds*, 50: 246-9.

(1958). Population and breeding environment of the St Kilda and Fair Isle Wrens. *Brit. Birds*, 51: 369-93. Autumn immigration of Redwings *Turdus musicus* into Fair Isle. *Ibis*, 100: 582-604. Bergmann's rule and obligatory overseas migration. *Brit. Birds*, 51: 209-32.

(1959). Changes of mating within a colony of Arctic Skuas. *Bird Study*, 6: 51-60. The September drift-movements of 1956 and 1958. *Brit. Birds*, 52: 334-77.

(1960). The work of the British bird observatories. *Proc. XII. Internat. Orn. Cong.*, 2: 749-57. Moult as a study in field-taxonomy. *Bird Migration*, 1: 171-5.

(1962). The nature of 'leading-line' behaviour. *Bird Migration*, 2: 176-82.

(1963). Movements as an indicator of population changes. *Bird Migration*, 2: 207-23. Aspects of autumn movements at the bird observatories in 1962. *Bird Migration*, 2: 224-51. The summer and autumn Crossbill irruptions of 1962. *Bird Migration*, 2: 252-60.

WILLIAMSON, K. and J. M. BOYD (1960). *St Kilda Summer*. London.
(1963). *A Mosaic of Islands*. Edinburgh.

WILLIAMSON, K. and P. DAVIS (1956). The autumn 1953 invasion of Lapland Buntings and its source. *Brit. Birds*, 49: 6-25.

WILLIAMSON, K. and A. BUTTERFIELD (1954). The spring migration of the Willow Warbler in 1952. *Brit. Birds*, 47: 177-97.

WILLIAMSON, K. and I. J. FERGUSON-LEES (1960). Nearctic waders in Great Britain and Ireland in autumn 1958. *Brit. Birds*, 53: 369-78.

WILLIAMSON, K. and SPENCER, R. (1960). Ringing recoveries and the interpretation of bird movements. *Bird Migration*, 1: 176-81.

WILLIAMSON, K. and WHITEHEAD, P. (1963). An examination of the Black-cap movements of autumn 1960. *Bird Migration*, 2: 265-71.

WILLIAMSON, K. and V. THOM (1955). Hudsonian Whimbrel at Fair Isle. *Brit. Birds*, 48: 379-81.

(1956). Thick-billed Warbler at Fair Isle. *Brit. Birds*, 49: 89-93.

WYNNE-EDWARDS, V. C. (1962). *Animal Dispersal in Relation to Social Behaviour*. Edinburgh.

INDEX

Abmigration, 151
Accentor, Alpine, 287
Ainsworth, G. H., 125, 297
Air-masses, 154, 159, 160-4
Albatross, Black-browed, 173, 253
Albatrosses, 'Starvation-period' in,
    118, 299
Albinism, Partial, in skuas, 89-91
Alexander, W. B., 125-6, 297
American birds in Europe, 155,
    234-5, 236-7, 239-41, 244-7,
    297, 299, 300
Anderson, L., 255
Anticyclones, 157, 161, 167-70, 174,
    177, 181-4, 187-9, 191-2, 194,
    198-9, 207-8, 218-24, 225-6
Archaeology at F.I., 24-6
Armada, Spanish, 38-9
Ashmole, M. J., 206, 297
Auk, Great, 271; Little, 271
Auks, 57-8, 67, 69
Austin, O. L., 93
Avocet, 267

'Back-track' migration, 152
Baird, J., 298
Bardsey, B.O., 146, 234
Barnes, G., 293
Baxter, Dr E. V., 125, 155-6, 251,
    297
Bedford, Mary Duchess of, xiii, 233,
    251, 297
Bee, Shetland, 175
Bee-eater, Carmine, 223; European,
    173
Bergmann's Rule, 213-15, 300
Bergstrom, A., 134
Birds-of-prey, 138, 142, 153, 163

Bittern, Little, 255
Blackbird, 19-20, 133, 144, 168,
    177-8, 205, 227, 229, 230-2,
    279-80
Blackcap, 153, 283-4, 301
Blake, C. H., 297
Bluethroat, 141, 217, 282
'Boat-day' at F.I., 11-13
Bonxie, 38, 49, 57-8, 60, 68, 71-82,
    96-7, 267
Booth, C. J., 260
Botni, Niels à, 90
Boyd, Dr J. M., 300
Bradwell B.O., 146
Brambling, 172, 205, 225, 230,
    294
'British List', 158, 233, 239
British Trust for Ornithology, xvi,
    126-7, 135, 144
Brownlow, H. G., 297
Bruce, R., xv
Brunt, D., 164, 297
Bryson, A. G. S., xiv
Bullfinch, 293
Bunting, Black-headed, 294; Corn,
    294; Lapland, 144, 172, 189-93,
    203-4, 210, 295, 300; Little,
    158, 172, 295; Ortolan, 172,
    217, 294-5; Pine, 234, 294;
    Red-headed, 176, 294; Reed,
    171-2, 295; Snow, 190, 192-4,
    203, 227, 295-6,; Yellow-
    breasted, 294
Buntings, 153
Bustard, 228
Butterfield, A., 187, 297, 300
Butterfly migrants, 148
Buturlin, A. C., 104
Buys Ballot's Law, 167

303